Cyber Silhouettes
Shadows Over Information Operations

Timothy L. Thomas

D0943487

Foreign Military Studies Office (FMSO)
Fort Leavenworth, KS
2005

The author works for the Foreign Military Studies Office (FMSO), Fort Leavenworth, Kansas. FMSO is a component of the US Army's Training and Doctrine Command (TRADOC). The office is charged with preparing studies based on the reading of foreign and domestic publications and through contacts with a network of foreign and US military and civilian security specialists. FMSO analysts research, write, and publish from unclassified sources about military establishments, doctrines, and practices of selected foreign armed forces. It also studies civil-military and transnational security issues affecting the US and its military forces. FMSO products are prepared for the US Army and other services, the Department of Defense, and other nonDOD organizations to include the Treasury and Justice Departments.

DEDICATION

This book is dedicated to my wife of thirty-two years,
Christine Marie Aberegg Thomas.
I thank her for her patience and for her assistance in
editing this work.

TABLE OF CONTENTS

FOREWORD

This book explores the impact of the Cyber Age on military thinking and operations worldwide. Four issues are examined: the contrast between the concept of "cyber operations" used by civilians, including criminals and terrorists, and the concept of "information operations" used by armed forces; the differences in information operations (IO) theory among the US, Russian, and Chinese militaries; the manner in which militaries use information operations in peace and in war; and the impact of cyber and information processes on the mind, the military machine, and their interface.

Of special interest are the challenges that the author presents to American IO experts regarding their terminology and methodology. He clearly believes that IO terminology is inadequate as it stands and that its "core capabilities and supporting elements" need to be reevaluated. Mr. Thomas has been studying foreign IO for nearly ten years so he has an interesting perspective to offer. He has IO templates from other countries against which to make his comparison, a perspective possessed by very few Americans. Further, the author has recognized how cyber processes have allowed criminals and insurgents/terrorists to practice guerilla warfare tactics and illegal or extremist activities online. He contends that the subjective nature of war has changed again and now has a social context unlike any other time in history.

The military reader and security specialist should enjoy this perspective about the impact of cyber and information processes on our lives. They will especially enjoy the discussion of the tension between the two perspectives at the start of the twenty-first century. This work will lead to a better understanding of the complexity of our digitized lives, will offer new ideas for US armed forces to consider, and will help analysts identify potential danger zones.

Jacob W. Kipp
Director, Foreign Military Studies Office
September 2005

ACKNOWLEDGEMENT

The author used only open-source articles, books, and translations for the construction of this document. Since the author does not speak Chinese, he fully utilized the translation talents of people at the Foreign Broadcast Information Service (FBIS) for the Chinese documents accessed for this work. In addition to his own Russian translations and those of the Foreign Military Studies Office (FMSO) official translator, Mr. Robert Love, the author accessed FBIS for some of its Russian translations.

The author would like to thank the editors of the following organizations for permission to reprint articles he wrote for their journals: Parameters, Joint Force Quarterly, Military Review, The Journal of Information War, and Slavic Military Studies. He would also like to thank the editors of Russian Military Reform 1992-2002 for permission to print his chapter from that book and the editors of Challenges of Peace Support into the 21st Century at the Swedish National Defense College for permission to print his article from that publication.

Additionally, the author would like to extend a special thanks to Ms. Karen Matthews. Ms. Matthews is a coauthor of Appendix Three on cybercrime. She has a vast knowledge of the issues of computer crime and has extensive work experience in this area.

The graphic artist for the cover and section dividers of this work is Mr. Charles A. Martinson III of Fort Leavenworth. His creative design sets the tone for the book's content. Mr. Scott Henderson and Sergeant Ching Tuan provided a Chinese version of the term "cyber silhouettes" (which could also be translated as network-shadows or cyber snapshot) for the cover, and Mr. Njdeh Asisian provided a Farsi version for the same term (which could be translated as cybernetic shadows).

Finally, and most importantly, the author would like to extend his thanks to other coworkers at the Foreign Military Studies Office (FMSO) who have assisted him with various aspects of this and many other projects. Dr. Jacob Kipp, the FMSO director, offered comments and recommendations that improved the overall quality of the material herein; Mr. Lester Grau, Mr. Robert Love, and Dr. Geoffrey Demarest helped edit initial drafts; Mr. Karl Prinslow continually encouraged the author to tackle this project and provided him with associated materials; Ms. Alice Mink assisted with product support and clearance issues; and Mr. Stephen Gerecke and Ms. Linda Pride resolved computer issues. Without their continued support this project would not have been completed.

INTRODUCTION

This book examines the development and use of cyber processes in civilian society and in the military. It explores how these developments have impacted the nature of warfare and the application of warfare fighting techniques. The analysis includes a critique of US information operations (IO); a comparison of US, Russian, and Chinese IO; and a look at how criminals and terrorists use computers in their fight against nation-states. The analysis suggests that there are many "cyber" activities (cybermobilization, cybermanipulation, cyberrecruitment, etc.)[1] that do not conform to our core understanding of warfare—attack and defend. It is to these nontraditional activities that the US armed forces will have to pay more attention in the coming years.

The primary US military focus has been on areas such as information security, infrastructure protection, and the integration of technology with information operations concepts. This focus has shifted in meaning and emphasis over the years. It is clear that the initial IO writers did their best to describe how military operations were changing in the 1990s. This was a new area, and no one knew where we were headed. That we have ended up at this point in time with just minor modifications to our initial IO theory is a tribute to the foresight and wisdom of the first IO writers. The new <u>Joint Doctrine for Information Operations, Joint Publication 3-13</u> (draft) carries on this tradition of foresight and wisdom. Words are chosen with care and those that touch on legal issues have been omitted until further clarification is provided. Some words have been deleted from our vocabulary (such as information war) and other terms have been severely altered (such as information superiority).

However, during these revisions, a divide has emerged that must be sealed between civilian and military terminology. In the civilian world, the term "cyber" is used to explain issues representative of the Cyber Age. Over 150 cyber-related terms now exist. On the other hand, in the military world, the focus has remained on using the term "information" (information operations). A cyber-related term is listed only once (cyberspace) in the new JP 3-13 glossary. Information security, not cyber security, was and remains the key

---

[1] The explosion in cyber-related terms has created many neologisms—new words, usages, or expressions. An online search utilizing OneLook Dictionary Search, which reviews material in a variety of online dictionaries and other online reference sites, has shown how pervasive use of the term "cyber" has become. Over 150 words and phrases were found. For purposes of this book, words that create a functional unit and are formed with the combining form "cyber" are generally written as single words.

buzzword for IO writers. For example, a recent 2004 Joint Warrior Interoperability Demonstration (JWID), where information security issues would be expected to appear, cited nine of sixty-one trials as worthy of further exploration. These nine trials were: identity-based encryption, cross-domain information sharing, interoperable decision support for defense, enterprise application integration, interoperable alerts here and abroad, making visible the entire network, securing message exchanges across nations, multiple network access from one workstation, and automated information sharing among networks.[2] This strong emphasis on systems integration and information security and network issues is typical for a US military exercise. Cyber-related terminology does not appear with nearly the same frequency or emphasis in such exercises, if it appears at all.

The US military has been extremely successful in applying and integrating information capabilities into its fighting apparatus—so successful, in fact, that it may have become immune to an emerging need to look elsewhere for new ideas and trends. It is hard to tell those who have done so well for so long that they might be able to do better if they considered other options. The US military is more than willing to experiment with new Cyber Age equipment but just as unwilling to explore IO theory with the same abandon. Some IO tasks in Iraq and elsewhere, for example, were assigned to artillery personnel because they understood targeting, not IO theory and practice. This is simply wrong. Perhaps this is because the US military doesn't have an academy of military science as some nations do. Such an academy would provide for greater clarification of the capabilities, laws, methods, forms, and principles of IO.

The US military writes more on IO by order of magnitude than most countries. Still this doesn't mean the US has it all right or that it has thought everything through from various perspectives. That is why a review of IO developments in other nation-states and IO developments among transnational groups, such as terrorists and criminal elements, are of value. The review offers alternative ways of viewing twenty-first-century developments and presents a comprehensive outline of the impact of information or cyber technologies and concepts on military and national security affairs. Such an analysis also helps with the formulation of counterstrategies to a terrorist's cyber activities.

While the primary US emphasis on technology meets the demands of keeping the military-industrial complex engaged, the US tends to place less emphasis on some of the equally important developments in the fields of cross-

---

[2] Frank Tiboni, "Military Eyes New Technology," <u>Federal Computer Network</u>, 18 January 2005, from FCW.COM, 20 January 2005.

cultural awareness, psychological operations, and other issues of persuasion. As we have found in Iraq, technology is a force protector and force multiplier and even a combat minimizer (for example, leaflets produced by the 4th Psychological Operations [PSYOP] Group can reduce combat's intensity or length), but it is also insufficient to quickly conclude an insurgency. Information technology is a two-edged sword. It enables the small and the weak to use technology to their advantage just as it enhances the power of the strong.

Insurgents have conducted successful media operations that touch at the cultural roots of some Iraqis while frightening others with threats of execution and vivid war footage. For the first time in recent conflicts involving US forces, CNN has a competitor, and it is not another US station. It is al Jazeera, an Arab station that is closer to the heartbeat of the local population even if, from a Western perspective, it is less truthful and exploited for the wrong purposes. In addition to media exploitation, insurgents use the Internet to spread cyberfear and to conduct cybermobilization, cybermanipulation, and cyberdeception in ways that equal or surpass nation-state capabilities (since the latter has legal responsibilities that insurgents do not). Insurgents also capitalize on their innate understanding of Iraqi and Arab cultural awareness and mentality.

US Army Captain Bill Putnam served in Iraq for over a year as the head of an Open Source Intelligence Unit. Putnam believes animosity still runs high among Iraqis because the US is ineffective at disseminating its message to the Iraqi people. Most importantly, this is because the US military is determined "to make the Iraqi information environment conform to its information operations and public affairs doctrine on how things should be done, rather than vice versa."[3] Putnam believes the US is forcing its views on a situation where they don't fit. It is the classic "square peg in the round hole" syndrome. Perhaps this is because there is no counterpropaganda capability anymore in the US IO doctrine.

It is the author's desire that the following civilian and military overview will expand the reader's understanding of the implications and consequences of the Cyber Age. It is also an aim to offer recommendations that might assist in the further development of US IO theory and to offer an observation on the emerging worldwide Cyber Age environment in which US forces are operating and potential implications.

The author believes that we have progressed beyond the Information Age and a proper description of our current environment is the Cyber Age. Articles that the author wrote previously (some of which are included in this

---

[3] Bill Putnam, "Winning Iraqi Hearts and Minds," <u>Army</u>, January 2005, p. 7.

book) may contain the term Information Age which was appropriate for the time. The beginning of Chapter One explains the rational for this shift in emphasis.

Part One
Understanding Our Cyber Environment

PART ONE: UNDERSTANDING OUR CYBER ENVIRONMENT

Part One is composed of three chapters. They explore the current cyber environment in which societies, militaries, and transnational elements operate. This includes potential threats created by new technologies.

Chapter One questions whether the term Information Age is the correct name for the contemporary environment and examines how the subjective nature of war has evolved. The chapter then looks at the military concept of information operations and examines how cyber activities assist terrorists and criminals in conducting operations, recruiting new followers, and manipulating the activities of law enforcement and military officials trying to capture them. Security officials everywhere must study these unintended consequences of the cyber environment closely.

Chapter Two examines how al Qaeda has exploited the cyber environment and infrastructure that the civilian world has provided. Al Qaeda uses the net to conduct cyberdeception, cyberrecruiting and cybertargeting activities. Also examined is the manner in which terrorists use the Internet as a base of operations and some of the cyber-related dangers of the contemporary security environment.

Chapter Three examines further how terrorists use the Internet as a cybermobilization instrument and how terrorists use the Internet to conduct guerilla warfare online. These are two overlooked aspects of the cyber threat that need to be understood by organizations contemplating conflict with a savvy foe.

CHAPTER ONE: ENGAGING CYBER OR INFORMATION UBIQUITY?

Information Age or Cyber Age?

The world is constantly changing. However, change used to happen slowly. In the past, we moved gradually from the mechanized, to the motorized, and then to the industrialized age. Now the tempo of change has quickened. Today its pace is so great that we can't foresee all of the paths that change offers. This is especially true for the virtual world. There is no frame of reference to deal with it, and we are finding that the virtual world can create new and unusual alliances. It also creates confusion over concepts and terminology.

We are struggling with a variety of descriptors for the modern age. Do we live in the Information, Digital, Computer, or Cyber Age? Many people use the term "information age" because information is the predominantly visual manifestation of a series of processes. However, information has always been with us since man first started speaking and thinking. Exploiting information about the number and location of enemy forces, as well as the composition of his own force, was key to the decision-making of Genghis Khan. Does "information age" really define anything new?

A Google search for "definition of information age" revealed the following: (1.) the information age is an age in which computers are used by the masses and knowledge workers, whose work focuses on the use and manipulation of digital data;[4] (2.) "this period is marked by the increased production, transmission, consumption of and reliance on information. Many consider the new role of information to be changing our social and economic behavior as dramatically as did the Industrial Revolution";[5] and (3.) this is a period beginning in the last quarter of the twentieth century when information became easily accessible through publications and through the manipulation of information by computers and computer networks.[6]

A Google search for "definition of cyber" revealed the following: (1.) the prefix cyber is connected in some loose way to the world of computers or

---

[4] Valencia Community College at
faculty.valencia.cc.fl.us/jdelisle/lis2004/glossary.htm, downloaded May 2005.
[5] Harvard University at cyber.law.harvard.edu/readinessguide/glossary.html,
downloaded May 2005.
[6] Princeton University at www.cogsci.princeton.edu/cgi-bin/webwn, downloaded May 2005.

the Internet;[7] (2.) "cyber is a prefix related to computer networks. For example, cyberpal refers to friends made over the Internet";[8] (3.) "cyber is a prefix used to describe a person, thing, or idea as part of the computer and information age. Taken from kybernetes, Greek for 'steersman' or 'governor.'";[9] (4.) cyber is a prefix used to describe some element of the high-tech or information age;[10] and (5.) "cyber is usually used in connection with references to automated systems—both in terms of hardware and software."[11]

These definitions indicate that the focus of the modern age is on three things: information, the computer, and the computer network. It is the latter two that allow for the movement, sharing, amount, and access to the former. Computers, and more specifically the computer chip, are the enablers that allow the "production, transmission, consumption, and reliance" on information.

Industrialized capabilities were the cause of increased productivity and heightened efficiency in the early Industrial Age. This former age was termed the Industrial Age (cause) and not the Productivity Age (effect). It is the cause that was highlighted, not the effect. Now cyber (computer and network) capabilities are the cause that allow for the flow of huge amounts of data/information, the effect. If the cause is highlighted as in the Industrial Age, then we live in the Cyber Age and not the Information Age. This point of departure takes us in an entirely different direction than a focus purely on information.

The term cyber is pervasive in society, and it refers to many actions in a new way. A cyber-related activity usually refers to an event or process that took place on the Internet or in virtual reality. Today there is a dizzying array of terms with the "cyber" prefix that can easily compete with or even surpass information-related terms: cyberspace, cyberculture, cybercash, cybercafé, cyber-football injuries (suffered from playing video games), cyberjihad, cybercrime, cybermanipulation, cybermobilization, cyberlaw, cybersketches, cyberpsyop, cyberstrategy, cybernews, cyberthreats, cybercide, cybercable, cyberaddict, cybehound, cybermediary, cybermen, cybernate, cyberslacker, cyberslang, cybersoap, cyberspeak, cyberpicketing, cyberstalker, cybertourist, and cyberrecruiting to name but a few. A recent Newsweek article on "Virtual

---

[7] www.goodnewsgooddeeds.org/glossary.html as downloaded in May 2005.
[8] www1.sympatico.ca/help/Glossary/c.html as downloaded in May 2005.
[9] e-Tropolis Evanston at www.epl.org/community/technopolis/infrast_keyterms.html as downloaded in May 2005.
[10] www.help2go.com/modules.php as downloaded in May 2005.
[11] VHA Center for Engineering and Occupational Safety and Health at www1.va.gov/emshg/apps/emp/emp/definitions.htm as downloaded in May 2005.

Jihad" listed the terms cyberattack, cyberwar, cyberterrorism, cybervandalism, and cybersecurity in one short article.[12] A Google search for the term cyber yielded 25,600,000 hits!

The term "cyber" enjoys widespread use for good reason—it has been around for years. The word evolved from cybernetics, a term first written about at the end of the 1940s. The Merriam-Webster Online Dictionary defines cybernetics as "the science of communication and control theory that is concerned especially with the comparative study of automatic control systems (as the nervous system and brain and mechanical-electrical communication systems)."[13] Perhaps the most famous early cybernetic book was that of Norbert Wiener, who wrote Cybernetics, or Control and Communication in the Animal and the Machine. Later, in 1954, he wrote The Human Use of Human Beings. He stated that

> It is the thesis of this book that society can only be understood through a study of the messages and the communication facilities which belong to it; and that in the future development of these messages and communication facilities, messages between man and machines, between machines and man, and between machine and machine, are destined to play an ever increasing part.[14]

Cyber-based products have become the backbone of modern societies. They are used by a host of institutions and organizations to not only support their contemporary security environments but also to conduct their daily activities and advance their interests. Computer and telecommunication businesses across the globe battle one another for customers on each continent. In turn they create a communications infrastructure that enables both business and the population of these countries to operate with the efficiency and precision once reserved for government, military, and security services.

A look at the newspaper on nearly any day of the year confirms just how widespread cyber-related technologies have become. A recent report noted that the average Internet user in the US spends three hours a day online. Use of the Internet has thus replaced much of the time previously spent watching TV and performing other activities according to the Stanford Institute for the Quantitative Study of Society.[15] Other examples abound. Surgeons now use

---

[12] Michael Isikoff and Mark Hosenball, "Virtual Jihad," Newsweek, 10 February 2005, from CNO/IO Newsletter, Vol. 5, No. 10, 8-18 February 2005.

[13] Merriam-Webster Online Dictionary as downloaded on 20 February 2005.

[14] Downloaded from www.angelfire.com, "Norbert Wiener Quotes."

[15] John Markoff, "Internet Use Said to Cut into TV Viewing and Socializing," The New

cutting-edge robotics to operate on patients even from across continents. The Netherlands Intelligence Service has warned of radical Islamic ideology spreading to thousands of young Dutch Muslims through Internet sites and online chat rooms. US troops in Iraq crowd into an Internet café and contact family members using web cameras and instant messaging. In Chicago, an eBay auction of "Chicago Experiences and Treasures" ended recently. In Italy, police used technology to shave years off the facial image on the Shroud of Turin and offered a headline that said "Here is Jesus at Age 12 (According to a Computer)." What is interesting is that all of these reports appeared in the same paper on the same day. These aren't events happening over the course of a month or year but everyday.[16] They are the result of cyber processes, not information processes.

   Some of the uses of new cyber technologies are quite bizarre or unique because they are occurring for the first time. An Indian Muslim recently divorced his wife by email.[17] Iranian authorities are escalating their attempts to control "webblogistan," some 75,000 blogs that contain criticisms of Iran's leadership.[18] In Russia an email virus known as the Maslan-C worm that had an attached file called "Playgirls2.exe" attacked Chechen rebel sites.[19] The Indian government has asked Microsoft to digitally map its entire country.[20] The W32/VBSun-A worm, masquerading as a legitimate Tsunami relief effort email, spreads via email as does the Playgirl virus.[21] Hackers recently set up fake wireless base stations known as "evil twins" to trick laptop users into divulging their passwords after receiving an invalid password prompt.[22] The high-tech nerve center for President Bush's second inauguration was in northern Virginia, twenty-five miles from where he took the oath. Plasma screens beamed live video as computers tracked the skies and called up three-dimensional maps of any downtown area at the click of a mouse. Advanced

---

York Times, 30 December 2004 as downloaded from Johnson's List on 30 December 2004.

[16] The Kansas City Star, 26 December 2004, pp. A1, A2, A6, A12, A13, A20, and A27.

[17] Lester Haines, "Indian Muslim Divorces Wife by Email," The Register, 1 November 2004 as downloaded from the website http://www.theregister.co.uk.

[18] FBIS Analysis: "Internet War in Iran Heats Up; Government Jails Bloggers, Filters ISPs." Analysis posted on the FBIS website on 20 January 2005.

[19] John Leyden, "Playgirl Virus Attacks Chechen Rebel Sites," The Register, 9 December 2004.

[20] The Associated Press, "Microsoft to Digitize Indian Maps," Technologyreview.com, 12 January 2005 as downloaded 13 January 2005.

[21] Antony Savvas, "Worm Masquerades as Plea for Tsunami Aid," ComputerWeekly.com, 18 January 2005.

[22] Rena Millman, "Evil Twins Allows Hackers to Phish for Wireless data," http://www.scmagazine.com, 20 January 2005.

screening methods were used to check everyone who came near the event. Advanced sensors sniffed the air.[23]

While discussing how computers or cyber technologies can be used surreptitiously to communicate with members of a group, <u>New York Times</u> reporter Tom Zeller wrote that

> At one website, spammimic.com, a user can type in a phrase like "Meet me at Joe's" and have that message automatically converted into a lengthy bit of prose that reads like a spam message: "Dear Decision maker—Your email address has been submitted to us indicating your interest in our briefing! This is a one-time mailing and there is no need to request removal if you won't want any more."[24]

The words are pasted into an email message and sent. The receiver of the email, on the lookout for such a message, then pastes it into the machine's decoder to read the original message.[25] Thus the uses of computers and their related activities are spreading and becoming more creative. Militaries and law enforcement agencies are having a hard time staying ahead of this transnational creativity.

Professor B.J. Fogg of Stanford University is a leader in a more specialized use of cyber technologies, yet one most people haven't thought much about. It is the use of cyber technologies strictly for purposes of persuasion. He runs a persuasive technology laboratory at Palo Alto, California. Fogg and his staff are creating a "body of expertise in the design, theory, and analysis of persuasive technologies, an area called 'captology'."[26] Dr. Fogg introduces users to devices that remind, reward, or monitor behavior, and thereby influence attitudes.[27] Persuasive technologies can induce flattery, seduction, fantasy, competition, humor, positive reinforcement, and appeals to the conscience. The difficulty, of course, is deciding what is persuasion and not manipulation or coercion.[28] Dr. Fogg has written a book titled <u>Persuasive Technology</u> that has two chapters of particular relevance–"Persuasion in the Digital Age" and "Credibility and the World Wide Web." These chapters, as

---

[23] Sari Horwitz and Spencer S. Hsu, "Inaugural Security Draws on Latest Technologies," WashingtonPost.com, 10 January 2005, p. A1.
[24] Tom Zeller, Jr., "On the Open Internet, a Web of Dark Alleys," <u>The New York Times</u>, 20 December 2004.
[25] Ibid.
[26] "Captology: Computers as Persuasive Technologies," at http://captology.stanford.edu.
[27] Taken from http://captology.stanford.edu/Examples/examples.html.
[28] Gary H. Anthes, "Persuasive Technologies," <u>Computerworld</u>, 28 June 1999, p. 76.

well as the Appendix "Summary of Principles," should hold special prominence for people studying how advertisers use these techniques and, additionally, how terrorist websites have succeeded at times in influencing people to their side.

Cyber products are the current rage. The names of these products are confusing (with combinations of capital letters and numbers) and sometimes misleading. It is also difficult to tell what the products do. The MOTO RAZR V3 is a phone, not a razor. The Monaco V4 is a concept watch, not a car. If listed separately from the product itself, the names are even more unintelligible. The Toshiba 26HF84, the Samsung MM-A700, the Suunto n3i, the MuVo Slim, the MyFi, and the Panasonic PV-GS120 are a high-definition wide-screen TV, a "smart watch," an MP3 player, a Sprint phone, a portable satellite radio, and camcorder, respectively.[29] Cyber terminology is confusing too. According to a recent BBC report, the average home computer user is not sure about the meaning of pharming (fraudsters redirect net users from legitimate to fake sites); phishing (fake email or popup scams to get you to reveal personal information for criminal gain); rogue dialer (software that installs itself on computers and changes settings to dial a premium rate number instead of usual dialup accounts); spyware (small programs that secretly monitor sites visited); keylogging (software/hardware to track keystrokes on a computer to gather passwords and credit card numbers); and other terms that all warn people about online security threats.[30]

Thus, the effect of cyber-based technologies on the population as a whole is huge and not limited just to information. There are emotional, societal, economic, psychological, and political effects in addition to easy access and sharing of information. There is a mind-boggling array of cyber technologies that control many aspects of our daily activities and numb the average consumer with their ubiquity. New technologies have enabled the civilian world to work faster and more efficiently. They ease us through our daily lives, assist us in times of trouble, help us to enjoy our entertainment time more clearly and deeply, keep us more closely connected to family, inform us of local and international events of importance, and amaze us with their spread and increasing accessibility. Governments and businesses worldwide are wired to receive news instantaneously and are using cyber technologies to either do their jobs better or to keep them informed about competitors. Many of these devices were financially out of reach to the average consumer at the start of the Cyber Age, but they are now available to the masses as witnessed by the plethora of cell phones in the hands of teenagers and families of all incomes. For example, there are now over 159 million cell phones in the US and, even more amazing,

---

[29] These items were taken from Time, 29 November 2004, pp. 63-136.
[30] "'Geek Speak' Confuses Net Users," BBC News, 6 April 2005 from news.bbc.co.uk.

more than 194 million in China. But this is just the effect on society at large. What has been the effect on various military organizations around the world? Have they embraced cyber-related issues or avoided them?

The Emergence of the Civilian and Military Cyber Battlefields

Non-state entities (terrorists and criminal agents) use these same networks and products to conduct their "business." They seldom use the terms cyber or information operations, although most civilian agencies and the media describe their activities as cyber-related. For example the media describes insurgent activities in Iraq and Israel as part of a virtual or cyberjihad, as cyberterrorism, or as the beginning of an Interfada. Terrorists and criminals feed off civilian and military technological advancements and use them to coordinate and advance their causes. Countering these activities employed by insurgents has proven most difficult in Iraq.

Computers enable criminal, terrorist, and insurgent capabilities. Cyber capabilities allow information to be manipulated, stolen, or held hostage, for example; and they allow criminals, terrorists, and insurgents to conduct guerilla warfare tactics and illegal or extremist activities online. Cyber capabilities have introduced identify theft, financial fraud, and cyber money laundering into our lives. This has changed the subjective nature of war, adding a social context unlike any time in history.

Cyber processes work in near-stealth mode. Electrons carry the "threat" of encryption or manipulation or some other capability, moving silently and surreptitiously around the world. These packets of electrons use the same networks and platforms that civilians use to conduct their everyday business. Today's criminals, terrorists, and insurgents use their computer skills and off-the-shelf cyber purchases (equipment ranging from frequency intercept devices to mini-spy cameras) to conduct activities that cast cyber silhouettes of influence and agitation over the much more lethal and powerful information operations of modern armies. The title for this book, Cyber Silhouettes, was chosen for this reason.

The cyber silhouettes cast by insurgents are not the traditional military ones of precision, speed, and efficiency. Instead these silhouettes are those of manipulation, perception, recruitment, mobilization, fear, and intimidation, among others. Quite often militaries and their associated intelligence agencies, while able to comprehend the outline of these silhouettes, have no arrow in the quiver that is flexible enough to target, eliminate, or control them. Their arrows were designed for other purposes such as the nation-state threat of the past. That is, a cyber threat enhances activities that an armed force is not prepared to handle at this time.

19

This means that we are truly in a new phase of warfare, a phase in which civilians cannot have armies stand between them and the enemy to the degree they once did. Cyber processes are the means through which terrorists and insurgents get information spread, read, and acted upon. In the past, criminals, terrorists, and insurgents lacked media outlets and the means to transmit information about their cause. Their doctrine and successes remained in the minds of extremists or on the pages of a typewriter. There was no outlet to convey their ideas to the public. The Cyber Age has changed that.

Cyber warfare is invisible yet ubiquitous and has a tremendous psychological overtone. The latter is the result of the amplitude produced from the use of cyber products. Satellite reporting insures that coverage is not only immediate but focused on what the reporter in the field decides to report. This initial reporting causes a psychological impact, whether it is crowds cheering over a downed aircraft or crying children bending over an injured parent. In this sense, amplitude is immediate and can be immense, shaping the story for days to come.

Western news coverage of websites friendly to al Qaeda enhances this psychological impact. Coverage of beheadings or film footage of insurgents' operations contributes to their propaganda and ensures its immediate spread as breaking news. By posting their own news online, insurgents also evade any editing process that the Arab or Western world might impose.[31] Al Qaeda has its own Internet journals, and the number continues to grow. In March the jihadi magazine Dhurwat al-Sanam made its first appearance. The issue contained edicts from Osama bin Laden and Abu Musab al-Zarqawi, denunciations of the recent elections in Iraq, and attempts to avoid dissension within the ranks. According to one source, two other prominent al Qaeda associated online journals, Sawat al-Jiahd [Voice of Jihad] and Maaskar al-Battar [al-Bataar Training Camp] ceased publication a few months ago.[32] Thus, Iraq has shown that even in stability or low-intensity operations where Internet support and use is limited, insurgents still rely heavily on the use of computers, networks, and high-tech equipment to plan and conduct operations and to communicate with one another.

Hackers are another type of cyberbattlefield threat to societies in that they can encrypt financial files or manipulate information. Civilian organizations are forming up in coalitions and battle groups on the Internet just

---

[31] Reuters, "Terrorism on the Web," www.cnn.com, 30 March 2005.

[32] Sudha Ramachandran, "Jihad's Latest 'Rag' Hits the Internet," Asia Times, www.atimes.com, 31 March 2005.

as armies do on the battlefield to conduct counterinsurgency warfare. For example, an anti-hacker alliance of top Internet Service Providers (ISPs) was recently formed, similar in function to a coalition of troops sent to stop hostile activity. They united to share attack profiles to stop Internet attacks as far from target areas as possible. The alliance included such important providers as BT Group, Deutsche Telekom, MCI, NTT Communications, Cisco Systems, and EarthLink, among others. Their realization is that "the operating principle of the technologies underlying the Internet will not allow hackers to be defeated."[33] Thus the goal is to improve the exchange of information among Internet providers as the best available method. Forming this coalition of ISPs is a first step. Civilian organizations are investing in computer tactics and strategies and in countercomputer activities as well. More interesting for purposes of this study, however, is that the Cyber Age has spawned a new age of military theory and practice.

Instead of studying opposing armies, many civilians today, both private citizens and security organs, study Internet terrorist sites. The website http://haganah.org.il is dedicated to, as the site says, "confronting the global jihad online." Instead of publishing training manuals, the Internet site offers insurgents a chance to use online tutorials about handling weapons or planning attacks. An Internet posting of 30 March 2005, obtained by NBC news, offered a missile tutorial. The targets were not military aircraft but civilian airliners.[34]

To view our borders, much like military units observe their perimeters, companies such as VistaScape offer a master system combining views from hundreds of cameras with GPS data that focuses on moving targets, digital borders, and final details from other sensors (infrared, chemical sniffing, etc.).[35] A Florida lawmaker plans to introduce legislation to remotely inspect boaters returning from Caribbean ports with videophones and biometric technology.[36]

Information Operations (IO) and the Military
The distinction in terminology between civilians and armed forces to describe the age in which we live is interesting. By focusing on the term cyber, civilians and some federal media outlets talk directly about the myriad ways

---

[33] Computer Crime Research Center Staff, "Top World ISPs Unite in Fight against Hackers," www.crime-research.org, 31 March 2005.
[34] Lisa Myers and the NBC investigative unit, "Al Qaeda Web Message Offers Missile Tutorial," msnbc.msn.com, 30 March 2005.
[35] "The All-in-One, Widescreen Security Cam," Wired, March 2005, p. 028.
[36] Greta Wodele, "Florida Lawmakers Want Remote System to Inspect Boaters," National Journal's Technology Daily, downloaded from the www.govexec.com on 5 April 2005.

that computers are affecting our industries, our social setting, and even the way our brains process information. Cybersecurity is a focus for these institutions and the government. For example, in February 2003, President George W. Bush issued a "National Strategy to Secure Cyberspace" which outlined five cyberspace-security priorities. The Department of Homeland Security has also tried to strengthen cyberspace security with a number of steps. These include building cybersecurity operations with a National Cyber Security Division; establishing a Cyber Security Readiness and Response System; sponsoring cybersecurity education and training; creating a Government Forum of Incident Response and Security Teams (GFIRST); partnering with the Multi-State Information Sharing and Analysis Center; implementing a process to maintain a Common Vulnerability and Exposure, Common Malware Enumerator, and Open Vulnerability Assessment Language; establishing International Information Sharing Conference calls; and initiating an Internet Infrastructure Security Program.[37] The military, on the other hand, talks of information operations and information security.

The US military focuses on "information" as it relates to several well-established military capabilities (deception, psychological war, electronic war, and operational security) and one new item, computer network operations, which is limited primarily to attack and defend operations. The military pays almost no attention to cyber processes. A quick check of the military's dictionary, Joint Publication 1-02 (as amended through 30 November 2004), supports and demonstrates this. Only two cyber-related terms were listed, cyber counterintelligence and cyberspace, while there were thirteen information-related entries including a definition for the term "information." The new draft of Joint Publication 3-13, Information Operations, even eliminated cyber counterintelligence leaving cyberspace as the only cyber-related term. A social transformation is happening, and the subjective nature of warfare is changing yet the military is having trouble adapting fast enough. It appears stuck in old prisms and paradigms.

There are reasons for this. Modern military theorists have long held the view that warfare, if it were ever to occur in contemporary times, would be a struggle between nations in possession of precision-guided weapons that utilized computer chips to guide weapons and troops with accuracy, speed, and efficiency. It would be a system-against-system struggle. Fortunately, such a confrontation has never occurred. When the US has fought in conflicts around the globe, the confrontation has been one-sided. The US has not fought another high-technology force on the battlefield of equal or greater status than itself. To

---

[37] Press Release Fact Sheet, printed in Information Operations Newsletter, Mr. Jeff Harley editor, Vol. 5, No. 10, 8-18 February 2005.

date, military opponents have been Cold War armies, the armies of Third World countries, or insurgents—all with outdated military equipment.

The US military does have an organization with tremendous cyber capability. It is the Defense Information Systems Agency (DISA) that performs many computer security functions for the armed forces. DISA's website notes that it is a combat support agency responsible for planning, engineering, acquiring, fielding, and supporting global net-centric solutions to serve the needs of the President, Vice President, the Secretary of Defense, and other DOD components, under all conditions of peace and war. The DISA website states that the organization

> Provides a seamless, secure and reliable web of communications networks, computers, software, databases, applications and other capabilities that meet the information processing and transport needs of DOD. DISA also ensures the integration and interoperability of command and control, communications, computers and intelligence (C4I) systems.[38]

This organizational mission does not mention responsibility for the manipulation, perception, recruitment, mobilization, and fear and intimidation capabilities of insurgents. Rather the focus is on CNO activities such as processing information, integrating systems, and ensuring computer security.

Overall, the military's approach is more specific than the civilian approach, and it exploits traditional concepts (however the US military is currently updating its information operations doctrine to include several new components). Information security, the worldwide information grid and infrastructure, information attacks, and information operations are part of the information lexicon of the military. The US military does, of course, utilize numerous cyber influence concepts in its day-to-day activities. They just don't refer to them as such. Before and during combat in Iraq these activities involved the use of emails and the Internet to convey messages and intentions. Still, the military would describe these events as information and not cyber operations.

Over the past decade the definition of IO has evolved and taken on new elements and new meaning. Even today, however, uncertainty as to what is meant by the term and what it can do for the commander remains. This

---

[38] See Defense Information Systems Agency website at
http://www.disa.mil/main/about/missman.html

uncertainty is apparent in the fact that different definitions are still advanced by the Air Force and Army even while a new Joint Publication definition for IO is under development.

The US military, according to a November 2004 definition at the Department of Defense official dictionary website, <u>Joint Publication 1-02</u>, defined IO as "actions taken to affect adversary information and information systems while defending one's own information and information systems."[39] The US Army's <u>FM 3-13: Information Operations</u>, from November 2003 defines IO as

> The employment of the core capabilities of electronic warfare, computer network operations, psychological operations, military deception, and operations security, in concert with specified supporting and related capabilities, to affect or defend information and information systems, and to influence decision-making.[40]

The US Air Force, in their new doctrinal publication 2-5, January 2005, defines an information operation as

> Actions taken to affect adversary information and information systems while defending one's own information and information systems. Also called IO....*Information operations are the integrated employment of the core capabilities of influence operations, electronic warfare operations, network warfare operations, in concert with specified integrated control enablers, to influence, disrupt, corrupt or usurp adversarial human and automated decision making while protecting our own.* [41] (Note: The section in italics is denoted in their publication as "applying only to the Air Force and is offered for clarity.")

The second draft of <u>Joint Publication 3-13, Joint Doctrine for Information Operations</u>, posted on the Department of Defense website on 14 December 2004, defined IO as

> The integrated employment of the core capabilities of electronic warfare, computer network operations, psychological operations, military deception, and operations security, in concert with specified supporting and related capabilities, to influence, disrupt, corrupt or

---

[39] See http://www.dtic.mil/doctrine/jel/doddict/data.

[40] <u>FM 3-13, Information Operations</u>, November 2003, Glossary-12.

[41] Air Force Doctrine <u>Document 2-5, Information Operations</u>, 11 January 2005, p. 51 as downloaded from the Internet.

usurp adversarial human and automated decision making while protecting our own."[42]

If this definition is approved, it will replace the definition cited earlier from JP 1-02. All past IO definitions defined IO as the ability to attack others' systems while defending its own. The new Joint Publication definition, if approved, resembles the Air Force definition in that it doesn't attack and defend systems but rather is defined as the ability to "influence, disrupt, corrupt or usurp adversarial human and automated decision making while protecting our own."

As you can see, the speed with which definitions are changing and the variations of core capabilities listed is indicative of the struggle to understand IO in general. The Air Force definition is the real renegade of the bunch. It does not include military deception and operational security in its definition as core capabilities as the Joint and Army definitions do.

One of the biggest problems with the service-oriented definitions is that they do not offer countercapabilities to the propaganda advanced by insurgents or other organizations via the Internet or other media means as a core or supporting/related capability. Countercapabilities are listed as a supporting activity and only counterintelligence is included in the new JP 3-13 draft. It may be that with the focus on information, the ability of enemies to conduct cyber-related actions is not properly contemplated. Counter- or even pre-emptive IO or cyber activities are extremely important in fighting an insurgency. Counterpropaganda is a term that appears to be missing. Perhaps counterinfluence could be substituted for counterpropaganda if the latter is unacceptable.

It is also possible to offer a new definition for an information operation based on an examination of foreign and domestic IO and cyber issues. The following is a definition that takes into consideration all of these factors:

> An IO is a number of technical, influence, and effects-causing operations (plus their countercapabilities) used from peacetime to postconflict scenarios to achieve a stated goal via means of destruction, persuasion, protection, control, or neutralization. These activities are aimed at the decision-making of leaders, combatants, and the general populace, and include all means to gather and distribute information.[43]

---

[42] Joint Publication 3-13, Joint Doctrine for Information Operations, Second Draft, 14 December 2004, GL-12.
[43] Author's definition.

Civilians, on the other hand, are not so limited in their application of cyber capabilities and thus have a broader palette of options for describing new events. The military has no way to address the myriad number of terms such as manipulation, mobilization, recruiting, squatting and at least a hundred other "cyber" word combinations. It is important that the military address this crucial shortcoming in its theory because these cyber-related actions affect the military. As documented in the conclusion, this shortcoming has affected the US military in Iraq even when the event occurs far from Iraq. For example, Omar Bakri Mohammed, an extremist London cleric, recently used live broadcasts on the Internet to call the young to Jihad.[44] In effect he is relying on cyber-based technologies to conduct cybermanipulation, cyberrecruiting, and cybermobilization activities that will affect our forces on the battlefield.

Some armies use different information terminology, however, and define terms that the US has avoided. A Russian information operation, for example, does not consist of the same elements as a US military information operation. It only has two core capabilities, information-technical and information-psychological. In addition, Russian theorists define in detail the term "information weapon"—a term the US does not define.

Regarding a Chinese perspective on information operations, one need only look at the writings of renowned Chinese IO expert Shen Weiguang. He noted

> Information has become as strategic a resource as material and energy. The information industry has become a national pillar industry, and information elements have become the most important production elements...it is necessary to establish a world information security committee to organize the research and control of information warfare theory, technology, and equipment as well as information security issues.[45]

Shen has also recommended the development of rules of engagement for the current environment and the requirement to begin discussion on developing the theory of information deterrence. Clearly other nations are examining IO with criteria that differ from the US. They also appear stuck in the lexicon of the past.

---

[44] Sean O'Neil and Yaakov Lappin, "Britain's Online Imam Declares War as He Calls Young to Jihad," timesonline.co.uk, 17 January 2005.

[45] Shen Weiguang, "Checking Information Warfare—Epoch Mission of Intellectual Military," Jiefangjun Bao [PLA Daily Newspaper], 2 February 1999, p. 6 as translated and downloaded from the FBIS website on 2 February 1999.

However, just as cyber activities have introduced a change in the subjective nature of warfare in the civilian world, so-called information technologies have also changed the way militaries fight, maneuver, and organize. These cyber-based technologies have enabled the armed forces of many nations to observe, orient, decide, and act faster than ever before possible on the battlefield. The US military has a host of technical (cyber-based) information-gathering devices at its disposal to allow it to do so, and they form the core of its operations. These include sensors, reconnaissance satellites, remotely piloted vehicles (RPVs) with cameras, and wireless intercept devices. The Global Positioning System (GPS) is a system of twenty-four satellites and ground stations that calculate positions with extreme accuracy. As a result GPS assists precision-guided munitions to seek and target enemy actions with extreme accuracy. American soldiers possess global positioning systems to insure that they stay out of the way of these weapons. Missile defense systems, early warning radars, nuclear facilities, and all of our telecommunication facilities depend on the functioning of cyber technologies. The next generation of secure communications satellites, based on Advanced Extremely High Frequency (EHF, radio frequency in the 3-30 GHZ band) technology, is now under construction. This entire array of equipment assists the military to attain battlefield awareness quicker and more accurately than an enemy force, thereby allowing it to act first in battle. But are these really "information technologies?" Yes, these devices relay information. But isn't it the cyber-processor that is new? Information relayed by semaphore played the same role as a computer years ago, simply passing data. But the cyber aspect is what is new. Line of sight is no longer needed. The cyber semaphore today connects continents.

The military-industrial complex and military colleges are developing cyber technologies in various ways. One of the most interesting is the use of persuasive technologies with military application. For example, in the case of two sides engaged in conflict, cyber technologies have been used to digitally persuade combatants not to fight. During the 1990s war in the Balkans, after nearly three years of fierce fighting among the factions in the former Yugoslavia, the international community finally persuaded the Presidents of Bosnia, Croatia, and Serbia to sit down together and discuss how they could end the bloodshed. This meeting took place at Dayton, Ohio, in the fall of 1995. Cyber processes played a prominent, even decisive role in convincing the three leaders that the Dayton Accords would be administered fairly and without prejudice. Mapping and satellite data were the two pieces of cyber-produced information used most often. US military scientists would also benefit by studying the potential military applications of both persuasive and counterpersuasive technologies in light of the extensive insurgent use of websites for mobilization and manipulation purposes.

Unintended Consequences of Cyber Age Technologies

There is not a criminal or terrorist group with its own computer chip factory or military-industrial complex. Yet criminal and terrorist groups are able to access products either by purchasing them, stealing them, or trading for them; and they are able to spread their doctrine and connect with allies as never before due to their empowerment by cyber processes. Purchasing commercial satellite images or off-the-shelf information technologies (such as spyware materials, intercept devices, and other technology available at Radio Shack or on e-Bay) are two such examples. Using the Internet as a media device akin to the New York Times for publishing articles or CNN for photographing and running videos is another plus for transnational groups.

It was not expected that terrorists and criminals would use the Internet to conduct cybermobilization, cyberplanning, cyberfear, and cybermanipulation activities. Law in most civilized countries forbids such activities. But because of the anonymity of the Internet, the ability to conduct these activities from far-off locations without fear of law enforcement agencies, and their total disrespect for the law, terrorists have little fear of being found and prosecuted. Further, a terrorist or insurgent cares very little about web credibility factors. Nation-states have to worry constantly about this issue. The terrorist or insurgent will put out any information that fits a specific need without worrying about being "called" on it for accuracy.

Off-the-shelf communication technologies, such as decoding and intercept devices, have enabled terrorists, insurgents, and criminals to coordinate and perform key functions similar to modern army staffs in the sense of covertness, integration of effort, and speed. Remote digital devices, such as car door openers, are used to detonate an insurgent's improvised explosive devices (IEDs). Surveillance cameras and voice intercept devices are available to the general consumer (and the insurgent/terrorist), and this allows them to plan ambushes with timeliness and precision. Before 9/11, websites contained schematics and sometimes even the plans of sensitive facilities that enemy operatives may still someday use. Information in a captured al Qaeda manual noted that "public information can provide 80% of the information needed about a possible target."[46] A recent Associated Press report is indicative of this trend. The report was about Google's new search tool that includes satellite images. The viewer gets an overhead shot of a site and driving directions to it. This information previously was owned by Keyhole Corporation and cost users $29.95 to download a version of Keyhole's basic software package. Google

---

[46] "Al Qaeda Surveillance Techniques Detailed," USA Today, 29 December 2004 as downloaded from the Internet at www.usatoday.com.

bought Keyhole and now offers free access to these maps.[47] Thus terrorists/insurgents don't have to do some of the reconnaissance of a target as they once did—it is provided for them in a highly transferable and accurate form.

Osama bin Laden did not define IO and probably never discussed IO in detail with his subordinates the way an American commander would do. He does not worry about legal constraints or "psyoping" his own people. He has no access to the devices produced by a military industrial complex but instead focuses his force on just the opposite capability—how to counter surveillance techniques such as sensors, satellites, RPVs, and wireless intercepts. He, his men, and other terrorists worldwide do, however, utilize technological devices in the manner in which normal citizens do. For example, Iraqi militants used Google to find the name of an Australian reporter they took hostage. They did so to investigate his work before deciding whether or not to release him.[48]

A terrorist focuses on influencing public opinion and conducting offensive influence operations via the Internet and other media outlets. The Internet serves as a mini-TV station, an outlet for terrorist propaganda that simply was not available in the past. These resources promote terrorist attack successes and serve as a conduit through which to relay simple messages from bin Laden and other terrorist leaders. Bin Laden is expert at buttressing Arab opinion with his TV and Internet messages that touch the souls and spirits of exasperated Arabs. He is a credible figure to many as he extols al Qaeda successes, gives directives, and offers moral support. US media and other international communication stations often pick up these broadcasts and replay parts of them for US audiences. While bin Laden relays his message, US forces are slow to respond. Usually this is because the CIA or some other agency is busy deciphering the message and trying to substantiate its authenticity. In the meantime, bin Laden moves on to his next planning sequence. The inability to respond quickly puts the US in a defensive mode from which it is hard to communicate worldwide and influence large geographical populaces.

Former CIA director George Tenet had more dire warnings about Internet use. He noted that greater government regulation of the Internet and telecommunications networks in general are needed to guard against terrorist attacks. He worries that terrorists might try to couple a telecommunications attack with a physical attack. Tenet believes that even though we are accustomed to using the Internet in a free and open society with no control or

---

[47] "Google Maps Lead the Way," The Associated Press, 7 April 2005, as downloaded from www.denverpost.com.
[48] "Militants Studied Internet," Kansas City Star, 20 October 2004, p. A15.

accountability that we will eventually need to give way to governance and control.[49] Others agree with Tenet's assessment. In the near future there may be real tension between those advocating freedom of speech and those who want more restrictions on the net.

In the age of the new persuaders, through the use of cell phones, the Internet, and alternate news sources, transnational groups are empowered by media outlets that present their position unaltered and unfiltered by governments or communication laws. This is the soft side of a terrorist influence operation, where bin Laden or al Zarqawi come into your home on the evening news. They plead with their "brothers" to rid the country of the hated "infidels," and under such pretenses, bin Laden doesn't look that vile to some audiences. He does not worry about lying or about altering facts. There is no interview with him, and impartial audiences ask no questions. Such people do not exist in his circle. US audiences, on the other hand, are predisposed to listen to all sides of a story, and many give bin Laden a chance to explain himself. Islamic extremists are not so congenial. For them there is only one story and that is theirs.

The TV station al Manar is another good example of a terrorist organization using the media for its purposes. Based in Lebanon, it is the official station of Hezbollah, an Islamic terrorist group. US State Department spokesman Richard Boucher noted that a group could be placed on a terrorist list if it "commits or incites to commit any terrorist activity." The al Manar station has been charged with doing just this type of activity. The station, for example, has urged attacks against US forces in Iraq. This is not freedom of speech, Boucher added, but "a question of incitement to violence."[50] Terrorists have also used the Internet to chastise clerics for not supporting their "resistance movements." One audiotape played on the Internet noted that Sunni Muslim clerics had "let us down in the darkest circumstances and handed us over to the enemy…Hundreds of thousands of the nation's sons are being slaughtered at the hands of the infidels because of your silence."[51] The tape was posted on an Islamic website known as al Qala'a. The site has been a mailbox for Islamic militant groups.[52]

---

[49] Chris Strohm, "Tenet Warns of Terrorists Combining Physical, Telecommunications Attacks," VEXEC.com, 1 December 2004 as downloaded from http://www.govexec.com.

[50] "Hezbollah's Terrorist TV Station," 21 December 2004 as downloaded from http://www1.voanews.com.

[51] John F. Burns, "Tape Condemns Sunni Muslim Clerics for Abandoning Iraqi Resistance," The New York Times, 25 November 2004, p. A22.

[52] Ibid.

The important point to underscore is that cyber-age technologies that persuade or influence audiences psychologically through information, disinformation, or deception are ubiquitous and available to anyone on any continent whether it is a US soldier in a high-tech force or a terrorist in the desert. Legal organizations and entities have developed most of these technological devices, but they are available to anyone including religious zealots, terrorists, dictators, and so on.

But this is only a discussion of the soft side of terrorism—the use of the media. A growing danger is the terrorist's slow but steady acquisition of digitally enhanced, miniaturized technologies. These devices, at the heart of recent reports on the use of laser devices to blind airline pilots or the Chechen suicide bombers who sneaked explosives onto two Russian domestic flights within minutes of one another, will become more prevalent in the next five years. Terrorists are on the lookout for small, dirty bombs and for biological or chemical agents that can be dispersed into large population settings. All of these agents will be much harder to uncover as miniaturized technologies continue to proliferate.

This description of the issues and uses of cyber technology offered above explains some of the "cyber silhouettes" that now are part of our lives. There are an ever-increasing number of cyber-related devices that are being forced upon us faster than we can comprehend their functioning or, more importantly, their eventual consequences. However, this is a fact we must accept and to which we must adapt. The good side is represented by cyber equipment's many benefits. In the end we are relying daily on cyber-based technologies whether it is to help us with mundane tasks or to communicate with friends and family on the Internet. The bad side comes into play as the functionality falls into the hands of terrorists or criminals and the purpose becomes explosive. Another indicator that we do not understand how to integrate our efforts is the disparity in language and thus focus among civilians, the federal government, and the military. If the saying is true that "how you understand something determines what you will do with your day" then we are all going in different directions.

CHAPTER TWO: AL QAEDA AND THE INTERNET: THE DANGER OF "CYBERPLANNING"[53]

Introduction

We can say with some certainty, al Qaeda loves the Internet. When the latter first appeared, it was hailed as an integrator of cultures, and a medium for businesses, consumers, and governments to communicate with one another. It appeared to offer unparalleled opportunities for the creation of a "global village." Today the Internet still offers that promise, but it also has proven in some respects to be a digital menace. Its use by al Qaeda is only one example. It has also provided a virtual battlefield for peacetime hostilities between Taiwan and China, Israel and Palestine, Pakistan and India, and China and the United States (during both the war over Kosovo and in the aftermath of the collision between the Navy EP-3 aircraft and Chinese MiG). In times of actual conflict, the Internet was used as a virtual battleground between NATO's coalition forces and elements of the Serbian population. These real tensions from a virtual interface involved not only nation-states but also non-state individuals and groups either aligned with one side or the other, or acting independently.

Evidence strongly suggests that terrorists used the Internet to plan their operations for 9/11. Computers seized in Afghanistan reportedly revealed that al Qaeda was collecting intelligence on targets and sending encrypted messages via the Internet. As recently as 16 September 2002, al Qaeda cells operating in America reportedly were using Internet-based phone services to communicate with cells overseas. These incidents indicate that the Internet is being used as a "cyberplanning" tool for terrorists. It provides terrorists with anonymity, command and control resources, and a host of other measures to coordinate and integrate attack options.

Cyberplanning may be a more important terrorist Internet tool than the much touted and feared cyberterrorism option—attacks against information and systems resulting in violence against noncombatant targets. The Naval Postgraduate School (NPS) defined cyberterrorism as the unlawful destruction or disruption of digital property to intimidate or coerce people.[54] Cyberplanning, not defined by NPS or any other source, refers to the digital coordination of an integrated plan stretching across geographical boundaries

---

[53] This chapter is the complete version of an article by the same name that appeared in Parameters, Spring 2003, pp. 112-123.

[54] Patricia Daukantas, "Government Computer News via Infowar.com," 14 December 2001, from http://www.infowar.com.

that may or may not result in bloodshed. It can include cyberterrorism as part of the overall plan. Since 9/11, US sources have monitored several websites linked to al Qaeda that appear to contain elements of cyberplanning:

- alneda.com, which US officials said contained encrypted information to direct al Qaeda members to more secure sites, featured international news on al Qaeda, and published articles, fatwas (decisions on applying Muslim law), and books.
- assam.com, believed to be linked to al Qaeda (originally hosted by the Scranton company BurstNET Technologies, Inc.), served as a mouthpiece for jihad in Afghanistan, Chechnya, and Palestine.
- almuhrajiroun.com, an al Qaeda site which urged sympathizers to assassinate Pakistani President Musharraf.
- qassam.net, reportedly linked to Hamas.
- jihadunspun.net, which offered a 36-minute video of Osama bin Laden.[55]
- 7hj.7hj.com, which aimed to teach visitors how to conduct computer attacks.[56]
- aloswa.org, which featured quotes from bin Laden tapes, religious legal rulings that "justified" the terrorist attacks, and support for the al Qaeda cause.[57]
- drasat.com, run by the Islamic Studies and Research Center (which some allege is a fake center), and reported to be the most credible of dozens of Islamist sites posting al Qaeda news.
- jehad.net, alsaha.com, and islammemo.com, alleged to have posted al Qaeda statements on their websites.
- mwhoob.net, and aljehad.online, alleged to have flashed political-religious songs, with pictures of persecuted Muslims, to denounce US policy and Arab leaders, notably Saudi.[58]

While it is prudent to tally the Internet cyberplanning applications that support terrorists, it must be underscored that few if any of these measures are really anything new. Any hacker or legitimate web participant can employ many of these same measures for their own purposes, for business, or even for advertising endeavors. The difference, of course, is that most of the people on

---

[55] Jack Kelley, "Militants Wire Web with Links to Jihad," USA Today, 10 July 2002, from CNO/IO Newsletter, Vol. 2, No. 29, 8-14 July 2002.
[56] Ibid.
[57] Yossi Melman, "Virtual Soldiers in a Holy War," Ha'aretz, http://www.haaretz.com, 17 September 2002.
[58] Habib Trabelsi, "Al Qaeda Wages Cyber War against US," Middle East Times, Dubai, June 27 2002, rpt. in CNO/IO Newsletter, Vol. 2, No. 28, 1-7 July 2002.

the net, even if they have the capabilities, do not harbor the intent to do harm, as does a terrorist or Al Qaeda member.

Terrorist Methodologies

Highlighting several of the more important applications helps attract attention to terrorist methodologies and enables law enforcement agencies to recognize where and what to look for on the net. Sixteen measured are listed here for consideration. More could be added.

The Internet can be used to put together profiles. Internet user demographics allow terrorists to target users with sympathy toward a cause or issue, and to solicit donations if the right "profile" is found. Usually a front group will perform the fundraising for the terrorist, often unwittingly. Email fundraising has the potential to significantly assist a terrorist's publicity objectives and finances simultaneously.[59]

Word searches of online newspapers and journals allow a terrorist to construct a profile of the means designed to counter his actions, or a profile of admitted vulnerabilities in our systems. For example, recent articles reported on attempts to slip contraband items through security checkpoints. One report noted that at Cincinnati's airport, contraband slipped through over 50 percent of the time. A simple Internet search by a terrorist would uncover this shortcoming, and offer the terrorist an embarkation point to consider for his or her next operation. A 16 September report noted that US law enforcement agencies were tracing calls made overseas to al Qaeda cells from phone cards, cell phones, phone booths, or Internet-based phone services. Exposing the targeting techniques of law enforcement agencies allows the terrorist to alter his or her operating procedures. The use of profiles by terrorists to uncover such material greatly assists their command and control of operations. The implication is that in a free society such as the United States, you can publish too much information, and while the information might not be sensitive to us, it might be very useful for a terrorist.

Internet access can be controlled or its use directed according to the server configuration, thus creating a true ideological weapon. In the past, if some report was offensive to a government, the content of the report could be censored or filtered. Governments cannot control the Internet to the same degree they could control newspapers and TV. In fact, the Internet can serve as a terrorist's TV or radio station, or his international newspaper or journal. The

---

[59] Patrick S. Tibbetts, "Terrorist Use of the Internet and Related Information Technologies," unpublished paper, School of Advanced Military Studies, Fort Leavenworth, Kansas, June 2002, p. 20.

web allows an uncensored and unfiltered version of events to be broadcast worldwide. Chat rooms, websites, and bulletin boards are largely uncontrolled, with few filters in place. This climate is perfect for an under funded group to explain its actions or to offset both internal and international condemnation, especially when using specific servers. The Internet can target fence sitters as well as true believers with different messages, oriented to the target audience.

In the aftermath of the 9/11 attacks, al Qaeda operatives used the Internet to fight for the hearts and minds of the Islamic faithful worldwide. Al Qaeda described several internationally recognized and respected Muslims who questioned the attacks as hypocrites. Al Qaeda ran two websites, alneda.com and drasat.com, to discuss the legality of the attacks on 9/11. Al Qaeda stated that Islam shares no fundamental values with the West and that Muslims are committed to spread Islam by the sword. As a result of such commentary, several Muslim critics of al Qaeda's policies withdrew their prior condemnation.[60] Ideological warfare worked.

The Internet can be used anonymously, or as a shell game to hide identities. Terrorists have access to Internet tools to create anonymity or disguise their identities. Online encryption services offer encryption keys for some services that are very difficult to break. The website spammimic.com offers tools that hide text in "spam," unsolicited bulk commercial email. Speech compression technology allows users to convert a computer into a secure phone device. Network accounts can be deleted or changed as required. For example, Internet users can create Internet accounts with national firms such as America Online (AOL), or can even create an AOL Instant Messenger (AIM) account on a short-term basis. In addition, anonymous logins are possible for many of the thousands of chat rooms on the net. If desired, the user can access cybercafés, university and library computers, or additional external resources to further hide the source of the messages.[61] An al Qaeda laptop found in Afghanistan had linked with the French Anonymous Society on several occasions. The site offers a two-volume Sabotage Handbook online.

Not only are anonymous methods available for the people who use the Internet, but at times Internet service providers (ISPs) unwittingly participate in serving people or groups for purposes other than legitimate ones. The al Qaeda website www.alneda.com was originally located in Malaysia until 13 May. It reappeared in Texas at http://66.34.191.223/ until 13 June, and then reappeared

---

[60] Paul Eedle, "Al Qaeda Takes Fight for 'Hearts and Minds' to the Web," Jane's Intelligence Review, August 2002, rpt. in CNO/IO Newsletter, Vol. 2, No. 33, 5-11 August 2002.
[61] Tibbetts, pp. 7-9.

on 21 June at www.drasat.com in Michigan. It was shut down on 25 June 2002. The ISPs hosting it apparently knew nothing about the content of the site or even the fact that it was housed on their servers.[62] This shell game with their website enabled the al Qaeda web to remain functional in spite of repeated efforts to shut it down. Cyberdeception campaigns will remain a problem for law enforcement personnel for years to come.

The Internet produces an atmosphere of virtual fear or virtual life. People are afraid of things that are invisible, and things they don't understand. The virtual threat of computer attacks appears to be one of those things. Cyberfear is generated by the fact that what a computer attack *could* do (bring down airliners, ruin critical infrastructure, destroy the stock market, reveal Pentagon planning secrets, etc.) is too often associated with what *will* happen. News reports would lead one to believe that hundreds or thousands of people are still active in the al Qaeda network on a daily basis just because al Qaeda says so. It is clear that the Internet empowers small groups and makes them appear much more capable than they might actually be, even turning bluster into a type of virtual fear. The net allows terrorists to amplify the consequences of their activities with follow-on messages and threats directly to the population at large, even though the terrorist group may be totally impotent. In effect, the Internet allows a person or group to appear to be larger or more important or threatening then they really are.

The Internet can be used to spread disinformation, frightening personal messages, or horrific images of recent activities (one is reminded of the use of the net to replay the murder of reporter Daniel Pearl by his Pakistani captors). Virtually, it appears as though attacks are well planned and controlled, and capabilities are genuine. Messages are usually one-sided, however, and reflect a particular political slant. There is often little chance to check the story and find out if it is mere bravado or fact. The Internet can thus spread rumors and false reports that many people, until further examination, regard as facts.

Recently, the Arab TV station al Jazeera has played tape recordings of bin Laden's speeches and displayed a note purportedly signed by him praising attacks on an oil tanker near Yemen, and on US soldiers participating in a war game in Kuwait. These messages were picked up and spread around the Internet, offering virtual proof that bin Laden was alive. Most likely, bin Laden was seriously injured (which is why we haven't seen him in over a year), but his image can be manipulated through radio or Internet broadcasts so that he appears confident, even healthy.

---

[62] Eedle, "Al Qaeda Takes Fight."

The Internet can help a poorly funded group to raise money. Al Qaeda has used Islamic humanitarian "charities" to raise money for jihad against the perceived enemies of Islam. Analysts found al Qaeda and humanitarian relief agencies using the same bank account numbers on numerous occasions. As a result, several US-based Islamic charities were shut down.[63] The Sunni extremist group Hizb al Tahrir uses an integrated web of Internet sites from Europe to Africa to call for the return of an Islamic caliphate. The website states that it desires to do so by peaceful means. Supporters are encouraged to assist the effort by monetary support, scholarly verdicts, and encouraging others to support jihad. Bank information, including account numbers, is provided on a German site, www.explizit-islam.de.[64] Portals specializing in the anonymous transfer of money, or portals providing services popular with terrorists (such as the issue of new identities and official passports) are also available.[65]

The fighters in the Russian breakaway republic of Chechnya have used the Internet to publicize banks and bank account numbers to which sympathizers can contribute. One of these Chechen bank accounts is located in Sacramento California, according to a Chechen website known as amina.com.

Of course, there are other ways to obtain money for a cause via the Internet. One of the most common ways is credit card fraud. Jean-Francois Ricard, one of France's top anti-terrorism investigators, noted that many Islamist terror plots in Europe and North America were financed through such criminal activity.[66]

The Internet is an outstanding command and control mechanism. Command and control, from a US military point of view, involves the exercise of authority and direction by a properly designated commander over assigned and attached forces in the accomplishment of the mission. Personnel, equipment, communications, facilities, and procedures accomplish command and control by assisting in planning, directing, coordinating, and controlling forces and operations in the accomplishment of a mission.

Command and control on the Internet is not hindered by geographical distance, or by lack of sophisticated communication equipment. Antigovern-

---

[63] Colin Soloway, Rod Nordland, and Barbie Nadeau, "Hiding (and Seeking) Messages on the Web," Newsweek, June 17 2002, p. 8.

[64] "Sunni Extremist Group Hizb al-Tahrir Promotes Ideology on the Internet," downloaded from the FBIS website on 5 February 2002.

[65] C. E. Manin, "Terrorism and Information Communication Technology," La Tribune, College Interarmees de Defense, April 2002, p. 112.

[66] Michael Elliot, "Reeling Them In," Time, 23 September 2002, p. 33.

ment groups present at the G8 conference in Cologne used the Internet to attack computers of financial centers and to coordinate protests from locations as distant as Indonesia and Canada. Terrorists can use their front organizations to coordinate such attacks, to flood a key institution's email service (sometimes as a diversionary tactic for another attack), or to send hidden messages that coordinate and plan future operations.

The average citizen, the antigovernment protester, and the terrorist now have access to command and control means, limited though they be, to coordinate and plan attacks. Further, there are "cracking" tools available to detect security flaws in systems and try to exploit them. Attaining access to a site allows the hacker or planner to command and control assets (forces or electrons) that are not his. The Internet's potential for command and control can vastly improve an organization's effectiveness if it does not have a dedicated command and control establishment, especially in the propaganda and internal coordination areas. Finally, command and control can be accomplished via the Internet's chat rooms. One website, alneda.com, has supported al Qaeda's effort to disperse its forces and enable them to operate independently, providing leadership via strategic guidance, theological arguments, and moral inspiration. The site also published a list of the names and home phone numbers of 84 al Qaeda fighters captured in Pakistan after escaping from Afghanistan. The aim presumably was to allow sympathizers to contact their families and let them know they were alive.[67]

The Internet is a recruiting tool. The web allows the user complete control over content, and eliminates the need to rely on journalists for publicity. Individuals with sympathy for a cause can be converted by the images and messages of terrorist organizations, and the addition of digital video has reinforced this ability. Images and video clips are tools of empowerment for terrorists. More important, net access to such products provides contact points for men and women to enroll in the cause, whatever it may be.[68] Additionally,

> Current versions of web browsers, including Netscape and Internet Explorer, support JavaScript functions allowing Internet servers to know which language is set as the default for a particular client's computer. Hence, a browser set to use English as the default language can be redirected to a site optimized for publicity aimed at Western

---

[67] Paul Eedle, "Terrorism.com," The Guardian, 17 July 2002, as downloaded from the FBIS website on 17 July 2002.
[68] Tibbets, p. 37.

38

audiences, while one set to use Arabic as the default can be redirected to a different site tailored toward Arab or Muslim sensibilities.[69]

This allows recruiting to be audience- and language-specific, enabling the web to serve as a recruiter of talent for a terrorist cause. Recently, the Chechen website qoqaz.net, which used to be aimed strictly against Russian forces operating in Chechnya, changed its address to assam.com, and now includes links to Jihad in Afghanistan, Jihad in Palestine, and Jihad in Chechnya. Such sites give the impression that the entire Islamic world is uniting against the West, when in fact the site may be the work of just a few individuals.

The Internet is used to gather information on potential targets. The website operated by the Muslim Hackers Club reportedly featured links to US sites that purport to disclose sensitive information like code names and radio frequencies used by the US Secret Service. The same website offers tutorials in viruses, hacking stratagems, network "phreaking" and secret codes, as well as links to other militant Islamic and cyberprankster web addresses.[70] Recent targets that terrorists have discussed include the Center for Disease Control and Prevention in Atlanta; FedWire, the money-movement clearing system maintained by the Federal Reserve Board; and facilities controlling the flow of information over the Internet.[71] Attacks on critical infrastructure control systems would be particularly harmful, especially on a system such as the Supervisory Control and Data Acquisition (SCADA) system. Thus any information on insecure network architectures or non-enforceable security protocols is potentially very damaging.

Terrorists have access, like many Americans, to imaging data on potential targets, as well as maps, diagrams, and other crucial data on important facilities or networks. Imaging data can also allow terrorists to view counterterrorist activities at a target site. One captured al Qaeda computer contained engineering and structural architecture features of a dam, enabling al Qaeda engineers and planners to simulate catastrophic failures.[72]

With regard to gathering information through the Internet, on 15 January 2003 Defense Secretary Donald Rumsfeld observed that an al Qaeda training manual recovered in Afghanistan said, "Using public sources openly

---

[69] Ibid., p. 34.
[70] Mark Hosenball, "Islamic Cyberterror," Newsweek, 20 May 2002.
[71] Tom Squitieri, "Cyberspace Full of Terror Targets," USA Today, 5 June 2002.
[72] Barton Gellman, "FBI Fears Al Qaeda Cyber Attacks," San Francisco Chronicle, 28 June 2002, pp. 1, 10.

and without resorting to illegal means, it is possible to gather at least 80 percent of all information about the enemy."[73]

The Internet puts distance between those planning the attack and their targets. Terrorists planning attacks on the United States can do so abroad with limited risk, especially if their command and control sites are located in countries other than their own. Tracing the route of their activity is particularly difficult. The net provides terrorists a place to plan without the risks normally associated with cell or satellite phones.

The Internet can be used to steal information or manipulate data. Ronald Dick, director of the FBI's National Infrastructure Protection Center, considers the theft or manipulation of data by terrorist groups as his worst nightmare, especially if the attacks are integrated with a physical attack such as on a US power grid.[74] Richard Clark, chairman of the President's Critical Infrastructure Protection Board, said the problem of cybersecurity and data protection had its own 9/11 on 18 September 2001 when the Nimda virus spread through Internet-connected computers around the world, causing billions of dollars of damage. Nimda's creator has never been identified. This virus, hardly noticed in the wake of the airliner attacks and anthrax scares, set off a chain reaction among software companies (including Microsoft) to get very serious about plugging vulnerabilities.[75] In the fall of 2001, a number of unexplained intrusions began occurring against Silicon Valley computers. An FBI investigation traced the intrusions to telecommunication switches in Saudi Arabia, Indonesia, and Pakistan. While none were directly linked to al Qaeda, there remain strong suspicions that the group was somehow involved.[76]

The Internet can be used to send hidden messages. The practice of steganography, which involves hiding messages inside graphic files, is a widespread art among criminal and terrorist elements. Hidden pages or nonsensical phrases can be coded instructions for al Qaeda operatives and supporters. One recent report noted,

> Al Qaeda uses prearranged phrases and symbols to direct its agents. An icon of an AK-47 can appear next to a photo of Osama bin Laden facing one direction one day, and another direction the next. The color

---

[73] "Citing Al Qaeda Manual, Rumsfeld Re-Emphasizes Web Security," InsideDefense.com, http://www.insidedefense.com/, 15 January 2003.
[74] Gellman, pp. 1, 10.
[75] John Schwartz, "Despite 9/11 Warnings, Cyberspace Still at Risk," The Post Standard (Syracuse, N.Y.), 11 September 2002, pp. D-10, 11.
[76] Maria T. Welch, "Accumulating Digital Evidence is Difficult," The Post Standard, 11 September 2002, pp. D-9, 11.

of icons can change as well. Messages can be hidden on pages inside sites with no links to them, or placed openly in chat rooms.[77]

In addition, it is possible to buy encryption software for less than $15. Cyberplanners gain an advantage in hiding their messages via encryption. Sometimes the messages are not even hidden in a sophisticated manner. Al Jazeera television reported that Mohammed Atta's final message (another advantage of the Internet—the impossibility of checking sources) to direct the attacks on the Twin Towers was simple and open. The message purportedly said, "The semester begins in three more weeks. We've obtained 19 confirmations for studies in the faculty of law, the faculty of urban planning, the faculty of fine arts and the faculty of engineering."[78] The reference to the various faculties was apparently the code for the buildings targeted in the attacks.

The Internet allows groups with few resources to offset even some huge propaganda machines in advanced countries. The web is an attractive device to those looking for a way to attack major powers via the mass media. The "always on" status of the web allows these individuals not only to access sites day and night but also to scold major powers and treat them with disdain in a public forum. The web can be used to counter facts and logic with the logic of the terrorist. There is no need for the terrorist organization to worry about "the truth," because ignoring facts is a standard operating procedure.

Al Qaeda uses polemics on the net not only to offset Western reporting, but also to counter Muslims who don't toe the party line. It defends the conduct of its war against the West and encourages violence. The web is important to al Qaeda because it can be used to enrage people and neutralize moderate opinion. The website of the Center for Islamic Studies and Research (according to one source, a made-up name), for example, has 11 sections, including reports on fighting in Afghanistan, world media coverage of the conflict, books on jihad theology, videos of hijackers' testaments, information about prisoners held in Pakistan and Guantanamo Bay, and jihad poetry.[79]

It does not pay for any major power to lie, as facts can be easily used against them. Even in the war in Chechnya, there were times when the Chechens would report a successful ambush of a Russian convoy, and the Russians would deny the event ever happened. To prove their point, the Chechens would show video footage of the ambush on the Internet, thus

---

[77] Ibid.; Soloway, Nordland, and Nadeau.
[78] Melman.
[79] Eedle, "Terrorism.com."

offsetting the credibility of the Russian official media and undercutting the power of their massive propaganda machine. Al Qaeda officials are waiting to do the same to Western media reporting if the opportunity presents itself.

The Internet can be used to disrupt business. This tactic requires precise timing and intimate knowledge of the business climate in the target country. It attempts to harm businesses by accusing them of guilt by association.

Hezbollah, for example, has outlined a strategy to cripple Israeli government, military, and business sites with the aim of disrupting normal economic and societal operations. Phase one might be to disable official Israeli government sites; phase two might focus on crashing financial sites such as those on the Israeli stock exchange; phase three might involve knocking out the main Israeli internet servers; and phase four might blitz Israeli e-commerce sites to ensure the loss of hundreds of transactions.[80] A final phase could be to accuse companies that do business with a target government as guilty by association and call for a boycott of the firms' products. Arab terrorists attacked Lucent Technologies in a round of Israeli-Arab cyberskirmishes, for example.[81] All of these plans require insider knowledge in order to carry out the operation in a timely and accurate manner.

The Internet can mobilize a group or Diaspora, or other hackers to action. Websites are used not only to disseminate information and propaganda. They also are used to create solidarity and brotherhood among groups. In the case of Islamist terrorist organizations, the Internet substitutes for the loss of bases and territory. In this respect the most important sites are alneda.com, jehad.net, drasat.com, and aloswa.org, which feature quotes from bin Laden tapes, religious legal rulings that justify the terrorist attacks, and support for the al Qaeda cause.[82] In addition, website operators have established a site that is "a kind of database or encyclopedia for the dissemination of computer viruses."[83] The site is 7hj.7hj.com, and it aims to teach Internet users how to conduct computer attacks, purportedly in the service of Islam.[84]

---

[80] Giles Trendle, "Cyberwars: The Coming Arab E-Jihad," The Middle East, No. 322 (April 2002), p. 6.

[81] Tim McDonald, "Fanatics with Laptops: The Coming Cyber War," NewsFactor.com via Yahoo! News, 16 May 2002.

[82] Melman.

[83] Ibid.

[84] Ibid.

The Internet takes advantage of legal norms. Non-state actors or terrorists using the Internet can ignore Western notions of law and focus instead on cultural or religious norms. At a minimum, they ignore legal protocols on the Internet. In addition, they use the net to break the law (when they hack websites or send out viruses) while at the same time the law protects them (from unlawful surveillance, etc.).

International investigations into such behaviors are difficult to conclude due to the slow pace of other nations' investigative mechanisms, and the limited time that data is stored.[85] However, in the aftermath of the events of 9/11 in the United States, the terrorists' actions actually initiated several changes in the US legal system that were not to the terrorists' advantage. For example, in the past, the privacy concerns of Internet users were a paramount consideration by the US government. After 9/11, new legislation was enacted.

The controversial USA Patriot Act of 2001 included new field guidance relating to computer crime and electronic evidence. The Patriot Act is designed to unite and strengthen the United States by providing the appropriate tools required to intercept and obstruct terrorism. It establishes a counterterrorism fund in the Treasury Department, amends federal criminal code that authorizes enhanced surveillance procedures, provides guidelines for investigating money-laundering concerns, removes obstacles to investigating terrorism (granting the FBI authority to investigate fraud and computer-related activity for specific cases), and strengthens criminal laws against terrorism.[86]

The "Field Guidance on New Authorities that Relate to Computer Crime and Electronic Evidence Enacted in the USA Patriot Act of 2001" provides the authority to do several things. Authorizations include: intercepting voice communications in computer hacking investigations; allowing law enforcement to trace communications on the Internet and other computer networks within the pen register and trap and trace statute ("pen/trap" statute); intercepting communications of computer trespassers; writing nationwide search warrants for email; and deterring and preventing cyberterrorism. The latter provision raises the maximum penalty for hackers that damage protected computers (and eliminates minimums); states that hackers need only show intent to cause damage, not a particular consequence or degree of damage; provides for the aggregation of damage caused by a hacker's entire course of conduct; creates a new offense for damaging computers used for national security and criminal justice; expands the definition of a "protected computer"

---

[85] Manin, p. 112.
[86] See "Bill Summary & Status for the 107th Congress," http://thomas.loc.gov/cgi-bin/bdquery/z?d107:HR03162.

to include computers in foreign countries; counts prior state convictions of computer crime as prior offenses; and defines computer "loss." In addition, the guidance develops and supports cybersecurity forensic capabilities.[87]

The Internet can be used to divert attention from a real attack scenario. Al Qaeda can plant threats on the Internet or via cell phones to mislead law enforcement officials. Terrorists study how US operators collect and analyze information, and thus how we respond to information.

Terrorists know when their Internet "chatter" or use of telecommunications increases, US officials issue warnings. Terrorists can thus introduce false information into a net via routine means, measure the response it garners from the US intelligence community, and then try to figure out where the leaks are in their systems or what type of technology the United States is using to uncover their plans. For example, if terrorists use encrypted messages over cell phones to discuss a fake operation against, say, the Golden Gate Bridge, they can then sit back and watch to see if law enforcement agencies issue warnings regarding this particular landmark. If they do, then the terrorists know US officials are listening to their communications.[88]

Conclusions

In conclusion, it should be reiterated that cyberplanning is as important a concept as cyberterrorism, and perhaps even more so. Terrorists won't have an easy time shutting down the Internet. Vulnerabilities are continuously reported and fixed while computers function without serious interference (at least in the United States). One hopes that law enforcement and government officials will focus more efforts on the cyberplanning capabilities of terrorists in order to thwart computer attacks and other terrorist activities. At a minimum, America can use such measures to make terrorist activities much harder to coordinate and control. Paul Eedle, writing in The Guardian, summed up the value of the Internet to al Qaeda:

> Whether bin Ladin or al Qaeda's Egyptian theorist Ayman al-Zawahiri and their colleagues are on a mountain in the Hindu Kush or living with their beards shaved off in a suburb of Karachi no longer matters to the organization. They can inspire and guide a worldwide movement

---

[87] See "Field Guidance on New Authorities that Relate to Computer Crime and Electronic Evidence Enacted in the USA Patriot Act of 2001," http://www.cybercrime.gov/PatriotAct.htm.
[88] John Diamond, "Al Qaeda Steers Clear of NSA's Ears," USA Today, 17 October 2002, CNO/IO Newsletter, 23-30 October 2002, pp. 17-18.

without physically meeting their followers—without knowing who they are.[89]

Such is the power and danger of cyberplanning.

---

[89] Eedle, "Terrorism.com."

CHAPTER THREE: CYBERINSURGENCY

Introduction

In the Industrial Age an insurgency was easily localized due to the limited means available to spread the insurgent's ideology. Insurgents had only word of mouth, the effects of their actions, and the local media's coverage of events to spread their ideas. A message could take days to distribute and might be limited to a few individuals. These facts severely limited command and control, recruiting, fundraising, and consequently the development of a mass insurgent base. Since mass mobilization was difficult, armed conflict became the primary means to advance a cause.

Insurgencies of the Cyber Age are aimed at, and able to reach, large numbers of people. The starkest difference is the insurgent's capability to reach disenfranchised members of a mass base in a direct manner via the Internet. As one specialist noted about Muslims in Europe "the Internet stands in for the idea of the ummah, the mythologized Muslim community."[90] This virtual ummah "inspires people not only to love their country but to die for it."[91] Further, the Internet provides the means to conduct virtual operations according to the insurgent's needs. Most often this results in cyberrecruiting, cyberplanning, cyberfear, cybertargeting, cyberreconnaissance, and cyberfunding operations in addition to purely offensive operations such as virus attacks. Most Western security specialists are preoccupied with cyberterrorism and cybercrime that results in a focus on cybersecurity operations. Thus the Western focus is different than the insurgent's focus.

The Internet also offers insurgents the ability to use tested guerilla techniques and operating procedures online (dead drops, anonymity, hit-and-run tactics, surprise and ambush, hostage-taking, reconnaissance, and deception). While not subscribing to all of these techniques, insurgents have adopted some of them. In addition to creating a global village, the Internet has also created an insurgent's operational paradise. Without fancy command and control, intelligence, and surveillance equipment, insurgents can accomplish some of the same missions that these high-tech and expensive systems conduct.

US army doctrine defines an insurgency as

An armed political movement aimed at the overthrow of a constituted government, or separation from it, through use of subversion and armed

---

[90] Lawrence Wright, "The Terror Web," The New Yorker, 2 August 2004, p. 49.
[91] Ibid.

conflict. It is a protracted politico-military struggle designed to weaken government control and legitimacy while increasing insurgent control. Political power is the central issue in an insurgency."[92]

Further, an insurgency has as its goal "to mobilize human and material resources in order to form an alternative to the state."[93] The real hidden danger of the Internet is its high-speed connection that can spread an insurgency's ideological and theoretical philosophy almost without time, space, or financial limitations. This offers the insurgent the capability to speed up the formation of a base of support (mobilizing those human and material resources with long inbred grievances) and to create an alternative to the state's ideology. The Internet thus helps insurgents weaken government control and legitimacy, thereby subverting local authorities just as the definition of insurgency requires.

This article describes how the Internet enables insurgents to mobilize a base of support, expand their influence, and potentially conduct guerilla warfare on the Internet. The continuing stream of insurgents flowing into Iraq today, perhaps, best reflects the Internet's success in these areas.

Context

While they continue to focus on physical and barbaric actions that induce terror (such as improvised explosive devices [IEDs], car bombs, hostage-taking, etc.), today's insurgents are also savvy and informed. They are adept at using Internet information and other media sources against us, replaying the attacks over the net to reinforce success and multiply the effects of attacks. Insurgents understand the importance of supporting virtual activities that potentially can mobilize thousands of people. For most American security specialists, the primary threat associated with the Internet remains cyberterrorism, which involves the destruction (physical action) of networks through the use of electrons or other devices. This fact is reflected in the West in the number of university and military courses dedicated to the theory of cyberterrorism. No such courses are available on cyberplanning or cybermentality or cyberexploitation of the masses.

Insurgents in the Information Age are capable of overcoming most of the limiting constraints imposed by media outlets during the Industrial Age. Today, according to Gabriel Weimann of the US Institute of Peace, there are more than 4,000 insurgent and terrorist websites.[94] The huge number of

---

[92] FMI 3-07.22, Counterinsurgency Operations, August 2004, p. 1-1, used with permission of the authors.
[93] Ibid.
[94] Lawrence Wright, p. 50.

websites has made it nearly impossible for law enforcement personnel to contain the scope and spread of an insurgent's message. Most Internet Service Providers (ISP) don't even know that their servers contain this type of information. The sheer volume of data, coupled with the fact that ISP owners often contract with other companies for the maintenance of their sites, allow web page content to be easily overlooked. If the ISP providers discover unacceptable content and shut down the websites, the insurgents can easily move their websites to alternative locations.

As a result, the Internet has become a communication and ideological paradise for insurgents. One recent book titled <u>The 39 Principles of Jihad</u> by Mohammad Bin Ahmad Al-Salem (a possible pseudonym) on the principles of jihad (a holy war waged on behalf of Islam as a religious duty) emphasized this notion. Principle 34 of the book's 39 principles of jihad was "electronic jihad." That is, waging war via the Internet. Believers are called to join a jihad through participation in Internet forums. Participants are asked to defend Islam and the Mujahideen, to preach Jihad, and to encourage Muslims to learn more about their duty.[95]

Countries battling insurgents need to examine the use of the Internet from a new angle. For the past ten years, Westerners have considered the Internet to be a part of their operating environment. They have understood its impact on democratic politics and assumed that other countries would use the Internet in a similar manner. Two problems stand in the way. First is the problem of legal regulation of the Internet—what can and cannot be shown, and how it can be used. Insurgents do not face this limitation. They use the Internet as they see fit without political or legal restrictions. Second, Westerners underestimate, or simply cannot comprehend, the Internet's impact on disadvantaged societies and its ability to mobilize and empower the disenfranchised. Insurgents try to boost their images with their targeted audiences by boasting online about bombings and killing hostages. They can also offer logic and legitimacy for their actions based on religious or ideological sources. Perhaps a new focus is needed on regions, ideologies, and religions instead of countries.

It is clear that there is a need for a closer look at all of these issues as the Internet is currently being used to reach a mass base. Insurgent websites are truly the planning and motivational grounds for future conflicts and battles.

---

[95] Joel Leyden, "Al Qaeda: The 39 Principles of Holy War," <u>Israel News Agency</u>, 4 September 2003 as downloaded from http://www.israelnewsagency.com/Al Qaeda.html.

Adaptive Insurgent Organization and Doctrine

The primary elements of an insurgent organization are its leadership, combatants, cadre, and mass base according to US army doctrine.[96] In the Cyber Age each of these elements has presented new challenges to the West. Leaders conduct command and control from distances that are miles, if not continents away from their base via the net, and they can conduct dead drops, send hidden messages, and control forces instantaneously in ways never before imagined. Combatants no longer have to be just fighters, either. They can also be computer operators, computer repairmen, or the owners and operators of servers, among other jobs. Cadres are the political activists of the insurgency. They are the main ideologues or website masters as well as those responsible for collecting local contributions based on net advertisements. These fundraising activities are conducted in the heartland of the enemy, often hidden as contributions to charities or disguised as legitimate businesses. The mass base is composed of the followers of the movement. Today the mass base is composed of dissatisfied elements found in chat rooms from Idaho to Baghdad. Now, from the privacy of one's home, all of these elements are executable. The mobilization of a much larger virtual supporting base has enabled the initial smaller "actionable" armed conflict of physical terror to expand instead of shrink as the insurgency progresses. It is possible to call people to the battle from far away via the Internet, as is being done in Iraq. The Internet has thus caused a significant increase in the virtual and real influence of the elements of an insurgent organization.

Two types of offensive actions are key components of insurgency doctrine according to US army publications: armed conflict and mass mobilization. The Western press is full of reporting on the issue of armed conflict in Iraq and other places. There is a historical record of insurgent/guerilla actions that support armed violence and cause reporters to observe and write from this point of view. These reports include life and death accounts from mobile (hit-and-run) and stationary tactics, the use of surprise and ambush via IEDs and car bombs, and hostage-taking among many other actions. The aim of armed conflict is to enhance the visibility of an ideology, to attain notoriety, and to attempt to win a political victory over an opponent. Group members (with the possible exception of charismatic leadership) try to remain anonymous, publicizing only the name of the group and its manifesto until victory is close to being assured. Such reporting is sensational and mainstream.

The new breed of insurgent leaders uses the Internet to offer their vision and lend legitimacy of their actions to the masses. It is a quiet aspect of

---

[96] Ibid., pp. 1-2.

insurgency, but equally as deadly, since it recruits new fighters for the ranks. In the past this simply wasn't possible unless a media outlet sympathized with the insurgents. Now, after an insurgent action is recorded and played on the Internet, local media more often than not pick up on the event and replay it several times for the population in an affected region. Then, the broadcast is repeated hundreds of times by media outlets in other countries as well. Osama bin Laden uses the Internet or al Jazeera to broadcast his short- and long-term goals and ideological messages, as do the leaders of the Chechen extremist movement. Then the Western media picks them up and replays them for Western consumption creating a cyberecho. Other websites replay the Western broadcasts. These replays add legitimacy and strength to the insurgent's cause within impoverished areas—in particular as the media attempts to explain real or perceived grievances that touch the souls of the virtual community. Further, if the logic of the insurgent has a religious base it can tempt like-minded believers all over the world to support the cause.

America has shown how its population uses the Internet to gain support for a cause on many occasions. Internet polls are conducted daily on issues as mundane as who would be the favorite to win an Emmy award or who should be the most valuable player in a baseball season. In the 2004 Democratic primary elections in the US, candidate John Dean used the Internet to marshal the support of young people all across the country. Insurgents do the same with the young people in their parts of the world except that these young people are following the Internet out of ideological zeal, not for something as mundane as the Emmys. Insurgents share with the young their common objectives and ideas for the development of political power or a desired end-state. This tactic is particularly effective in poverty-stricken areas where promises of a better lifestyle and imposed justice can undo the perceived injustices of countries and past leaders covering decades of rule.

Mobilizing the Masses
The insurgent's achievement of mass mobilization through the Internet is not as dramatic as the life and death struggles of armed conflict for media outlets. Thus it receives far less coverage and understanding. But the Internet is a forum for achieving mass mobilization since it is accessible and controllable.

This is most apparent in the Arab world where long-held grievances against countries (Israel) and kingdoms (Saudi Arabia) manifest themselves on the net in the form of mass condemnations and demands for action. The presence of coalition forces in Iraq exacerbates these feelings. These are the sites accessed by the disenfranchised so that they can hear the words of people of like minds. Websites such as CNN do not offer the same type of mental refuge or understanding.

It is clear that Osama bin Laden realized the importance of the mass media and the necessity to mobilize the masses several years ago. Journalist Lawrence Wright noted that bin Laden emboldened his Internet warriors with his bragging about successes and desire to rid the world of "infidels" via assassinations and other operations. Users began to discuss bin Laden's appeal among themselves with postings on message boards. These boards also posted declarations, recordings, and other material. In Wright's opinion the Internet helped to arouse other Muslims and Arabs by explaining terrorism's "sacramental role," and the Internet helped to immortalize bin Laden. [97]

Bin Laden believes the Internet can help subvert Western public opinion. Journalist Allan Cullison obtained an al Qaeda "owned and operated hard drive" from a computer in northern Afghanistan in the autumn of 2001 during the fighting against the Taliban. He wrote about its contents for the Atlantic Monthly in the summer of 2004. In a 3 October 2001 message from bin Laden to Mullah Omar that Cullison recovered, bin Laden noted the requirement to conduct a media campaign to fight the enemy's publicity. The goal was to create a rift between the American people and their government (and stop the US campaign in Afghanistan) by demonstrating:

- The government would lead them into further losses of lives and money.
- The government is sacrificing the people to serve the interests (particularly Jewish interests) of the rich.
- The government is leading them to war in order to protect Israel.
- America should withdraw from the current battle between Muslims and Jews.[98]

Bin Laden has not been particularly successful with this methodology. Rather his ranting has impacted his own people more than Westerners, emboldening them to further action.

CDs are circulating in Iraq and Kuwait purportedly on behalf of Abu Musab al Zarqawi, al Qaeda's primary leader in Iraq. The CDs appear to be aimed at recruiting fighters. They include interviews with suicide bombers as well as religious and war hymns. Zarqawi is the narrator.[99] Rita Katz, director

---

[97] Wright, pp. 50-53.

[98] Alan Cullison, "Inside Al Qaeda's Hard Drive," The Atlantic Monthly, September 2004, paper received via email.

[99] "Zarqawi's Disk Demonstrates Suicide's Pre-Nuptial Rites," DEBKAfile Special Report, 7 August 2004 from http://www.debka.com

of the SITE Institute, a nonprofit group in the District monitoring terrorist sites for the federal government, believes that Abu Musab al Zarqawi, Iraq's most wanted guerilla leader, is revered due to the Internet.[100] Journalist Ariana Eunjung Cha summarized how these attributes of the Internet work for the terrorist:

> He calls himself Abu Maysara al Iraqi, or father of Maysara the Iraqi, and he's a master at being everywhere and nowhere in the virtual world, constantly switching his online accounts and taking advantage of new technologies to issue his communiqués to the world. Acting as a spokesman for Abu Musab al Zarqawi ...his words and images reach millions of people when they open their newspapers, turn on their TVs or go online in search of news. ...Abu Maysara declared in a Sept. 19 posting that he issues his reports so that his perspective "does not become lost in the media blackout that America imposes in order to deceive its people and its allies." ...With more than 1 billion linked computers, ...technology allows users to mask their identities and change them on a whim by throwing away old email accounts and creating new ones. ...A message that appears to come from Australia, for instance, may actually come from someone who has accessed the Australian computer by going through the Netherlands via South Korea (news - websites) after originating in Jordan.[101]

What are some other advantages that the Internet offers to the insurgent to mobilize the masses? The Internet offers flexible identity, the transmission of altered perceptions, equalized status, recordability, and control from a distance almost instantaneously. The outlets to communicate these methods were not available earlier, which limited the spread of an ideology's mass appeal. Now insurgents can use the Internet to conduct one-sided story telling. It also allows for the means to promote intent, actions, counterreactions, and is often quoted by the "real press" even in the West during a crisis. While civilized nations worry about a mixture of technical, diplomatic, and legal actions to be effective, terrorists worry about none of this. Finally, the insurgent is no longer confined to defensive, offensive, and stalemate operations as US army doctrine states. The forms or types of Internet actions are radically different. Insurgents can conduct command and control operations, recruit new members, develop profiles, raise funds for their cause, develop means to hide messages in photos or files, conduct counterpropaganda, and conduct ideological mobilization and manipulation, among other actions.

---

[100] Ariana Eunjung Cha, "From a Virtual Shadow, Messages of Terror, Washington Post, 2 October 2004, Internet version.
[101] Ibid.

With no filter or censor, the Internet can advance the most bizarre insurgent principles with little chance of being caught. The net can energize sympathy for a cause, operate as a psychological weapon that can enter a home anonymously, and can even invite guests to an insurgent gift shop to purchase or download emblems and slogans. Web postings are used to vindicate insurgent actions based on the logic of "no other choice than to act" or to "delegitimize the enemy" and can offer nonviolent solutions. In other words, the Internet can offer a kinder face for the insurgent, or it can offer harsh reality (beheading of an individual) for those who choose to support the "infidels."

Potential and Actual Insurgent Tactics on the Internet

Insurgent techniques have evolved and now include Cyber Age adaptations from their Industrial Age counterparts. This applies to both tactics and planning for an insurgency operation.

An example of a Cyber Age adaptation is the "dead drop." A dead drop is a method used to exchange secrets between two groups or among people who do not actually meet. In the past, an insurgent dead drop may have been a huge rock under which they placed the message or code. Another insurgent, aware of the rock's location, would then retrieve the message. In the Cyber Age, an insurgent can visit a cybercafé, write a draft message, put it in a file, sign off, and depart the premises. Because the draft was never sent, the Internet service provider (ISP) does not retain a copy. Later, even from another location thousands of miles away, another insurgent with knowledge of the same prearranged password and username can obtain access to the file, read the draft letter, and then erase it.[102] Thus the message is exchanged via a high-tech dead drop.

Al Qaeda computer expert Mohammad Naeem Noor Khan, arrested in Pakistan on 12 July 2004, had been creating websites and secret email codes to enable al Qaeda operatives to communicate with one another. He was arrested in a remote area of Pakistan far from the other al Qaeda hideouts.[103] Khan allegedly told interrogators that al Qaeda used websites and email addresses in Turkey, Nigeria, and tribal areas of Pakistan—that is, in the country of a NATO member, on another continent, and in a region where computer connections should be sparse, thus demonstrating the reach of an insurgent's net. Files were deleted after being read, and email addresses were used only two or three

---

[102] "Cyberspace Gives Al Qaeda Refuge," Jihad Watch, 16 August 2004 at http://www.jihadwatch.org.
[103] "Al Qaeda Computer Whiz Was Top Terror Planner: Security Official," Channelnewsasia.com, 4 August 2004.

times.[104] Thus, the Cyber Age is offering insurgents new tools of operational empowerment.

Insurgent website operators must remain anonymous, and so they create anonymous accounts. It usually is not known who is pressing the keys to publish the message. Insurgents use the net to conduct hit and run tactics, sending viruses out from one machine in a neutral location (cybercafé) and then moving to some safer computer sanctity. Further, the Internet provides insurgents with the logistic support they require. The Internet's infrastructure is continuously updated free of charge, and new methods to attack the Internet are continuously posted at hacker sites—again free of charge.

Reconnaissance of an objective is an important operation before an attack. Reconnaissance is also possible on the Internet to obtain vital information about attack objectives. This might occur before a computer attack or before an attempt to gain access to targeting information (such as a building design). It is not known if insurgents have used this technique, but it is important to note that although reconnaissance is an old tactic, new and possibly more effective methods of using it are available.

The SDBot.UJ worm offers an example of reconnaissance on the Internet. It scans passing traffic for patterns of data "that normally precede the transmission of a username and password." It then records the data sent immediately afterwards if it spots such a pattern. It does the same for electron packets containing PayPal, a web service for the transfer of money. Network reconnaissance is achieved through the use of a sniffer program, which monitors packets.[105] In this case insurgents may conduct reconnaissance to gain access to a computer to do one of several things: look for computer or network vulnerabilities, access sensitive files, or ascertain the level of police awareness of their activities.

Hostage-taking is possible via the Internet as well. Insurgents can break into a database and encode several important files. In order to get the "key" to unscramble the code, the owner of the file may have to pay a ransom. The important file thus becomes the hostage. Public opinion can also be held hostage. As is the case with the hostage-taking in Iraq, demands can be made for the withdrawal of troops or some other request. If these demands are not met, insurgents can demonstrate to the whole world how a person suffered or

---

[104] "Al Qaeda Suspect Reveals Communication Strategy," 4 August 2004, http://www.cnn.com.
[105] "Computer Worm 'Sniffs' out Passwords," NewScientist.com news service, 14 September 2004, p. 1.

was killed as a result. Public opinion becomes the greatest hostage of such actions, which results in more pressure on governments to concede to the insurgent's demands.

Deception and surprise are still cornerstones of an insurgent's operating techniques during conflict. Catching an opponent off-guard is crucial to success. Similar attack strategies and techniques can be used on the Internet. Most Internet users have been victimized to a degree by some of these methods. That is, the Internet is a place for mass psychological and virtual manipulation just as much as it is a place for mass mobilization. A recent example is an action appearing on spam messages that requests readers to "click here to remove." In actuality the action allows spammers to know that the junk mail messages are being read.[106]

Another common deception technique used online (again, it is not known if insurgents are using this technique) is "phishing." These are emails that appear to be from banks and other financial institutions asking for consumer credit card details—that is "phishing" for details. Insurgents could use this technique as an alternate funding mechanism to support their cause. They could pretend to send a user to a reputable site and then steal the user's money or identity. A vulnerability in Microsoft's Internet Explorer makes this technique appear even more legitimate. An email may load an actual bank website into the main Internet Explorer web page. A second, smaller popup page is then brought up. The location bar on the smaller page will be hidden so that the user doesn't know the page actually originated from another country. Because the site operator can recreate the page to mirror an actual bank site, a degree of trust is created in the mind of the user. The user enters his credit card information and unknowingly sends information off to the country involved. Antiphishing websites are even beginning to appear.

To overcome law enforcement efforts to catch them, criminals started sending image-based messages that can skirt most spam and other filters that rely on algorithms to seek out text strings. These new techniques involve steganography, or the embedding of text in an image.[107] Insurgents are believed to be using these techniques.

Another example of masking or deceiving computer users could be termed "hiding in plain sight." For example, many people have heard of .dll

---

[106] John Leyden, "Click Here to Become Infected," The Register online version, 22 September 2004.
[107] Dennis Fisher, "New Scam Tactic Hits Online," 13 September 2004, from http://www.eweek.com.

files and know they are an integral part of the Windows Operation System. Can you tell the difference between these two files, win32.d11 .exe and win32.dll.exe? The small font style almost obscures the difference in the actual file names. The name is not totally legible and the look-alike file could be anything someone installed on the machine. In this case all of the "L's" were substituted with "1's". When the computer user looks up the currently running processes in his Windows Task Manager, the switched letters are not so obvious. This program could be anything, from a keystroke logger, to a "zombie" bot used for Denial of Service attacks. Another form of hiding in plain sight would be if a person posts messages to a bulletin board that signals some event to members of al Qaeda via simple art forms on the message board. The person could change the position of an AK-47 on the screen or the direction that a "white horse" (a white stallion, according to another source, is purportedly the logo of al Qaeda)[108] is heading to signify the go ahead for an operation. So, while law enforcement officials are looking for hidden text or codes, the answer would be right there in plain sight.

The most clever example of how al Qaeda might mentally manipulate law enforcement through the Internet is to allow (on purpose) some of its messages to be intercepted by law enforcement agencies in order to do one of two things: either divert attention to places specified in the messages and then attack somewhere else, or to simply observe FBI warnings to see if someone picked up on the message and is thus watching or monitoring Internet traffic.

Conclusions

The move from Industrial Age to Cyber Age warfare has changed the speed and way wars are perceived. This results in increased mobilization potential for insurgents. Industrial Age insurgencies were localized, hierarchical, centralized, covert, and contained a single message. Propaganda was for leaders, and agitation materials took the form of written or spoken messages. Cyber Age insurgencies are global, networked, decentralized, overt or covert, and templated at specific target groups. They use messages that attempt to manipulate local Arab opinion with themes such as the humiliation of male prisoners or the violation of human rights at Abu Ghraib. Cyber Age insurgencies take advantage of instantaneous communications means (financed and developed by governments) to deliver messages before governments can block or challenge the statement except after the fact. Charismatic figures or those in charge of a community of believers deliver propaganda, and the

---

[108] Lawrence Wright, p. 50.

material is visual as well as written and spoken. It thus appears more real and legitimate.[109]

The important phrase in the definition of insurgency for purposes of this article is "a protracted politico-military struggle designed to weaken government control and legitimacy while increasing insurgent control." It is important because it may no longer be true that insurgencies are protracted in the old sense of the term. Rather, the period of time needed to wage conflict is cut, due to efficiencies offered by the Internet. The insurgency that developed in Vietnam in the 1960s took years to develop. When the US moved into Vietnam in 1964, it still took another four years for the media to really impact public opinion. When the US moved into Iraq in March 2003, it fought a totalitarian government with little to offer in the way of horizontal communications since it demanded total control. Now a year later, insurgents are attacking coalition forces at a rate of fifty or more incidents a day across Iraq, and the cause of the attack, as well as the casualty figures, are being manipulated by the insurgents at will across the Internet.

The use of propaganda on the Internet strengthens an insurgent's control over its followers and over governments by offsetting official statements through the use of pictures and mass mobilization. Insurgents request some type of action if demands are not met. Items such as photos of beheadings on the Internet grab the attention of potential combatants on both sides of the fight. Control may lie in understanding who delivered an acceptable message to the target audience first or in the most culturally appropriate way. Insurgents' use of the Internet weakens government control by undermining the perception or position of legitimacy in regard to ruling authority. If one cannot protect its citizens, then it is not a legitimate authority in the Arab world.[110]

For the insurgent, the Internet allows for the mobilization of all the various members of populations around the globe with similar grievances or like causes. They are able to unite in chat rooms, exchange opinions and plans, and never meet except virtually in a relatively short period of time. The Internet also allows for Cyber Age insurgents to use their guerilla tactics in an electronic way. These techniques are at risk in the same way as past insurgent actions. Insiders or captured computer hard drives inform law enforcement officials in the same manner that covert operators or captured documents did in the past. The problem for law enforcement officials is to maintain the pace of

---

[109] The author would like to thank Dr. Jacob Kipp, FMSO, for providing this information during review of this chapter.
[110] The author would like to thank Dr. Cindy Ayers, US Army War College, for providing this information during review of this chapter.

change and adapt to the insurgents' operating environments. As always, the insurgent attempts to stay one step ahead of the law or the military.

The primary conclusion to be drawn from this discussion is that the Internet is a true force mobilizer and thus multiplier. More attention needs to be paid to the Internet as an organizer of mass support and operational planner by all types of law enforcement agencies, the military, and homeland defense personnel. The Internet is facilitating mobilization of people faster than we can comprehend and respond. Similarly the Internet is a new operational ground for the employment of guerilla tactics and techniques that have proved themselves over time. It is apparent that in a virtual battle with insurgents, it will be difficult to remain ahead of the fight for legitimacy and the hearts and minds of the population, especially the disenfranchised.

Part Two

Terminology and Concepts

Information Warfare

Information Age

United States

INEW

Chinese

NCW

?

Russian

Information Operations

Informationization

PART TWO: TERMINOLOGY AND CONCEPTS

Part Two is composed of three chapters. They investigate the term information operations in-depth and explore IO paradigms from both a US and foreign perspective.

Chapter Four examines the US concept of information operations. It considers whether the paradigm chosen by the Defense Department was an accurate reflection of the terms "information" and "operation," and whether the concept IO now requires updating.

Chapter Five looks at the affect of specific linguistic, environmental, historical, philosophical, technical, and cultural elements in the US, Russia, and China on each country's military view of cyberactivities, information operations, and information warfare. The analysis results in three separate and varying approaches to the new security environment.

Chapter Six compares the US concept of network-centric warfare to its potential Chinese equivalent, "integrated network-electronic warfare." This similarity in concept, yet difference in terminology and application, of these IO subsets is discussed in this chapter.

CHAPTER FOUR: IS THE IW PARADIGM OUTDATED? A DISCUSSION OF US IW THEORY[111]

Introduction

Many military analysts believe the end of the Cold War signaled the close of the age of conventional weaponry. At this juncture, a switch was made to acquire weaponry based on technological achievements spawned by the so-called revolution in military affairs. This latter concept had been under consideration for several years. As one analyst noted

> Future historians might well cite the years 1993 and 1994 as the period during which the US military and associated national defense organizations identified Information Warfare as a conceptual vehicle for transitioning from the precepts of the Cold War into the new global realities of the Information Age. This concept is gaining momentum throughout the national security community at a breakneck pace.[112]

American industry and business were the first organizations to fully embrace the power of information-age technologies, and the military soon followed. The Internet as we know it was a military research project to develop redundant communication paths that would work if some communication nodes were destroyed. The Defense Department learned to utilize these technologies in logistics and administrative endeavors, and created attack and defend weaponry that could process information quicker and with greater precision than could its adversaries. The overwhelming effectiveness of this ability was most decisively demonstrated for the first time during the Gulf War. The coalition victory over Iraq was labeled as the first battlefield reliance on information technologies to achieve victory.

US military theorists attempted to describe this new emphasis on technology under the cover of a joint doctrine, Joint Publication 3-13, Joint Doctrine for Information Operations. Also discussed in the same volume was information warfare (IW). These concepts were new and as a result loosely defined, not completely mirroring the components of the terms that composed them. Those responsible for defining the terms were stepping into totally unmapped territory and had no frame of reference from which to work other

---

[111] This chapter is a slightly modified version of the author's opinion paper under the same name published in the Journal of Information Warfare, Vol. 2, Issue 3 2003, pp. 117-127.

[112] Bruce D. Berkowitz, "Warfare in the Information Age," In Athena's Camp (John Arquilla and David Ronfeldt, editors), RAND 1997, p. 179.

than the existing doctrines of psychological operations (PSYOP), operational security (OPSEC), military deception, and similar related topics. Their work was admirable. IO and IW were used as metaphors to express the technological transformation that was underway in times of peace and conflict, respectively.

Recently, however, conceptual writers working on IW doctrine have adopted some radical changes. Most important for purposes of this article is that IW has been removed from the Army's information-related terminology. The familiar term "information operations" now serves all functions associated with information-age processes and weaponry. Such a radical move indicates that the time is ripe for a review of some of the other concepts associated with information operations as well. As the analysis below demonstrates, some of the vital terms around which IO has been constructed remain loosely defined; some international terms that might support IO theory are totally absent from the US lexicon; and some new paradigms describing the Information Age are beginning to appear. This chapter makes several recommendations to tighten up terminology, especially the concept of information superiority, and focuses squarely on other potential paradigms for interpreting current and future developments, offering one paradigm for discussion.

Terminology and the IO/IW Paradigm: The Early Decisions
An authoritative definition of IO and IW reasonably should encompass the accepted meanings of three components: information, operations, and warfare. When the terms in JP 3-13 are examined, however, disconnects become apparent regarding how military analysts defined the terms some ten years ago and how they could have defined them. The old definitions worked because they were new and no one REALLY understood what the terms meant. After thousands of pages have been written on IO and IW, it is useful to quickly review these definitions, pointing out their deficiencies that were not apparent at the time.

Three authoritative sources are used here to examine the old definitions of information, operations, and warfare. The three sources are <u>Webster's Dictionary</u>; the Department of Defense's <u>Joint Publication 1-02, Dictionary of Military and Associated Terms</u>;[113] and <u>Joint Publication 3-13, Joint Doctrine for Information Operations</u>.[114] The reason for using a source outside of the military realm is obvious upon closer examination. First, one of the three terms (war) under discussion *is not defined in either JP 1-02 or JP 3-13*, and, therefore,

---

[113] <u>Joint Publication 1-02, Dictionary of Military and Associated Terms</u>, 12 April 2001, as amended through 9 January 2003, pp. 257-258.
[114] <u>Joint Publication 3-13, Joint Doctrine for Information Operations</u>, 9 October 1998, pp. GL-7, GL-8.

Webster's is necessary. Secondly, Webster's is a generally accepted source while both JP's contain military-related terminology that is not generally accepted by the academic community at large. The JPs have not been reconciled with general sources; rather words are defined from a military paradigm and may not mean what someone outside the military thinks they mean.

The two primary definitions for the word "information" found in Joint Publication 1-02 are "facts, data, or instructions in any form," and "the meaning that a human assigns to data by means of the known conventions used in their representation."[115] JP 1-02 defines an operation as "military action or the carrying out of a strategic, tactical, service, training , or administrative military mission; the process of carrying on combat, including movement, supply, attack, defense and maneuvers needed to gain the objectives of any battle or campaign."[116]

It would appear, based on a look at these definitions, that IO could have been defined from a purely military point of view in one of three ways. First, it could be a military action using facts, data, or instructions. Second, it could carry out a strategic or tactical military mission using facts, data, or instructions. Finally, IO is the process of carrying on combat, including attack and defense means, to gain the objectives of any battle or campaign using facts, data, or instructions. Joint Publications 1-02 and 3-13 defined IO as "actions taken to affect adversary information and information systems while defending one's own information and information systems." These official definitions mirror the potential definitions suggested above in a tangential manner. The official definition's focus is clearly on the information systems of equipment and not on mental perception or reaction (which is a huge component of IO) or on facts, data, or instruction. The gamut is insufficient to clearly define IO. The Army's relatively new Field Manual 3.0, Operations, describes the attainment of information superiority (the goal of IO according to FM 3.0) as capable of putting disparity in the enemy commander's mind between reality and his perception of reality. It thus discusses influencing the mind of the commander, giving more attention to PSYOP than did the old definitions of IO that relate

---

[115] Merriam-Webster's Collegiate Dictionary, Tenth Edition, Merriam-Webster, Incorporated, Springfield, Massachusetts, USA., 1998, p. 599. The primary definitions of information from Webster's dictionary are "the communication or reception of knowledge or intelligence, and knowledge obtained from investigation, study or instruction; intelligence, news, facts, data."
[116] Merriam-Webster's Collegiate Dictionary, p. 815. An operation is defined as the "performance of practical work or of something involving the practical application of principles or processes, an exertion of power or influence."

primarily to systems and equipment and give scant reference to the mind.

Similarly, IW should have been defined differently than it was in JP 3-13 and JP 1-02. War is defined by Webster's dictionary as a "state of usually open and declared armed hostile conflict between states or nations." JP 1-02 *does not define war*. This is an interesting point. How can one possibly define IW if we do not define "war"? The question is worth asking, for avoidance of controversy is hardly an acceptable price for lack of clarity. This can become a troubling condition. For example, consider the emphasis we put on the correct determination of an "objective" or a "center of gravity" as operational or strategic principles.[117] If we do not define the terms properly, can we make the proper determination? Was a weak definition the reason that IW is no longer in the US army's lexicon? If this is so, we will need to inform the international military community (coalition forces that support us), because they are still using the IW phraseology.

JP 1-02 defines IW as "information operations conducted during times of crisis or conflict to achieve or promote specific objectives over a specific adversary or adversaries." The latter part of this definition sounds more like the definition of an operation, in that an operation carries on combat to "gain the objectives of any battle or campaign." Further, the definition of war can only be inferred to mean "crisis or conflict" based on the definition of IW in JP 1-02. That is the only difference between IO and IW.

This problem is exacerbated when foreign concepts are bumped up against US concepts. For example, the 1986 Russian Military Encyclopedia defined "military information" (there was no entry for information) as "information of a military nature, as well as the process of transmission and receiving of such information." An "operation" was defined by the encyclopedia as

> An aggregate of battles, engagements, strikes and maneuvers, coordinated and interlinked in objective, tasks, place and time, by various force organizations, conducted simultaneously and sequentially according to a common concept and plan, to accomplish missions in a theater of operations, a strategic or operational sector, or within a specified period of time; a form of military operations.

"War" was defined as "a sociopolitical phenomenon, continuation of politics by violent means…armed struggle comprises the specific content of

---

[117] Discussion with Dr. Geoff Demarest, FMSO, on 14 November 2002.

war."[118]

If the definition of war as found in Webster's dictionary (JP 1-02 cannot be used since it does not define war) is combined with the definition of information from JP 1-02, then a sample definition of IW could be "open and declared armed hostile conflict between states or nations using data, facts, or instruction in any form." This definition would make little sense. A second potential definition might be "open and declared armed hostile conflict by nations or states that utilizes information or information-based systems and processes that could be used to attack human or system processors."

Even more to the point, information does not actually go to war against other information, further casting doubt on the idea of IW. Data or electron streams can be directed against one another to collide or interfere or influence movement, but they are not in open and declared "armed conflict." Electrons might collide with other electrons, laser beams may try to destroy computer chips, and directed energy beams may try to destroy satellites, but this is not "IW." Perhaps it could be called beam confrontation, or electron stream confrontation where computer chips and other data-processing elements are the objectives of attack. However, as noted above, this is a mute point. The US Army no longer has IW in its lexicon although it does remain in the digital version of JP 1-02.

Other Information-Related Terms
There are several nations, such as Russia and China that define other information-related issues. These include terms such as "information weapons" and "information-psychological" actions. JP 1-02 and JP 3-13 do not define an information weapon just as they do not define war. There appears to be a long-term unwritten policy in military circles in the US not to define an information weapon. Yet much of today's weaponry is loaded with computer chips and other information technologies that are the cornerstones of the Information Age. The Russians define information weapons in great depth and specificity. They ask "How can you have an information war if you do not have information weapons?" Can we have tank warfare without tanks? This term and others might be worthy of future consideration by IO specialists in this country. One of the greatest strengths of the US armed forces is its ability to learn from other armed forces (for example, the US studied and then adapted the term "operational art" from Soviet theoreticians). Perhaps now is the time to data mine foreign IO theory for some of the good ideas they have developed and see

---

[118] <u>Russian Military Encyclopedia</u>, Moscow 1986, pp. 151, 294, 514, and 515. Data-processing is not defined in the Soviet military encyclopedia.

if they are applicable to the US paradigm.[119]

For example, it is interesting to ask, some ten years down the road—why did US theorists, at the height of peace operations theory (peacemaking, peacekeeping, peace enforcement) at the end of the Cold War, develop the concept of IW instead of "information peace" (that is, how nations might use information technology to prevent conflict)? Why did we choose information warfare? The Soviet threat had evaporated, and a worldwide scare generated by a new term, IW, was the last thing Russian reformers needed. Many in Russia interpreted the term as a method of mind control. Now, however, the time appears right for cogent arguments to be advanced to reject or modify some terms and concepts and to promote new conceptual vehicles.

And there are terms in the US IO lexicon that could use a scrub. One of the most important is information superiority (IS). JP 1-02 defines IS as "that degree of dominance in the information domain which permits the conduct of operations without effective opposition." JP 3-13 defines IS as "the ability to collect, process and disseminate an uninterrupted flow of information while exploiting or denying an adversary's ability to do the same." If anyone reading this or any other article collects, processes, and disseminates the information therein, they do not necessarily have information superiority. What if all of the information in this article is misinformation? That does not provide information superiority, only information inferiority. To process is not to analyze. Or is it? One argument is that "process" is part of the intelligence cycle: converting raw data to a form that is usable by an analyst or for immediate action by a commander. That is, it hasn't been analyzed yet. It is only "useable" by an analyst. Another argument would indicate that "analyze" might be included in the term "process." The phrase "information-based processes" in JP 3-13 includes the term analysis ("processes that collect, analyze, and disseminate information using any medium or form"), making it appear that JP 3-13's authors do not make as big a distinction between process and analysis as might be implied. Perhaps too big a deal is being made of this slight oversight, but it would be nice to add the word "analysis" to the IS definition.

The reason for such additions is that processing and not analyzing information caused a huge waste of munitions during the air war over Kosovo as fighter pilots targeted mockups that appeared to be real targets. How else can one ascribe the difference in the number of tanks we thought we had "killed" in July of 1999 (according to General Wesley Clark, 110 Serb tanks) and the final tallies, some of which ranged as low as 26 tanks? And this occurred in the face

---

[119] See, for example, the work of Russian scientist Vitali Tsygichko. Dr. Tsygichko has broken information weapons into six categories.

of near total "information superiority" when no air force was flying against ours and we owned the airwaves! The US had "self-deceiving information superiority" as a result. FM 3.0 describes information superiority as "when commanders synchronize all three contributors (intelligence/surveillance/ reconnaissance, information management, and information operations) and it is greater than the enemy's." This descriptor considers that information has been processed and analyzed, one hopes, in order to attain information superiority.

One is left with the feeling that IW and some other information-related terms do not exist in a pure state but are simply metaphors for expressing aspects of war using high technology weapons or computers and, to a lesser extent, terms associated with psychological operations. But terminology is not the only concern with the old model that has served us so well for ten years.

IO applies to no specific or conceptual model (conventional, nontraditional, etc.) but instead conjures up a unique mental model composed of many elements that exist independent from other forms of warfare. FM 3.0, Operations, lists ten different "elements" of IO: military deception; counter deception; operations security; electronic warfare (e-attack, protection, support); information assurance; physical destruction; psychological operations; counterpropaganda; counterintelligence; and computer network attack and defense. Such a broad definition makes it hard to distinguish what IO is not, not what it is! Further, if IO's goal is to produce a disparity in the enemy commander's mind between reality and the perception of reality in order to disrupt the ability to exercise C2, as FM 3.0 notes, then IO is really nothing new. Deception has been doing this for years. The methods are the same, but the means (sensors, satellites, holograms, etc.) are different as well as the precision and speed of destruction involved. But IO is something new. Today, weaponry does more than just disrupt the ability to conduct C2 via deception or PSYOP. Now weaponry can shut down the data processors of both weapons (computer chips) and the mind (neurons). There is more at stake than just deception.

In its purest form, attacks with electrons, leaflets, or other means attack equipment or weaponry on the one hand, but also can attack the logic and decision-making capability of the commander on the other, according to Army FM 3.0. That is, there is a huge psychological component of IO, much greater than is generally implied or discussed. There are information operations against the brain on a daily basis in nations worldwide, especially in advertising and the mass media, where the goal is to influence or persuade through pure influence, debates, and tests of logic. Less considered is the more sinister form of an information operation against the brain that uses acoustics or other devices to shut down the normal processing of the brain, much like a laser tries to destroy computer chips. US specialists tend to put these operations out of the IO fold and into a field known as nonlethal operations. Most definitions of PSYOP are all about the first, or soft, use of IO; to influence the logic in someone else's head (leaflets, loud speakers, deception, etc.), or to use counterpropaganda as an element of defensive PSYOP. Soft PSYOP, however, is not the same as protecting the neurons in your head from being fried by a nonlethal device. Data attacks a human's logic in a soft IO PSYOP attack, and electronic or nonlethal streams of data attack neurons in the brain in a hard IO PSYOP attack. Lasers do the same to computer chips, but the latter is more easily identifiable with IO (physical destruction). What about mental destruction?

In summary, the theories of IO and IW have served the US well for the past ten years. They have given us a conceptual model through which to understand the changes that new technologies have brought us. This paradigm made sense ten years ago. But already, new models and concepts are emerging: Network-Centric War, effects-based strategies, asymmetric war, and operational prototyping are but a few of them. Some of these, based on the discussion above, most likely are already deficient since we have no definition of war! Others are being subsumed under the IO mantle.

Yet another model or paradigm, human and equipment data processors, is offered now for your consideration. It attempts to capture much of the discussion above in a simpler form and under an old term, data processing. It is nothing more than a suggestion, but it does offer an alternate way of viewing the problem.

"Data-Processing Operations:" Another Way to Think about the Information Age

The manipulation of data (information) has played an important role throughout the history of armed warfare. Before the creation of the computer chip (a data-processor), an information operation meant influencing or manipulating the actions of the decision-maker, the human. It was more of a psychological operation than an information operation. In reality, the attack was on a human's logic or on the emotion of fear. Just as today, data (leaflets, messages, newspapers, etc.) or activities (a show of force, atrocities, etc.) were the means to manipulate the data processor known as the mind via deception or intimidation. The transmission of data was slow in ancient times, and this also affected the manner in which data was analyzed.

Today, data processors in weapon systems have provided for the vast improvement in the acquisition and transmission of information, ensuring quick and precise attacks on targets even from standoff positions. Data processors allow commanders to mass effects quickly and precisely at decisive points across broad geographical areas. However, feeding false information into the data processor can still fool the logic of even a computer chip. Wrong information in: wrong information out. A computer chip does not have the ability to "fear" data, but it can be programmed to reject certain kinds of data.

Data processors form the core element, the heart if you will, of sensors, satellites, and computers. Thus, computer network operations (CNA, CND, and more recently computer network exploitation or CNE), or attacks on sensors or satellites, are in reality attacks against data processors. In like manner, psychological operations, deception, and even nonlethal operations are directed against the data processor known as the mind. PSYOP and deception have reached new levels of maturity in that holograms, morphed images, and other virtual representations of reality now have the potential to influence people like leaflets and loudspeakers once did. Nonlethal weaponry, such as acoustics or stun guns, is capable of momentarily shutting down the data processor known as the brain. Nonlethals can be influence means (leaflets, soft attacks) or incapacitating and even debilitating (hard attack) means. Unfortunately, this important latter attack method is not covered by present day IO theory in the US, which is focused on systems and equipment. "Nonlethals" are in a separate category for analysis.

People have ignored the fact that the mind has no firewall for too long. The primary emphasis on networks and pieces of equipment missed the most exposed computer/data processor on the battlefield, the human head. PSYOP and military deception are the only elements of those ascribed to IO that are concerned with the human information security feature, logic. A nonlethal substance is much more insidious—it attempts to alter or destroy the functioning of the brain's neurons just as an electron stream or laser beam attacks the data-processor known as the computer chip.

Further, in a recent interview with <u>Wired</u> magazine, Mr. Andrew Marshall of the Net Assessment's Office of the Pentagon underscored the importance of the mind and its implications for future warfare scenarios. He noted that

> People who are connected with neural pharmacology tell me that new classes of drugs will be available relatively shortly, certainly within the decade. These drugs are just like natural chemicals inside people, only with behavior-modifying and performance-enhancing characteristics. One of the people I talk to jokes that a future intelligence problem is going to be knowing what drugs the other guys are on.[120]

---

[120] Douglas McGray, "The Marshall Plan," <u>Wired Magazine</u>, 1 February 2002.

Thus the data processor, possessed by both equipment (computer chips) and humans (neurons), is the actual center of gravity of future attacks. The old IO/IW paradigm did not focus on the data processor as the objective of an attack, but rather offered elements and other descriptive criteria to describe IO. However, much of the problem with data processors is related to our reluctance to view a human as a data processor. We are not accustomed to doing so and don't feel comfortable putting nonlethals into the IO lexicon as a result. Physical destruction appears to have a comfort level of acceptance, but mental destruction does not.

Further, the human is always the interface between the input and output of data processing. The mind must not only ward off deception and acoustic attacks against it, it must also interpret what is downloaded from a computer or satellite, or acquired by counterintelligence means (for example, counter EW or HUMINT operations), or developed via counterpropaganda operations. Equipment can produce false outputs that the human interface must be coy enough to process, analyze, and interpret. Once again, the focus is on a human's ability to use proper logic to come to the correct conclusion. The computer-operator or machine-mind interface is one of those centers of gravity for the technological age that people seldom mention. The journal Technology Review recently wrote about this development, noting that efforts to link brains and computers could result in thought-controlled robots, enhanced perception and communications, and might make you smarter.[121]

Webster's dictionary defines data-processing as "the converting of raw data to machine-readable form and its subsequent processing (as storing, updating, combining, rearranging, or printing out) by a computer." The online American Heritage Dictionary defines a data processor as a device that performs operations on data; a machine for performing calculations automatically; or a person who processes data. JP 1-02 does not define data processing. This is not surprising since it is not a military-specific term, although military forces in almost every aspect of their day-to-day lives (like civilians everywhere) and wartime activities use its capabilities.

Knocking out or manipulating the organizer and distributor of data, the data processor, is the focus of the new paradigm. The data processor is the objective. As a result, it would be more correct to position data-processor wars at the top of the hierarchy of the concept and to position information as a sub-element, a means to influence the data processor. *Attacks on computers or the mind, whether electronic, laser, or other, are designed not to attack informa-*

---

[121] G. Huang, "Mind Machine Merger," Technology Review, May 2003.

tion but rather the data processor. In the case of a sensor, satellite, electronic warfare platform, or a computer, it is an attack on 1's and 0's of computer-based language or on the computer chip itself. With regard to humans, special light or TV frequencies that induce photoelectric epilepsy or other forms of debilitating light that attack the actual functioning of a human's data processor, the brain, are the areas of concern. Finally, regarding persuasion management or deception activities, these can be used against either equipment or a human.

If data-processing operations were broken down into two categories, equipment and the brain, what shape would the categories take? If one were to look at the elements listed in FM 3.0, psychological operations, military deception, counterdeception, counterpropaganda, and counterintelligence would be listed under the brain as elements designed to influence this data-processor. Nonlethals, not one of the elements in FM 3.0, would also have to be added to the list since they can shut down both logic and bodily functions. With regard to equipment, electronic warfare, information assurance, and computer network operations (CNA, CND, and CNE) would be listed. Of course, military deception is not purely a function of the human side of the equation. Military deception could be used against a piece of equipment's data processor just as easily as it could be used against a human. A sensor that is fed false signals is one example. Physical destruction and operations security also could fit both the equipment and brain categories.

Are there other paradigms besides data processing? Of course there are, and several were already listed. The one offered here is just a simple example, and far from the most creative. Most paradigms are susceptible to the same problems as IO and IW, however. They have to be properly defined, meaning they shouldn't offend more traditionally accepted definitions, but adapt to them. Care must be taken not to insist on mutually exclusive categories as IO and IW do. Another suggestion is to divide the conceptual model to describe technological change into three parts: kinetic warfare, electro-magnetic spectrum energy warfare, and PSYWAR (or influence war). Each would have specific subelements (deception, operational security, etc.). Or one could look at the technological revolution as simply dividing the pie into technology and psychological sectors. In any event, much conceptual thought is needed. Data processing is only one way to think about the problem, not a way to define it. And particularly with regard to nonlethals, there are a whole host of international laws that would affect the development of any mind-related concept.

Conclusions

The rapid pace of development in today's technology sphere indicates that the concept of "information warfare" that served a purpose for ten years is now somewhat dated, or at least in need of updating. IO begins before a crisis or conflict begins and is ongoing during the conflict. To say that military deception, OPSEC, PSYOP (look at the US use of leaflets and TV/radio today to influence the Iraqi population and soldiers long before actual conflict), and other elements of IO only occur during conflict is missing the point. It will be interesting to see if Pentagon theorists use IO to express a threat to the security of the country, a category of warfare, a method of defense, or leave it as the same conceptual umbrella for a host of operations, the function it served in the past. Or will a new prism of analysis replace IO itself?

Elements of the old metaphor are still applicable but a new conceptual model is needed, and especially one with more focus on the mind. The old concept of IO/IW looked almost exclusively at equipment and systems, and it gave scant notice to the mind except for soft PSYOP—counterdeception, counterpropaganda, military deception, and operational security. But, as pointed out in the text above, the focus was purely on how to influence the behavior and opinions of others, which does not concentrate on protecting the mind from either information that could influence behavior or attitudes or from weaponry that could upset the functioning of the brain's neurons. One way to potentially deter such attacks from occurring is, again, to ensure international laws are in place to warn about the consequences of such potential applications.

To underscore developments in this latter area, one need only look at the August edition of Newsweek. Inventor Woody Norris indicated that a device he created could put words or images into your head from 100 yards away. Military and law enforcement officials are closely monitoring the results of this experimentation. This development, if it turns out to work, would further emphasize the importance of protecting the mind. Just as data can be fed into a computer, Norris's invention would indicate that data can be fed into a person's mind as well.[122] The New York Times, Popular Science, and Business Week followed up with stories on Norris's invention a few months after the Newsweek article.

A clear future problem will be not only validating concepts in the US, but attempting to get nations across the globe to find a common language if/when the problem of IO/IW is brought before the United Nations. Just because we "invented" IW and the Army has now discarded it doesn't

---

[122] James Reno and N'Gai Croal, "Hearing is Believing," Newsweek, 5 August 2002, pp. 44-45.

necessarily mean that other nations will do the same. One Chinese officer, for example, noted that IW is ongoing all the time, and that IO only happens in wartime. A key Russian concept, around which that country has developed a doctrine and policy, is "information security." Both China and Russia define information weapons. All of these approaches are not explored fully in current US thinking. Of course, US policy makers have consciously decided to simply ignore some of these concepts for national security reasons, and their concerns are real.

It is unfortunate that the focus of defense departments worldwide is so focused on IO or IW and not on "virtual peacemaking" or "information peace" concepts. Information technologies were used extensively to keep the sides from fighting after US forces entered Bosnia, and a precedent was set. The presidents of Serbia, Croatia, and Bosnia-Herzegovina were influenced strongly by the use of information technology to come to a common agreement when their borders were divided. At Dayton, the presidents were placed in a room and shown a virtual flyover of crucial border regions. From information in the video, they were able to discuss and develop among them solutions to sensitive issues. Such use must be at the forefront of our efforts and not the afterthought.

In Iraq information technologies were used to ascertain if the US and other nations would eventually go to war. No one is talking about the UN's use of high technology as a "virtual peacemaking" or "information peace enforcement" operation. Rather, people only are thinking of IO use in a conflict. More attention needs to be focused on the persuasive influence of high technology developments and not just by the Pentagon. The State Department should be in the lead on this issue. They have developed a good grasp of virtual diplomacy issues and need to continue to push such agendas and methods for resolving issues via negotiations.

Whatever model is chosen to explain the emerging virtual world, it must be direct, reflect reality, and offer a way for thinking about the evolving nature of the world around us. IO and IW were excellent starters that helped military people understand the changing nature of technology. Now might be the time to move on to other ideas or to alter the initial IO and IW concepts.

CHAPTER FIVE: COMPARING US, RUSSIAN, AND CHINESE INFORMATION OPERATIONS CONCEPTS[123]

Introduction

Over the past ten years, the United States, Russia, and China have developed their own concepts of information warfare (IW), information operations (IO), and information superiority (IS). It is somewhat easy to ascertain the US approach to these concepts because the US publishes much of its doctrine in an unclassified format as Joint Publications (JP) or Field Manuals (FM). The US does indeed have a JP and FM on IO. Neither Russia nor China publishes such a document. Thus, the analyst is left to ascertain a plausible description of IW, IO, or IS based on reading academic and quasi-official military views.

The US armed forces expect to publish a new version of JP 3-13, Information Operations in 2005. The old document (1998) emphasized six offensive and eight defensive "assigned and supporting capabilities and activities."[124] The 1998 JP also emphasized the necessity of obtaining and maintaining information superiority during IO. Much emphasis is currently being placed on network-centric operations in US IO theory.

Russia has two aspects to its IO concept: information-technical and information-psychological. Not only are these different from the US's "assigned and supporting capabilities and activities," but Russia also views IS differently. Russian theorists place as much emphasis on "disorganizing" the enemy as they do toward achieving information superiority. In fact they believe the former produces the latter. Russia currently has not explained its equivalent concept of "network-centric operations" to Western audiences. However, Russia is developing the concept of an "information weapon" to great effect, a term the US State and Defense Departments do not define.

China has developed six "forms" (not capabilities or elements like the US but similar in content) for its IO concept: operational security, military deception, psychological war, electronic war (EW), computer network war, and physical destruction. Many Chinese military authors consider "control" to be nearly as important as information superiority. Again the former results in the latter. China's focus for attaining information superiority/control is built around the use of stratagems whereas the US focuses on speed and efficiency. China

---

[123] This article was posted under the same title on the Command and Control Research and Technology Symposium website in 2004.

[124] Joint Pub 3-13, Joint Doctrine for Information Operations, 9 October 1998, p. viii.

views network-centric operations in a slightly different manner than does the US, calling their nearly equivalent theory integrated network-electronic warfare or, as one Chinese expert explained, the "informationization of warfare."

This chapter develops a comparative view of these concepts and highlights strengths and weaknesses of each. As the comments demonstrate, these concepts may vary radically in the three countries under consideration. At times one can feel as if lost in the Bermuda triangle of IO terminology.

The United States

The definitions of information warfare (IW) and information operations (IO) have been under constant revision in the US. For comparative purposes two of the more recent definitions are presented here as refreshers.

Joint Publication 1-02, Department of Defense Dictionary of Military and Related Terms, defines an operation as "a military action or the carrying out of a strategic, tactical, service, training, or administrative military mission; the process of carrying on combat, including movement, supply, attack, defense and maneuvers needed to gain the objectives of any battle or campaign."[125] It would appear, based on an examination of this definition, that IO's definition should include the terms movement, maneuver, and objectives among other terms.

Joint Publication 3-13, Joint Doctrine for Information Operations (1998) and JP 1-02 (the latter last updated on 5 June 2003) both defined information operations as "actions taken to affect adversary information and information systems, while defending one's own information and information systems." Both publications defined IW as "information operations conducted during time of crisis or conflict to achieve or promote specific objectives over a specific adversary or adversaries."[126] Interestingly the new Army FM 3-13 of 2003 did not define information warfare thereby indicating a renewed emphasis on IO alone. Thus it is easy to see that even today, after some ten or so years, there is still much discussion about what IO and IW are or are not in the US armed forces.

In November 2003 the US Army released its new and updated version of FM 100-6, Information Operations, now called FM 3-13. It defined information operations as

---

[125] JP 1-02, Department of Defense Dictionary of Military and Related Terms, Internet version, last updated 5 June 2003.

[126] Joint Pub 3-13, Joint Doctrine for Information Operations, 9 October 1998, pp. I-9, I-11.

The employment of the core capabilities of electronic warfare, computer network operations, psychological operations, military deception, and operations security, in concert with specified supporting and related capabilities, to affect or defend information and information systems, and to influence decision-making.[127]

In this case the US Army is stating that it foresees five core capabilities but retained the wording for "supporting and related capabilities." IO, the manual asserts, encompasses attacking adversary command and control (C2) and protecting friendly C2. The proper combination of the two produces IS at decisive points. More important, however, is the assertion in the manual that IO allows commanders to mass the effects of the information element of combat power. IO and automated information systems and communications allow for staff processes to be shortened and decision cycles to be compressed. This increases operational tempo.[128]

The US Air Force, in their new doctrinal publication Document 2-5, Information Operations of January 2005, defines an information operation as

Actions taken to affect adversary information and information systems while defending one's own information and information systems. Also called IO. [The definition continues with an Air Force only application] Information operations are the integrated employment of the core capabilities of influence operations, electronic warfare operations, network warfare operations, in concert with specified integrated control enablers, to influence, disrupt, corrupt or usurp adversarial human and automated decision making while protecting our own.[129]

The second draft of Joint Publication 3-13, Joint Doctrine for Information Operations of 14 December 2004 defined IO as "the integrated employment of the core capabilities of electronic warfare, computer network operations, psychological operations, military deception, and operations security, in concert with specified supporting and related capabilities, to influence, disrupt, corrupt or usurp adversarial human and automated decision

---

[127] FM 3-13, Information Operations: Doctrine, Tactics, Techniques, and Procedures, November 2003, p. 13.

[128] Ibid., pp. v, vi.

[129] Air Force Document 2-5, Information Operations, 11 January 2005, p. 51 as downloaded from the Internet. Author's update as of January 2005.

making while protecting our own."[130] When approved, this definition will be included in JP 1-02.

Attaining IS remains the goal of IO as this condition allows commanders to seize, retain, and exploit the initiative. This can only be accomplished, of course, if the core capabilities of the US are superior to those of the opposing side not only in the technological sense but also in the manner in which the data obtained is analyzed and used. Seeing the battlefield first is not enough. As is often the case (witness subjects such as the operational art of taking down a huge city, or postconflict termination plans and measures), our commanders often are not taught how to analyze and use the information at their fingertips or what information to request. The attainment of IS may be short lived if analysis is not properly conducted. IS must support a commander's intent and his concept of operations.[131]

For this reason the author's IO definition advanced may provide a longer yet more comprehensive understanding of the subject.

Russia

IW and IO have been defined in several ways by Russian authors. Most use the term "war" instead of "warfare" (however, it will still be abbreviated as IW here). Without an authoritative publication like a JP or an FM, it is nearly impossible to get an official definition of either term, however. The 1986 Soviet Military Encyclopedia defined an operation as "an aggregate of battles, engagements, strikes and maneuvers, coordinated and interlinked in objective, tasks, place and time, by various force organizations, conducted simultaneously and sequentially according to a common concept and plan, to accomplish missions in a theater of operations, a strategic or operational sector, or within a specified period of time; a form of military operation."[132] War was defined in the military encyclopedia as "a sociopolitical phenomenon, continuation of politics by violent means... Armed struggle comprises the specific content of war."[133]

In the 2003 book An Introduction to the Formal Theory of Information War, Russian IW expert S. P. Rastorguyev discussed the concept of IW. It is worth examining Rastorguyev's concepts because he was commissioned a few

---

[130] Joint Publication 3-13, Joint Doctrine for Information Operations, Second Draft, 14 December 2004, GL-12.

[131] Ibid.

[132] Soviet Military Encyclopedia, Military Publishing House, Moscow 1986, p. 294.

[133] Ibid., pp. 514-515.

years earlier to write a book called <u>Information War</u> for the Security Council of the Russian Federation. He thus appears to be a very influential IW theorist.

Rastorguyev defined IW as "a battle between states involving the use of exclusively information weapons in the sphere of information models." The final objective of an information weapon's effect is the knowledge of a specific information system and the purposeful use of that knowledge to distort the model of the victim's world. He adds that there is no important difference between the terms IW, information struggle, and information battle.

Rastorguyev defined an information operation as "a sequence of actions to use an information weapon to achieve an assigned task." An information weapon, according to Rastorguyev, is

> A means directed at activating (or blocking) information system processes in which the subject using the weapons has an interest. An information weapon can be any technical, biological, or social means or system that is used for the purposeful production, processing, transmitting, presenting or blocking of data and or processes that work with the data.[134]

The use of an information weapon assumes that the following have been developed: (1) an analysis of the means and mechanisms for activating within an enemy system the self-destruction, self-control, and self-limitation programs installed in that system, (2) development of a specific information weapon, and (3) use of an information weapon against a given objective within the framework of the information operation under consideration. An information weapon must be used on an objective with maximum speed as compared to another type of weapon, inflict the necessary damage to the objective within the allotted time period, be sufficiently cheap and simple to produce, as compared to another type of weapon of the same action class, and be capable of mass production.[135]

Rastorguyev added that information weapons are the most significant weapons of the modern era for four reasons: they offer a much cheaper production of data due to the emergence of information technologies; they provide automated means for obtaining knowledge from data that has been created; they provide a great reduction in the cost and time for delivering information to practically any point on the planet due to the development of

---

[134] S. P. Rastorguyev, <u>An Introduction to the Formal Theory of Information War</u>, Moscow 2003, pp. 6-7.
[135] Ibid., pp. 7-8.

telecommunication assets; and they offer a great increase in the effectiveness of the impact of information. The latter is due to the emergence of sophisticated theories in the areas of programming for computers and neuro-linguistic programming for social systems, to include many methods and means for exerting an information-psychological effect.[136] Thus Rastorguyev discusses both the information-technical and information-psychological aspects of IO.

Breaking the subject of information war and information operations into two components, information-technical and information-psychological, and not into elements as the US armed forces does, started several years ago. For example, threats were listed as information-technical and information-psychological in both Russia's April 2000 military doctrine and in a year 2000 issue of the Russian defense complex journal Questions of Information Security. In the latter journal the information-technical confrontation was divided into technical intelligence devices, means and measures for protecting information, super-high-frequency weapons, ultrasonic weapons, radio-electronic countermeasures, electromagnetic impulse weapons, and special software and hardware. Information-psychological aspects included the mass media, nonlethal weapons, psychotronic tools, and special pharmaceuticals.

An October 2003 brochure "Urgent Tasks of the Development of the Russian Federation Armed Forces" also stated that information operations (IO) were a threat to the Russian Federation and its allies. IO was said to contain two aspects, information-technical and information-psychological operations.[137] In a 2003 issue of the military's authoritative journal Military Thought, author S. A. Bogdanov stated that the goals of contemporary armed struggle were obtainable by military, economic, and "information-technical and information-psychological" measures.[138]

Perhaps the most recent detailed article reflecting this breakdown into two major components was that of Captain First Rank (Reserve) R. Bikkenin. Writing in Morskoy Sbornik [Naval Journal] in October 2003 Bikkenin first pointed out that many players conduct information conflict at different levels. At the strategic level various ministries and departments are involved, and in wartime two or more fronts or fleets may perform strategic missions. At the

---

[136] Ibid., p. 9.

[137] Russian Ministry of Defense Brochure, "Urgent Tasks of the Development of the Russian Federation Armed Forces," as translated and downloaded from the FBIS website in January 2004.

[138] S. A. Bogdanov, "The Probable Appearance of Future Warfare," Voyennaya Mysl [Military Thought], 15 December 2003, as translated and downloaded from the FBIS website in May 2005.

operational level fronts, fleets, army, flotilla, and corps are involved. At the tactical level of information conflict formations, units, single ships, and army subunits are involved.[139] Bikkenin noted that information conflict has become a kind of military art wherein offensive and defensive actions are used to influence the intellect of civilians and servicemen. Information weapons are involved (a term which the US State and Defense Departments, as noted above, decline to define) and are defined by Bikkenin as:

> A means of eliminating, distorting or stealing information for the purpose of obtaining necessary data after penetrating the security system; blocking of access to information by its legitimate users; and in the final account, disorganization of all means of society's life support, including the enemy military infrastructure.[140]

Bikkenin thus uses disorganization instead of information superiority as part of his definition of an information weapon.

He then lists the fundamental components of information conflict as information-technical and information-psychological just as did Russia's military doctrine and the brochure on "Urgent Tasks." However, Bikkenin somewhat altered the subcomponents of these two aspects from past definitions. Under the former he listed the main targets of attack and defense as electronic assets, above all communications and telecommunications systems, and the Internet. Other aspects of the information-technical component of information conflict included disinformation, maskirovka [deception], intelligence, the science of cryptology, and steganography. Bikkenin pointed out that several new cryptographic algorithms have become widespread, particularly the RSA-algorithm and the El Gamal algorithm.[141]

In the case of the latter aspect, information-psychological, Bikkenin focused attention on the civilian population and servicemen. This IO aspect included the use of the mass media (press, radio, and television), leaflets, religious propaganda, and computer networks, especially the Internet, according to Bikkenin. Thus if Bikkenin's views are widely held, the Internet is now considered both an information-technical and information-psychological aspect of IW.[142] Of greatest surprise, however, was the introduction by Bikkenin of the

---

[139] R. Bikkenin, "Information Conflict in the Military Sphere: Basic Elements and Concepts," Morskoy Sbornik [Navy Journal], No. 10, 2003, pp. 38-40 as translated and downloaded from the FBIS website on 6 February 2004.
[140] Ibid.
[141] Ibid.
[142] Ibid.

religious propaganda aspect of IW. This addition is indicative of the influence that the Chechen conflict has had on Russia's society and armed forces. Russia's elite is clearly concerned about the impact of religious extremism on local conflicts and especially the effect of Wahhabism to coerce local residents to fight for their cause.

With regard to the information-technical aspect of IW, a 1999 article by Russian Defense Minister Igor Sergeyev highlighted the influence of the Information Age on Russia's military-technical policy. He listed the following as priorities for the Russian military in the coming years:

- Guided and electromagnetic energy weapons
- Cyberweapons
- Stealth unmanned combat platforms
- All-weather reconnaissance and accurate long-range weapons.[143]

The Russian military journal <u>Military Parade</u> offers analysts an updated perspective on how the military has focused on implementing Sergeyev's plan. For example, Issue One of 2003 had articles on drones and UAVs (a series begun in Issue Four of 2002), communication devices, radars with electronic beam control, laser information technologies for military and dual-use applications, modernizing tanks and infantry fighting vehicles with information technologies (thereby improving their combat potential), high-precision cruise missiles, digital mapping technologies, automatic control systems, and smart guidance systems. The issue also had an article on "High-Precision Weapon Systems Development Trends and their Role in Modern Armed Conflicts."

Issue Five of 2003 also contained several articles of interest from an information-technical viewpoint. Several stood out. These articles were about information technologies as tools of troop and weapon control, military satellite communications equipment, helmet-mounted vision systems, the Akveduk communications system, and high-precision anti-ship missiles belonging to the Navy.

The ongoing conflict in Chechnya has offered examples of both the information-psychological and the information-technical aspects of information conflict. Russian author V. V. Panchenkov explained the information-psychological defeat of the Russian armed forces in the First (1994-1996) Chechen Conflict and measures to correct the situation in the second (1999-

---

[143] Igor Sergeyev, "The Main Factors which Determine Russia's Military-Technical Policy on the Eve of the 21st Century," <u>Krasnaya Zvezda [Red Star]</u>, 9 December 1999, as translated and downloaded from the FBIS website on 6 February 2004.

present) conflict. In the first conflict, the Russian media was not under state control and was often financed by Chechens. Russia's Defense Ministry did not provide journalists with official information that the Russian public needed. As General of the Army Makhmut Gareyev noted, "no army can operate successfully if …it is being morally beaten down by its own compatriots and the media."[144] Information-psychological influence on the illegal armed formations was ineffective, Panchenkov added.

For the second conflict, information centers were established in two neighboring republics of Chechnya—Dagestan and North Ossetia. These republics served as staging areas for Russian journalists. Russian Defense Ministry officials supplied the journalists with videos and briefing material and escorted them to specific locations in Chechnya. In this way the information centers were able to better control information produced about the conflict.[145]

Panchenkov also noted the use of new measures to help establish the information-technical aspect of IW. At the start of the second conflict in Chechnya he noted that

> During 1999 more than 150 control points and radio-electronic facilities operating in the interests of the illegal armed formations were found. By the end of September, 77 of them had been destroyed by fire engagement, including 22 of the 38 radio broadcasting stations. The power was cut off from 18 radio-electronic facilities. Some 90% of the base stations (to include retransmitters) for radio relay, cellular, and other types of communications were either seized or put out of commission.[146]

China

When examining Chinese IW materials for the past decade, it becomes clear how serious a role IW is playing in the transformation of the People's Liberation Army (PLA) from a mechanized to an informationized force. For example, on 6 August 2003, Defense Minister Cao Gangchuan told a meeting of municipal government personnel, the PLA General Staff, and the Beijing Military Region staff that the defense buildup was aimed at gaining victory in IW. This IW directed effort also has the complete support of the Central Military Commission (CMC). Former Chinese President Jiang Zemin's son

---

[144] V. V. Panchenkov, "Lessons from the Information War in the North Caucasus," Vooruzhenie, Politika, Konversiia [Equipment, Politics, Conversion], No. 4, 2002, downloaded from the FBIS website on 5 February 2004.
[145] Ibid.
[146] Ibid.

Mianheng, by the way, was reported to be the nominee who would serve as an advisor for the 38th Group Army's digitization program. He will be responsible for digitizing weapons and command systems of the unit.

China's IW theory is closer in detail to the US Army's definition of IO. China has six core "forms" or subdivisions of IW, and not just two as Russia has. China's IW and IO definitions have changed through the years even though the components haven't. One Chinese IW expert noted a few years ago that "IW occurs all the time, in peace and war. It is part of the ideological struggle. An IO only occurs in wartime."[147] In 2002, the PLA's IW General Staff proponent, General Dai Qingmin, listed six forms of IW in the authoritative Chinese journal China Military Science: operational security, deception, computer network attack, electronic warfare, intelligence, and physical destruction. Two of these forms stand out: electronic warfare and computer network warfare. Dai also discussed China's concept of "integrated network-electronic warfare (INEW)", similar in content to the US concept of network-centric warfare. The concept refers to a series of combat operation actions with the integrated use of EW and CNW measures on the informationized battlefield. The actions are designed to disrupt the normal operation of the enemy's battlefield network information systems and protect one's own. The objective of INEW is to seize battlefield information superiority, according to Dai.[148]

Dai had earlier defined information operations as "a series of operations with an information environment as the basic battlefield condition, with military information and an information system as the direct operational target, and with electronic warfare and a computer network war as the principal forms."[149] In the same article he stated that contention for "information control" might become a focus of future war. Belligerents in a future war will contend for information superiority, but Dai maintained that information control was needed to create conditions for maintaining the initiative and winning final victory.[150]

---

[147] Author's discussion with Chinese IW expert, January 2001.
[148] Dai Qingmin, "On Integrating Network Warfare and Electronic Warfare," China Military Science, Feb 2002, pp. 112-117 as translated and downloaded from the FBIS website in October 2002.
[149] Dai Qingmin, "Innovating and Developing Views on Information Operations," China Military Science, August 2000, pp. 72-77 as translated and downloaded from the FBIS website October 2002.
[150] Ibid.

Dai listed three characteristics of information supremacy or superiority (IS): it is an integrated combat posture that can greatly affect the war as a whole; it allows freedom of movement in the information dimension and is conducted in three areas (electromagnetic space, computer network space, decision-makers' cognition and belief systems) and two levels (attack against information systems, attack against a human's cognition and belief system); and it influences events in the information dimension so as to affect events in the physical dimension.[151]

A review of China's open source literature reveals that its leaders intend to use IW in one of three ways depending on the geopolitical situation confronting them: as a tool of war, as a way to achieve victory without war, or as a means to enhance stability through the promotion of new military theories. These different methods will present a continual guessing game to the Western mind as it tries to ascertain the actual IW strength of the PLA: is the PLA "appearing weak when strong" or is it trying to "appear strong when weak?"

Several specific issues stand out in the open-source analysis of IW, IO, and IS theory that probably will carry over into the next ten years of PLA development. These items are:

- Joint offensive IW has become a closely studied subject by the Chinese leadership and is considered an important aspect for the attainment of victory in the Information Age.
- Psychological warfare will have an elevated role in future war.
- In nearly every training exercise a "blue IW-based army" has superiority in technology which forces a "red IW-deficient army" to rely on backup systems or the employment of counter tactics, which might indicate that the PLA expects to absorb a first IW strike.

It is evident from Chinese open-sources that reserve, militia, PLA, and civilian forces will conduct joint IW operations in the future and join hands against any intervening IW force. This integration is already underway as signified by the proposed establishment of a cyber security force. Qu Yanwen, a security specialist, has proposed that a cyber security force (CSF) be composed of members of the PLA, the Ministry of State Security and Public Security, and technical specialists. Currently Chinese political, economic, and military security is in danger due to the nascent stage of development of

---

[151] Dai Qingmin, "On Seizing Information Supremacy," China Military Science, April 2003, pp. 9-17, as translated and downloaded from the FBIS website in March 2004.

China's networks according to some reports. Weaknesses exist in financial network security, in the vulnerability of information networks of key organizations to cyberattacks, in insuring military information security, and in the control of information that can affect the stability of public order, according to a Chinese Naval News agency.[152] Within the PLA the Shijiazhuang Army Command College, the Navy Command Academy, the Air Force Command Academy, and the Second Artillery Corps Command Academy met in July 2003 to work out an overall joint teaching program for the three armed forces to share information resources and exchange experiences via the Internet.[153]

To demonstrate the emphasis on offensive IW one need look no further than the militia. Guangzhou City's militia has, for the past few years, focused on the requirements of the information battlefield. It was decided to organize a battalion headquarters (set up as a provincial telecommunications company and two other companies: a computer network warfare company and an electronic warfare company). The computer network company has two platoons, a network defense platoon and a network attack platoon, and the electronic warfare company has two platoons, one devoted to reconnaissance and the other to deception. However there is no training outline to follow since this unit is a newly emerging force. A draft "Training Plan for Militia Information Technology Elements" was developed from discussions with staffs of the Guangzhou Military Region. This year's training research included the topics of protecting one's own network security, searching for enemy network stations, and attacking enemy networks.[154]

Thus with this level of attention devoted to the militia, it is no wonder that the PLA has developed its own IW brigades that conduct offensive and defensive operations against one another. In March 2003 military representatives attending the National People's Congress (NPC) noted that IW units would soon be activated. These units had "already developed electronic jamming/bombardment weapons" capable of paralyzing all enemy electronic systems including the Internet and military command systems. The Chinese believe these weapons are more advanced than similar weapons in the US. Several trial units were already established, and a large portion of the budget

---

[152] Takungpao News, http:www.takungpao.com/news/2003-11-30/MW-203198.htm, Naval News http://jczs.sina.com.cn/2003-11-30/167226.thml, 30 November 2003.
[153] http:www.pladaily.com.cn/gb/pladaily/2003/07/31/20030731001027, from FBIS document CPP 20030811000030.
[154] Ye Youcai, Zhou Wenrui, "Building a High-quality Militia Information Technology Element," Guofang, 15 September 2003 p. 45 as translated and downloaded from the FBIS website on 15 September 2003.

would go to developing IW units.[155] On 4 November 2003, Jiang Zemin asked the armed forces to build IW units to win in IW. New types of soldiers with new military theories are needed to do this he added.[156]

The theory of psychological warfare has tremendous significance and value to China. Chinese theorists are attempting to develop an updated ideology and strategy of psychological warfare—one that will focus on intimidation and on exploiting the differences between Eastern and Western mentalities. The PLA intends to establish a command structure for psychological warfare as well as create special units that will attempt to overcome Chinese inferiority in high-tech weapons.[157] More importantly, since Chinese theorists appear to believe that because modern psychological warfare can help ensure stability and shape national-security thinking, the concept is more applicable in peace than in war.[158]

In offering a recommendation for future psychological-warfare forces in China, Major General Xu asked Chinese leaders to:

- Develop a psychological-warfare system that integrates specialized and nonspecialized personnel and that emphasizes China's special characteristics.
- Establish a psychological-warfare coordination agency at the national level to provide guidance and coordination for national psychological-warfare actions.
- Establish a psychological-warfare command agency under the unified leadership of the Central Military Commission and the party committee.
- Establish several types of psychological-warfare scientific research agencies in order to guide both national and military work.
- Establish a specialized psychological-warfare corps that would form a consolidated and effective psychological attack force.
- Develop a modernized basis for psychological-warfare material and technical equipment.

---

[155] Mingpao News, 12 March 2003.
[156] The Sun Daily News <http://the-sun.com.hk/channels/news/20031105/20031105012934.html>, 5 November 2003.
[157] Ibid.
[158] Xu Hezhen, "Focus on Psychological War Against the Background of Grand Strategy," Zhongguo Junshi Kexue [China Military Science], Number 5, 2000, pp. 67-76, as translated and downloaded from the FBIS website on 11 December 2000.

- Form a psychological-warfare mentality by developing psychological-warfare education for the masses and for all commanders in the military.[159]

In conclusion Chinese military theorists apparently believe they have found a willing, relatively inexpensive and malleable ally in IW—an ally that can enable China to catch up with the West in both strategic military and international status. Success in these areas could lead China to play an important strategic deterrent role (or potential troublemaker) in the Asia-Pacific region in the future and to gradually emerge into an economic competitor worthy of close scrutiny. China sees a strategic opportunity to leap frog the age of mechanization and move directly into the age of information, a move full of positive aspects for the Chinese military.

Conclusions

Cyber and information technologies are the supplemental formations and troops of twenty-first-century armed forces that support the traditional forces of the US, Russia, and China. They require that the focus or concentration of effort be on operational effectiveness, manipulation, and speed as well as the principle of concentrating military strength. The West should examine Russian and Chinese approaches for new areas of emphasis. Such areas include new criteria for figuring correlation of forces, the new emphasis on cognitive factors, and the alternatives to IS (disorganization in the case of Russia and control in the case of China) among other issues. While it was easy to measure the intent of steel in the form of a tank it will be much more difficult to measure the intent of an electron, and to conduct the consequence management assessments for electronic and other cyberactivities.

It is hoped that all countries engaged in the development of IW forces will learn to talk and negotiate with one another perhaps through the establishment of an IW hotline between governments. Since it will be more difficult to know who or what is attacking a nation in the age of information, communications will become even more important and vital to our national security than they were in the past. Everyone will know immediately if a nuclear device is detonated but not everyone will know as quickly if an electronic attack is launched on a nuclear power station, for example. The former will bring death and destruction while the latter may only initially produce darkness. In the Information Age it is possible to mask attacks and make them appear to come from someplace other than the attacks origination. A hotline will enable clarification of attack status and allow nations to correspond

---

[159] Ibid.

and sort out what happened thereby reducing misunderstanding over a very serious issue. In fact such a hotline should be collocated with the current nuclear hotline. The Y2K hotline between Russia and the US was an example of such a link.

Thus for the US military, a force focused on information superiority, dominant maneuver, digitized operations, and information assurance, a study of Russian and Chinese IW/IO methods would be not only advisable but should be required. Such a study might uncover inherent IW weaknesses in the US system when analyzed through the thought process of another ideological prism or framework. The absolute worse mistake that America can make is to use its own process for uncovering vulnerabilities exclusively since there are other problem-solving schemes (the dialectic) available that offer other scenarios. It is worth the time of the US analytical community to analyze IW/IO strategies and tactics from all points of view and not just the empirical US approach. China and Russia have been able to learn from the mistakes of others and are already becoming IW forces with which to reckon since they bypassed major mechanized age stumbling blocks. IW has allowed both countries to skip over some technological developments, to use discoveries in the West to save time and money or to, as the Chinese say, "borrow a ladder to climb the tree."[160] The Chinese believe that losers in IW will not just be those with backward technology; they will also be those who lack command thinking and the ability to apply strategies.

---

[160] Wang Jianghuai and Lin Dong, "Viewing Our Army's Quality Building from the Perspective of What Information Warfare Demands," Jiefangjun Bao [PLA Daily Newspaper], 3 March 1998, p. 6 as translated and downloaded from the FBIS website on 16 March 1998.

CHAPTER SIX: CHINESE AND AMERICAN NETWORK WARFARE[161]

China published the fourth version of its white paper on national defense in December 2002.[162] The document received positive comments from US analysts for its greater sophistication than previous versions and mild criticism for its continued lack of detail. Subjects addressed included China's security situation, defense policy, armed forces, international security cooperation, and arms control and disarmament. But there was a noticeable lack of attention to *information warfare* (IW) and *information operations* (IO), subjects to which the congressionally mandated DOD study, "The Military Power of the People's Republic of China," paid particular attention in 2002.[163] In addition, China's 2004 white paper failed to address IW but focused on the revolution in military affairs and the topic of informationalization, which was mentioned more than 20 times.

This 2002 white paper, however, did note that information technologies (IT) have helped stretch the battlefield into "multidimensional space, which includes the land, sea, air, outer space, and electron." The last term, in US documents, usually refers to the information sphere. The form of war, the paper added, is becoming information oriented. High technology was listed as an acquisition priority, and 20,000 km of optic fiber cable was laid in western China, while in October 2000 the General Staff organized a computer networking and electronic countermeasure exercise around Beijing. Finally, the paper noted that in 2001, many People's Liberation Army (PLA) studies and exercises explored the features and patterns of an integrated network-electronic warfare (INEW) concept. Thus, while not specifically highlighting IW or IO, information-related topics were mentioned.

INEW is worthy of further note. Earlier in 2002, in the journal China Military Science, Major General Dai Qingmin, head of the 4th Department of the General Staff, explained the concept, which he had first mentioned in the

---

[161] This chapter under the same title appeared in Joint Force Quarterly (JFQ), Issue 38, 3rd Quarter, July 2005, pp. 76-83. It contains additional information omitted from the published article due to length.

[162] China's National Defense in 2002, white paper (Beijing: Information Office of the State Council of the People's Republic of China, December 2002), as downloaded from www.aseansec.org/ARF/ARF-DWP/China-2002.doc.

[163] See Annual Report on the Military Power of the People's Republic of China (Washington, DC: Department of Defense, July 2002).

August 2000 issue of that journal. Parts of Dai's 2002 article contradicted the white paper. For example, he stated that the concept placed more emphasis on active offense, whereas the paper emphasized a traditional active defense focus. Dai equated INEW with IO, which the white paper did not, noting that it "serves as information operations theory with Chinese characteristics." It is strange that the 2002 Pentagon report on China did not mention this concept, a theory that appears to be a half cousin to the wildly popular Pentagon transformation concept of "network-centric warfare" (NCW).

This article compares General Dai's INEW concept with the US network-centric warfare concept and highlights their strengths and weaknesses. Many issues arise. For example, both concepts evade the fog and friction of war, assuming perfect information and ignoring those problems at their own peril. Further, both are bathed in their own cultural environments. The United States used a business metaphor when discussing NCW. Dai, on the other hand, noted that INEW refers to an overall concept, method, and strategy for guiding IO, not a set of hardware and software or a single system, and puts "the wings of network warfare on traditional electronic warfare." Clearly, moving from kinetic to network-based warfare will be an interesting transformation as different nations look at new developments in their own ways.

Integrated Network-Electronic Warfare

Dai's 2002 article, "On Integrating Network Warfare and Electronic Warfare," noted several topics of interest:

- IO contradictions
- IO centers of gravity
- Network weaknesses
- Importance of IT training
- Achieving information superiority
- Definitions of information war and other terms, all with Chinese characteristics.[164]

Dai argues that IW is composed of six "forms": operational security, military deception, psychological war, electronic war (EW), computer network war, and physical destruction. He made only one further reference to psychological operations in the article and never again mentioned operational security,

---

[164] Dai Qingmin, "On Integrating Network Warfare and Electronic Warfare," Zhongguo Junshi Kexue [China Military Science], Vol. 15, No. 2 (February 2002), pp. 112-117, translated and downloaded onto the Foreign Broadcasting Information Service (FBIS) website.

military deception, and physical destruction. Electronic warfare and computer network warfare thus captured most of his attention.

INEW, according to Dai, refers to a series of combat operations that use the integration of electronic warfare and computer network warfare measures to disrupt the normal operation of enemy battlefield information systems while protecting one's own, with the objective of seizing information superiority—similar to the US definition of IO. While network war disrupts processing and use of information, EW disrupts acquisition and forwarding of information. The core of computer network warfare is to "disrupt the layers in which information is processed, with the objective of seizing and maintaining control of network space." EW is targeted at networked information systems and informationalized weapons in order to increase combat effectiveness. INEW is essential for the system-versus-system confrontation on the informationalized battlefield.

Dai did not use the term "network centric," although there seem to be similarities between his and American concepts. For example, a subtitle on the cover of a US publication, Network Centric Warfare, states that the concept is for "developing and leveraging information superiority." The INEW objective, according to Dai, is not to develop and leverage but simply to seize information superiority.

INEW emphasizes integrating combat operations by merging command, forces, objectives, and actions. Command integration is its unified planning, organization, coordination, and control. Forces integration is its use in a complementary manner. Objective integration is its simultaneous use against enemy command, control, communication, computers, intelligence, surveillance, and reconnaissance (C4ISR), while action integration is its coordination to produce combined power. Dai listed the characteristics of INEW as its comprehensive nature, its integrated methods and expansive nature ("battlespace"), and the integrated nature of its "effectiveness." Forces integration implies the synthesis of platforms with networks.

The concept has a comprehensive effect on the enemy when it destroys C4ISR, according to Dai, thereby constraining decision-making and strategic planning. C4ISR systems are integrators and force multipliers, the focal point of IO. Dai did not address what would happen if INEW only damaged or disrupted systems, but one can imagine that the effects would be severe if not disabling. Integrated INEW methods can be developed into a unified plan and organization for action, and the expansive nature of battlespace (Dai implies an informationalized battlefield replete with information-based systems) allows for noncontact and nonlinear operations as well as full-depth integrated attacks.

Finally, the main targets are enemy military, political, economic, and social information systems, making the potential effectiveness greater than any traditional combat operation form.

Dai used the term "system" over forty times and stated that these systems are used to attack, weaken, destroy, or paralyze enemy systems. Since systems are the lifeblood of an economy, they are targets. Some are centers of gravity. He implied that INEW will exert tremendous disruption or damage well beyond the battlefield, reaching into societal, political, and economic relations in new ways. The Chinese recognize that if a network is destroyed, people and weapons cannot link up in an integrated fashion even if they are unharmed, and they are unable to exert nearly the same effect as they can when integrated.

Information operations revolve around destroying enemy systems and protecting friendly ones. Acquiring and forwarding information relies on electronic warfare, while processing and using the information relies on computer networks. INEW provides the means to participate in the system-versus-system confrontation and for attaining information superiority since systems are centers of gravity for combat forces. People and weapons become insignificant when not structured within a system. This concept appears similar to the US idea of systems integration except for its emphasis on ideology and philosophy. However, nowhere does Dai entertain fog and friction in the Information Age; he presents his argument as if there were no such problems.

The Chinese see the main combat contradiction (a dialectic point of view) as being between starting and stopping the flow of information in both the electromagnetic sphere and the space occupied by networks. An example of a successful operation would be disrupting information processing and obtaining control over network space, thereby disrupting the enemy knowledge system and preventing commanders from obtaining information required to make decisions. The struggle for information superiority is vital since it is a precondition for seizing sea, air, and space superiority.

Dai stated that China must transform its military focus from electronic warfare alone to include network operations. The emphasis on information operations, as represented by INEW, must be on acquiring both defensive and offensive equipment. Further, it is "important to take the initiative and effectively destroy the enemy's electronic information systems."

When discussing China's "two transformations," Dai again emphasized the active offense. He noted that the first transformation means changing from just EW to several forms and methods, such as INEW. The second transformation is to emphasize both defense and offense, with the "priority being the development of offensive information operations equipment." Again, this goal directly contradicts the emphasis in the white paper on the active defense. It is not clear whether the Chinese deliberately downplayed offensive operation in the Information Age or it was a rebuff to Dai's article. With regard to strategy, Dai noted that China must make breakthroughs at weak points, seize the commanding high ground, leap out of the dead ends, coordinate development, and grasp key junctures.

Finally, Dai noted that implementing INEW required an "information warfare personnel development plan." Information operations command personnel who understand technology and can manage as well as staff personnel and trainers are needed to teach and carry out ideological work. Combat personnel are needed to study, research, train, and fight. Finally, it is necessary to develop competencies for merging networks and electronics. Academies must develop specialized courses, deepen reforms, and send large numbers of multitaltented IO personnel to units.

Putting the INEW plan into action will require the use of theoretical achievements and modeling the battlefield deployment and other situational aspects of an enemy force. Perhaps this is being accomplished via computer network brigades or reserve IW units serving as opposition forces against PLA. In China, theory guides training, and rules and regulations are produced from evaluating the training.

Most likely, Dai's article was condensed from his earlier work, <u>An Introduction to Integrated Network-Electronic Warfare</u>. One critique of that work stated that the concept of INEW demonstrated that China no longer only learns from foreign militaries but has developed innovative theories with special Chinese military features. Further, the critique reiterated (as did Dai's 2002 article) that systems represent the center of gravity of combat forces and that systems integration uses information as a control mechanism to form a combat capability greater than the sum of its parts.[165] To American IO theorists, however, the Chinese approach does not appear to have as many special "Chinese characteristics" as it purports. INEW sounds similar to American theory of a few years ago, when system-of-systems research was more fashionable.

In fact, not only Chinese but also some US commanders highly regard electronic warfare, even at the expense of computer network attack. For

---

[165] "Introduction to Integrated Network-Electronic Warfare," <u>Jiefangjun Bao</u> [PLA Daily Newspaper](26 February 2002), p. 6, from the FBIS website.

example, General Hal Hornburg, USAF, Chief of Air Combat Command, noted that IO should be separated into three areas: manipulation of public perception, computer network attack, and electronic warfare. Only the latter should be assigned to the warfighter.[166]

In a 2000 article in <u>China Military Science</u>, Dai stated that the means of integrated application of information fighting will initially be the integrated application of networks and electronics and that the key to gaining the initiative in IO lies in the establishment of an "active offensive." Dai also noted that an IO is a series of operations with an information environment as the basic battlefield condition, with military information and an information system as the direct operational targets, and with EW and a computer network war as the principal forms.[167] His emphasis on INEW was thus clear over three years ago.

Dai further noted that IOs are both confrontations focusing on forces and arms and, more importantly, trials of strength focusing on knowledge and strategies, meaning the emphasis should be on strategies. As technology has reinforced human initiative, it has also highlighted the role played by a confrontation of strategies. Now traditional strategic theories are being rethought, new strategies mapped out, and new confrontation strategies advanced. Dai speaks of:

> Informationalized arms and equipment, which will, together with information systems, sound, light, electronics, magnetism, heat, and so on, turn into a carrier of strategies, thereby extending the field of strategic thinking and application of strategies; enabling us to map out a strategy from the angle of technology, technological equipment, and techniques; and helping us study and develop some new methods for applying a strategy by technological means. Thus, we're able to map out strategies aimed at applying technology to a battlefield; organically integrate technology with a strategy; add strategic wings to technology or scientific and technological genes to strategies; match technology with strategies; make strategies complement technology; or apply strategies in light of technology.[168]

---

[166] David Fulghum, "USAF Redefining Boundaries of Computer Attack," <u>Aviation Week and Space Technology</u>, Vol. 158, No. 9 (3 March 2003), p. 33.
[167] Dai Qingmin, "Innovating and Developing Views on Information Operations," <u>Zhongguo Junshi Kexue</u>, [<u>China Military Science</u>] Vol. 13, No. 8 (20 August 2000), pp. 72-77, from the FBIS website.
[168] Ibid.

Network-Centric Warfare

Early in 2003, US Army Lieutenant General Joseph Kellogg, director of command, control, communications and computer systems (C4) for the Joint Staff, stated that the US concept of network-centric warfare (NCW) is composed of three equal parts, technology, organization, and culture. Technology is the enabler in the equation and must be interoperable. Kellogg was less clear in explaining that culture involves taking risks while insuring that failures do not occur and that organizations must center on creating an environment for speed with only a single overall commander.[169]

In 1998, Vice Admiral Arthur K. Cebrowski, USN (Ret.), the director for space, information warfare, command and control (N-6), and John Garstka, the scientific and technical advisor for the directorate for C4 systems on the Joint Staff (J-6), wrote an article focused on business adaptations to the Information Age:[170]

- The power of network-centric computing comes from information-intensive interactions between large numbers of heterogeneous computational nodes in the network.
- Competitive advantages come from the co-evolvement of organizations and processes to exploit information technology, employing network-centric operational architectures consisting of a high-powered information grid, a sensor grid, and a transaction grid.
- The key to market dominance lies in making strategic choices appropriate to changing ecosystems.

The authors then noted that network-centric operations offered the same dynamics to the military. Strategically, that meant understanding all the elements of battlespace and battle time; operationally, it meant mirroring business ecosystem linkages among units and the operating environment; tactically, it meant speed of operations; and structurally, it meant that network-centric warfare required sensor and transaction grids and an information grid supported by command and control processes needing automation for speed. NCW reportedly enabled a shift from attrition warfare. Speed enabled a force to have more battlespace awareness, mass effects instead of forces, and foreclose enemy courses of action. It also offset disadvantages in numbers, technology, or position and was capable of locking out alternative enemy strategies and locking in success.

---

[169] Dan Caterinicchia, Federal Computer Week, 23 January 2003.
[170] Arthur K. Cebrowski and John J. Garstka, "Network-Centric Warfare: Its Origin and Future," US Naval Institute Proceedings, 124, No. 1 (January 1998), pp 28-35.

This list is significantly different from Dai's, with its focus on contradictions, ideology, and centers of gravity. This is not surprising since different cultures will interpret the interaction of systems in different ways. It reinforces Kellogg's comments about technology, organization, and culture as the components of NCW. Of concern, however, is once again the notable absence of focus and discussion on the fog and friction of technology in a real-time battlespace. The US concept appears to rely on speed to overcome all obstacles. The concept seems to focus on "the content, quality, and timeliness of information moving between nodes on the network" and dismisses misinformation or deception. Loren Thompson, chief operating officer of the Lexington Institute, commented about over reliance on business strategies while critiquing a 2002 article by Admiral Cebrowski on NCW:

> Let me conclude by answering Cebrowski's question as to why commercial development cycles are so much shorter than military ones. The reason is that it's harder to get to geocentric orbit than the grocery store, that no one is shooting at the Coca Cola Co., and that private-sector executives don't rewrite their business plans every time a consultant comes up with a new idea.[171]

There also appear to be built-in contradictions in the concept. For example, the authors note that NCW strength is designed to "offset a disadvantage in numbers, technology, or position." Further, "We must change how we train, organize, and allocate resources if the United States decides to fight on an NCW rather than a platform-centric basis."[172] Yet, the authors twice note that a sensor or engagement grid must be coupled in time to shooters, and the DOD report to Congress on NCW stated, "Battlefield entities (platforms, units, sensors, shooters) must be designed 'net ready.'"[173] This reliance on interoperability is not given the place it deserves by US theorists. Rather, the idea of moving from platform to NCW takes center stage when in fact the move is from platforms to net-ready platforms. This interoperability resembles the integration process the Chinese stress.

Cebrowski and Garstka underscored that NCW made the whole greater than the sum of its parts, which the Chinese INEW concept also noted, with the

---

[171] Loren Thompson, "Dot-Com Mania," Defense News, 28 October -3 November 2002, p.12.
[172] Cebrowski and Garstka.
[173] Art Money, Report on Network Centric Warfare: Sense of the Report, March 2001, as downloaded from the Internet at
http://www.dodccrp.org/NCW/NCW_report/report/ncww_cover.html.

latter perhaps mimicking the American authors. In contrast to the Chinese, Cebrowski and Garstka used the term "system" sparingly; however, systems remain important to the US concept.

John Garstka, David Alberts, and Federick Stein wrote Network Centric Warfare in 1999. The book defines NCW as: an information superiority-enabled concept of operations that generates increased combat power by networking sensors, decision-makers, and shooters to achieve shared awareness, increased speed of command, higher tempo of operations, greater lethality, increased survivability, and a degree of self-synchronization.[174] The authors imply integration of platforms and networks by including sensors and shooters in their definition. Again, however, fog and friction are ignored.

In October 2002, Cebrowski wrote that any weapon system must be on the net to remain viable—the concept of a net-ready platform. If such interoperability is not available, the program is subject to cancellation. Risk is managed by increasing the breadth of capabilities to cover gaps.[175] Can simply increasing capabilities reduce fog and friction? Doesn't surprise or disruption mean anything for theory? Cebrowski also noted that aircraft and other joint capabilities in Afghanistan were empowered by high-speed NCW principles. However, problems remained, such as minimal information filtering and decision aids for field commanders.[176]

The DOD report to Congress about NCW stressed many of these points.[177] It noted that interoperability must not be abandoned ("a critical mass of connectivity and interoperability is necessary to both encourage and support new ways of doing business"[178]), and that impediments to the program must be overcome. However, the report does assert that "NCW is to warfare what e-business is to business" and "no single platform or sensor is the heart of the system."[179] The first statement again overemphasizes the business-military comparison, and the latter implies that platforms remain vital to the NCW concept. We are not moving from platforms to NCW, but from platform to an integrated or interoperable form of platforms and nets.

---

[174] David Alberts, John Garstka, and Frederick Stein, Network Centric Warfare, C4ISR Cooperative Research Program (CCRP) Publication Series (Washington, D.C.: National Defense University Press, 1999), p 2.
[175] Arthur Cebrowski, "New Rules, New Era: Pentagon Must Embrace Information Age," Defense News, 21-27 October 2002, p. 28.
[176] Richard W. Mayo and John Nathman, "ForceNet: Turning Information into Power," Proceedings, February 2003, p. 43.
[177] Annual Report.
[178] Money.
[179] Ibid.

Chinese IW expert Wang Baocun, writing in <u>China Military Science</u>, discussed the US concept of network-centric warfare from a Chinese perspective. He did not compare NCW with INEW, although he noted that China must study the theoretical and practical aspects of other countries' efforts to develop an information-based military in order for China to do the same. He further stated that China must develop a comprehensive electronic information system and that such systems should be integrated.[180] To that degree, Wang appears to echo Dai.

Comparing the NCW and INEW

The two explanations above represent the basic views of Chinese and US specialists on network-related concepts. Clearly these are ideas for the present and immediate future and will form the basis of both countries' transformations. However, the terms should be examined against other paradigms as well. Admiral Cebrowski is a proponent of alternate or even multiple concepts. He stressed that "one best way" should not be pursued, as there may not be one architecture or standard. Rather, competing concepts should be debated. And interestingly enough, the view from a "bottom-up" perspective is different from the view at the top. Those at the bottom have other points for the authors to consider.

First, it is unfortunate that the authors who proposed these concepts did not venture into detailed definitions, for this lack has confused readers. For example, Cebrowski and Garstka used the terms "network-centric computing," "network-centric operations," and "network-centric war" in their seminal article without defining them. Readers were left with the impression that they are interchangeable sound bites for an idea. A citation at the end regarding NCW came closest to a definition, noting that it is "applicable to all levels of warfare and contributes to the coalescence of strategy, operations, and tactics. NCW is transparent to mission, force size and composition, and geography." This definition was updated in Network Centric Warfare, by Alberts, Garstka, and Stein, which Cebrowski reviewed. Their definition is better but still needs specification, such as an explanation of what a network "war" means. Would confrontation or struggle work better, for example? Do networks really "war" with one another?

The terminology problem is important because if we are attempting to sell a concept, we need a thorough understanding of what we are selling. The

---

[180] Wang, Baocun, "The Future Warfare for Which the US Military Is Making Preparations: Network-Centric Warfare," <u>Zhongguo Junshi Kexue</u> [<u>China Military Science</u>] (20 October, 2002), pp. 133-143, as translated and downloaded from FBIS.

authors appeared to be describing warfare enabled by speed of awareness and shared knowledge to bring effects to bear on targets in a timely and accurate manner. Thus, NCW is an enabler much like other developments in the mechanized age, albeit a quantum leap, to act as a combat facilitator, especially of battlefield awareness. Communications have always acted as enablers, facilitators, and coordinators of battlespace awareness, just not to the same degree as sensors and satellites. Terms such as "network assisted platform operations," "network-coordinating engagement operations," or simply "network-centric operations" appear as appropriate as NCW. The INEW concept suffers from the same imprecision. In many ways INEW sounds like an updated version of NCW except for its EW and stratagem links.

Second, many NCW authors describe a movement away from platforms to networks in their discussion of theory, then use an integrated or interoperable model of platforms and networks to describe their concept, which again shows lack of precision. Further discussion of the move from kinetic to combined kinetic, electronic and network-based warfare would have assisted understanding. NCW does not occur in isolation. If it did, no one could use it because it would not control or be connected to anything; it would just be a grouping of sensors and nodes joined to a network that produces information. Rather, the concept implies that sensors are part of systems integrated into platforms. Weapons, weapon systems, and platforms are plugged into the sensor, information, and transaction grids that comprise NCW at the moment, and they will be with us for some time. Platforms launch weapons and have nodes where network information is integrated into the targeting and protection mechanisms of the platform. Predators are platforms that use networks. The INEW concept used the word "integrated" while NCW theorists used "interoperable" for KC-135 aerial refuelers that possess routers, antennas, and other equipment so the aircraft can transmit battlespace information among units.[181]

Third, the NCW discussion suggests that the concept alone is sufficient to make a nation great and modern. The American metaphor is that if it works for business, it will work for the military. The difference is that in the military, people plan on destroying the networks through high-tech weapons, making the systems useless. Or they try to deceive sensors and satellites, which does not happen often in business because it runs on information in a more perfect form. The military does not possess perfect information to the degree the market does; therefore, economic superiority may not translate into military superiority. Most important, there is no discussion of what might happen if such

---

[181] Joab Jackson, "Network-Centric Warfare Comes of Age," <u>Washington Technology</u>, 21 October 2002, a WT special report.

a system meets a like system or if there is even partial disruption. Kosovo, Somalia, and Bosnia were not confrontations between modern systems, but rather of modern against antiquated systems. So there is little consideration of the impact of the fog and friction of war on NCW and INEW. And there remain problems of available bandwidth, mission priorities and access to networked platforms, and the number of combat systems that must be coordinated—over 400 by some accounts.[182]

Further, smaller countries are already developing ways to negate NCW and INEW, including simple offsets such as small devices that fool global positioning system-guided weapons as they approach a target set. Potential enemies are also undoubtedly looking into ways to provide false information that our systems will speedily process and turn into fire-for-effect missions that are inefficient or perhaps even damaging, using NCW to get into the observe-orient-decide-act loop. Networks have vulnerabilities that are too seldom discussed. What happens to NCW and INEW when parts of the net go down? How do they rearm/react/readjust? Kellogg stated that even "the cryptology being used by terrorists to protect their data and communications is as good, if not better, than DOD's solutions."[183] This implies that NCW cannot operate as businesses do, because the net will be attacked and suffer damage.

Fourth, the network-centric concept is technology-focused, while INEW possesses a strong stratagem element. This difference is important. It is how INEW plans to "defeat the superior with the inferior." The Chinese have noted that Asian analysts think in terms of stratagems and Western planners in terms of technology. Western strategists should be aware of this perspective. Perhaps the Pentagon should start thinking about using NCW together with stratagems.

Alfred Kaufman, a study director at the US Institute for Defense Analyses, agrees that technology has too prominent a place in our military thinking, so much so that it dictates military strategy. He wrote that NCW theory has resulted in "the virtual collapse of the intellectual structure that was erected to control the development of Western military technology." He believes that the Pentagon hopes that commercial innovation will bring to war and to national security the same benefits it brings to commercial enterprises. In his view, NCW is flawed because it:

---

[182] Alex Salkever, "The Network is the Battlefield," Business Week, 7 January 2003.
[183] Dan Caterinicchia, "Kellogg Describes Cyber Battlefield," Federal Computer Week, 5 March 2003.

- Overestimates man's capacity to deal with contradictory information.
- Ignores the true nature of the enemy and drives him to asymmetric strategies.
- Ignores the dynamic nature of combat and bureaucratizes war.
- Assumes that military victory is an end in itself.[184]

Fifth, consideration is given to the human in the loop, yet one wonders if a proper parallel should be drawn between NCW/INEW and human network attacks (HNA). NCW and INEW discuss the importance of training and educating personnel to conduct themselves as well as to run a network-oriented staff. US theory now includes discussions of effects-based operations to demonstrate how NCW can be used to affect humans and objectives in a sequenced manner. Addressing the human as a network might be the next logical thinking. Not doing so reinforces the Pentagon's one-sided focus on technology. HNA refers to the ability of weapons, including nonlethals, to shut down the operating systems of people, who have their electric circuitry in the form of neurons. Properly targeted, this type of attack can make it difficult for humans to enter the decision-making cycle to assist in processing and selecting targets, the fail-safe aspect to NCW and INEW. No one is writing about human-centric operations that are also key to continuing network-centric operations. Again, this topic was not the focus of the authors addressing NCW and INEW, but their innovative concepts can be carried further into the human domain.

Sixth, the United States needs to study foreign IO and NCW related concepts if it is to understand how to work with or against the cyber-age systems of other countries. It is clear that China studies Pentagon thinking. At Chinese bookstores there are hundreds of US books translated from English, especially in the IO area. No such bounty on Chinese thinking can be found in American bookstores.

Finally, and most importantly, Dai noted that INEW is an offensive strategies based on acquiring both defensive and offensive information operations equipment, "with the priority being the development of offensive information operations equipment." Further, it is "important to take the initiative and effectively destroy the enemy's electronic information systems."[185] The focus on the active offense is totally lacking in the NCW discussion, as is the Chinese focus on applying strategies to offset inferiorities

---

[184] Alfred Kaufman, "Caught in the Network," <u>Armed Forces Journal</u>, February 2005, pp. 20-22.
[185] Dai, 2002.

in technology and equipment. The latter focus is really on the decision-maker's mind, with strategies being the means and perception management the ends.

The good news is that the initial discussion of NCW is over, and the concept has received feedback from both private and public sources. This has provided substance to Admiral Cebrowski's foresight that more than one idea should be pursued. China is lacking in that area. The INEW topic has not been publicly critiqued. Perhaps the dialectic of point and counterpoint works better in Western culture based on its willingness to confront ideas with counters or better ideas. In many ways China merely mirrors what happens in the West in the NCW arena, but the West must be acutely aware of the Chinese nuances and mirror imaging.

Milan Vego, for example, wrote a critique of NCW, pointing out several concepts that should be addressed.[186] Loren Thompson, noted above, offered nearly a point-for-point rebuttal of the Cebrowski's article.[187] Such evaluations have been sorely lacking from the one-sided American debate. Even if NCW is but an instrument to get more appropriations for systems out of the budget process, it is worth examining the idea now instead of allocating money and complaining later about a fancy system that glossed over details.

As Vego noted, NCW is probably here to stay, but it is not a panacea. It lacks human factors and basic empirical evidence. Thompson added that it is akin to transferring the dot-com mania into the military field, and we must be aware of the problem set that comes with it. Vego and Thompson may or may not be correct, but they have filled a void (most likely in China, too, since the latter has a voracious appetite for anything written on NCW in this country). Their critiques have offered other angles at a minimum.

US decision-makers, many with business backgrounds, must not apply their business experience to the military arena. The concept worked well, but in an environment totally divorced from the battlefield. China, on the other hand, will continue to load its INEW concept with Chinese characteristics, or so they say. Their metaphor will be shaped by the words of famous strategists and consider the use of deception and surprise while the United States focuses on speed of response and efficiency. One important distinction in the Chinese approach, however, is that INEW would be used to attack economic, political, societal, and military networks.

---

[186] Milan Vego, "Net-Centric is Not Decisive," Proceedings, January 2003.
[187] Loren Thompson, "Dot-com Mania," in Letters, Defense News, 28 October - 3 November 2002, p 12.

Cultures eventually produce metaphors. General Kellogg noted that culture involves taking risks while insuring that failures do not occur. Does the US risk overdependence on speed and prowess at the expense of other factors, while China tries to defeat the superior with the inferior, using good but not outstanding technology combined with stratagems? Both concepts lack ways to block failure in an age of continued fog and friction. We are uncertain what happens if our risk taking fails. No one wants to talk about that. And, as the conflict in Iraq extends and diverts funding from the transformation effort, we may be closer than we think to confronting the risks discussed here.

Part Three

Case Studies

PART THREE: APPLICATIONS AND CASE STUDIES IN PEACE AND WAR

Part Three is composed of four chapters. They examine the impact, both potential and actual, of cyber technologies on military conflicts and peacekeeping operations.

Chapter Seven examines how virtual processes can prevent or resolve conflict between participants. The chapter also describes how virtual processes were used to quell the fighting in Bosnia and how these processes offer hope as a crisis management, preemptive, or preventive means to stop conflict from occurring or to limit its spread.

Chapter Eight examines the concept of information superiority as it applied to the NATO intervention in Kosovo in March of 1999. The conclusion drawn by the author is that even with total information superiority, NATO still was fooled by the Serbian armed forces on several occasions. This indicates that there is still much tension between IO theory and the practice of IO in the field.

Chapter Nine explores the United Nation's interest in exploiting cyber-based technologies to help the peacekeeper maintain law and order. In effect, peacekeepers are transforming into "policekeepers." They must confront unruly mobs and criminal elements as well as maintain the peace. Cyber technologies can greatly assist their efforts.

Chapter Ten outlines how Russia applied its IW concept in the second Russian-Chechen conflict (1999 and still ongoing as this chapter goes to print in the fall of 2005). A short summary of the Chechen application of the information-psychological aspect of IW is included. Students of military history can learn much about the low-intensity IW environment from a study of the experiences of both sides in this conflict.

CHAPTER SEVEN: VIRTUAL PEACEMAKING: A MILITARY VIEW OF CONFLICT PREVENTION THROUGH THE USE OF INFORMATION TECHNOLOGY[188]

Introduction: What Is Virtual Peacemaking?

While on patrol in Bosnia, an American lieutenant colonel was confronted by an irate Croat who, with an old map in his hand, told the officer that he was on his territory. Referring to his own map, the officer replied that he wasn't and offered to go one step farther to prove his point. Taking out his Global Positioning System (GPS), he entered data and showed the Croat the results. "Sir," the LTC said, "I have consulted the cosmic tribunal (three satellites), and they have proven me correct. Excuse us. We have to continue with our mission."

Today there are many such occurrences when information technology (IT) is consulted to provide accurate and timely information. IT has the potential to become a huge conflict prevention tool or mechanism, an area largely underutilized. Traditionally, crisis managers and conflict resolution academicians attempted to prevent conflict through diplomatic, economic, cultural, and finally nonlethal means. If these steps failed, then the international community deployed military forces to exert pressure on potential combatants. The use of information developments now must be added to this process or progression. IT's data-processing systems connect people, places, concepts, and organizations with speed and accuracy, significantly upgrading the conflict prevention methods and integrating other conflict prevention means. Through developments such as the Internet, IT offers the potential to reach both ruling elites and individuals in societies contemplating conflict whether they have access to the technology or not.

The application of IT to processes that influence or regulate our lives has spawned a host of new concepts. Perhaps the most important is the concept of "things virtual." These "things virtual," as but one example, allow people to experience concepts or illusions temporarily simulated or extended by computer software. "Things virtual" explain processes we can see and use but which we can't directly touch or feel. Some of these processes are familiar to

---

[188] This chapter was first published under the same title as an article in <u>Challenges of Peace Support into the 21st Century</u>, The Swedish National Defence College, Stockholm, 26-27 September 1997, pp. 179-213. It has been slightly modified for length and context. A second version of the article appeared as "Preventing Conflict through Information Technology," <u>Military Review</u>, December 1998/January-February 1999, pp. 44-57.

us—virtual reality games, for example, are available to children. It is possible to order virtual flowers for loved ones via the Internet; and virtual environments allow scientists to explore molecular structures, architects to walk clients through their designs, and Ford Motor Company to teach forge hammer operators how to stamp out connecting rods.[189] Branches of government now study concepts such as virtual diplomacy, virtual justice, and virtual communications.

It seems only natural then to develop or apply virtual processes that help prevent conflict. Computer simulations, IT use by diplomats in negotiating processes, and IT use by militaries to monitor locations or find minefields are a few of many potential applications. This concept, hereafter termed virtual peacemaking, is defined as:

> The use of virtual processes of information gathering, analysis, and communication (through the use of information technologies) for simulated or training exercises as well as real-world scenarios by diplomats, mediators, negotiators, military leaders, and other individuals or groups to end a dispute and resolve the issues that led to it before conflict occurs.[190]

The definition of peacemaking utilized in the collation was taken from the 1997 version of Army Field Manual (FM) 101-5-1, Operational Terms and Graphics. Here, peacemaking is defined as "the process of diplomacy, mediation, negotiation, or other forms of peaceful settlements that arranges an end to a dispute and resolves issues that led to it."[191] Peacemaking, in the opinion of the US Army's Peacekeeping Institute at Carlisle, Pennsylvania, refers to the term as used in 101-5-1 but, in addition, encompasses military support to preventive diplomacy as incorporated in the umbrella concept of peace operations.

---

[189] W. Wayt Gibbs, "Taking Computers to Task," Scientific American, July 1997, p.84.
[190] This definition was generated by collating the main ideas from two definitions, that of virtual diplomacy and that of peacemaking. This past April, at the opening session of a conference on "Virtual Diplomacy," the President of the United States Institute of Peace, Richard Solomon, defined virtual diplomacy as "an exploration of how our world is being transformed by the global information revolution, one that assesses new technologies of data processing and communication to prevent, more effectively manage, or resolve international conflict." He added that virtual diplomacy is designed to help explore the possibility to decrease conflict through virtual processes of information gathering, analysis, and communication. Richard Solomon, US Institute of Peace Conference on Virtual Diplomacy, 1-2 April 1997, Washington, D.C.
[191] Army Field Manual (FM) 101-5-1, Operational Terms and Graphics, 1997, p. I-119.

The most important part of this definition is the last few words–that the use of these processes will happen "before conflict occurs." Also of importance is the term information technology, which forms the core element of virtual peacemaking processes, and is often used as a specific reference point by discussants of conflict prevention who do not use the broader term virtual peacemaking.

This paper focuses on the military aspect of virtual peacemaking, those virtual information technologies the military can use to prevent conflict. First, it discusses the goals, interests, and value of virtual peacemaking. Second, it discusses the environment in which militaries conduct operations today and the applicability of virtual peacekeeping to this environment. Third, it discusses the information technologies available. Finally, the limitations, problems, and dangers involving the military use of virtual peacemaking are explored.

It will be helpful to review a related use of IT that served as the catalyst for the idea of virtual peacemaking before beginning the detailed examination. This use was the crafting and implementing of the Dayton Accords negotiation process, which allowed the international community not only to manage the Bosnian crisis but also to find some resolution. So far, the process has successfully endured the challenges to peace for nearly two years. Future historians will look on the Accords as the first major successful application of IT to assist in the conflict prevention process, in this case via "virtual crisis management."

The Dayton Accords
"In peace operations...perception is reality."[192]

After nearly three years of fierce fighting among the factions in the former Yugoslavia, the international community finally persuaded the Presidents of Bosnia, Croatia, and Serbia to sit down together and discuss how they could end the bloodshed. This meeting took place at Dayton, Ohio, in the fall of 1995. IT played a prominent, even decisive role in convincing the three leaders that the accords would be administered fairly and without prejudice. Mapping and satellite data were the two pieces of information technology used most often. Similar procedures could prove useful for virtual peacemaking, it appears.

---

[192] Kenneth Allard, "Information Operations in Bosnia: A Preliminary Assessment," Strategic Forum, Institute for National Strategic Studies, Number 91, November 1996, pp. 1-4.

A huge TV screen was located in the room where these leaders met. A replica of the conference working map on the table in front of them was shown on the screen. This allowed the leaders to keep their fingers on the changing Inter-Entity Boundary Line that marked where the boundaries for their countries would lie. This was the chief area of contention. Mappers would

> Digitize the line and import the information into a terrain visualization system called PowerScene (an advanced software architecture for terrain visualization), showing a 3-dimensional terrain perspective to depict where the line apportioned the land. Negotiators could also use the system to further refine the proposed line. For example, if the line cut through a building, the line could be moved to either side of the building and viewed on the screen.[193]

Current mapping for the software was accomplished by using real-time satellite images from "flyovers." This three-dimensional, moving model of Bosnia's terrain was combined with PowerScene software (which purports to have no limitations on image source, scale, or breadth). Imagery of varying resolution from satellites, aerial photographs, and other sources were integrated into a seamless image on the screen. Maps and cultural features were worked into the display as well, since the imagery was correlated with real-world coordinates.[194]

Working with legal experts, the mappers exported information to an 8mm tape and hand carried it to the Joint Topo Tactical Operations Center (JTT), located three-quarters of a mile from the delegates' quarters, for hard copy production. Sometimes the information was piped through fiber optic cables linking the JTT to the Remote Replication System support function to expedite production. The numerous changes kept the mappers very busy, with as many as 600 maps produced a day. Line drawings were digitized and put on a 1:600,000 UNPROFOR road map, where a transparent overlay was created and matched to a Defense Mapping Agency 1:50,000 Topographic Line Map, and replicated on a bubble jet printer.[195] The software almost eliminated misunderstanding over boundaries, thereby building confidence, mustering support, and saving time.

Aviation Week and Space Technology indicated that PowerScene had uses other than mapping. PowerScene had also helped coerce the participants by demonstrating to the Serbian, Croat, and Muslim leaders that NATO

---

[193] "DMA Support to the Peace Talks," Online. Internet. 15 March 1997, p. 1, http//www.dma.gov/inf...acts/site/mappers.html.
[194] PowerScene, advertising overview handout, November 1995.
[195] "DMA Support to the Peace Talks," p. 2.

warplanes were very capable of precisely hitting targets if the fighting did not stop. That is, the possessor of these technological capabilities linked to simulation and mapping alone was able to demonstrate in a benign form its potential military power. Today

> PowerScene is being used in Bosnia to support command, control, communications and intelligence. If the commanding general wants to know what the road looks like from point A to B, or the line of sight from a mountain, the system is ideal.[196]

After the peace agreement was initialed, representatives from the three sides continued to exploit this virtual reality view of the zone of separation.[197] They went on a simulated flight along the 650-mile-long border to determine, in some cases, on which side of a road the boundary should run.[198] The flight lasted nearly nine hours. Thus, the application of virtual crisis management at Dayton helped eliminate mistrust and disinformation, and it served as a confidence building measure.

During the implementation phase of the treaty, reinforcing mechanisms were essential to the successful implementation of the peace accords while IT continued to play a major role. Helicopters, equipped with a new method to digitize the attack helicopter's gun-camera footage, exposed Dayton Accord violators by photographing their infractions. Occasionally, peacekeepers presented evidence of a violation to leaders of the nation or group breaching the Accord to compel compliance. At times, cross hairs were trained on the equipment in the photographs to demonstrate the precision of the technology. The implied message was taken to heart by the transgressors.[199]

Information technology also connected NATO Headquarters with IFOR; the Internet kept troops informed of events at home; and a joint information bureau provided timely information and helped insure compliance with the Dayton Accords. The bureau provided daily advice to the division

---

[196] Joseph Anselmo, "Satellite Data Plays Key Role in Bosnia Peace Treaty," Aviation Week and Space Technology, 11 December 1995.

[197] Virtual reality is "an interactive technology that creates an illusion, still crude rather than convincing, of being immersed in an artificial world." Philip Elmer-Dewitt, "Cyberpunk," Time, 8 February 1993, p. 60. Another source defines virtual reality as "a realistic simulation of an environment, including three-dimensional graphics, by a computer system using interactive software and hardware." See Webster's Pocket Dictionary, Random House Inc., 1993, p. 735.

[198] Eric Schmitt, "High Tech Maps Guided Bosnia Talks," The New York Times, 24 November 1995, p. 1.

[199] Allard, p. 4.

commander and operated together with the operations, intelligence, and civil affairs elements. It has helped manage a multitude of tasks and missions, and it offered journalists a unified, coherent view of the situation from an IFOR/SFOR standpoint. Clearly a key lesson learned, whether in the negotiation room or in the zone of separation, is that in peace operations in Bosnia, "perception is reality."[200] Managing this effort was possible because the agreement was in place before troops were deployed to the field.

What Are the Military Goals, Interests, and Value of Using Virtual Peacemaking?

The military's goal regarding virtual peacemaking is to apply technologies to conditions generated by a new world environment, turning this integration into military plans and operations to resolve disputes before they transform into conflicts. Just as diplomats use virtual processes (communications, negotiations, etc.) to keep a disagreement "within bounds," the military must use virtual processes to guide or force (when necessary) the militaries of disputing nations away from conflict. Military planners and operators do this by providing channels for anger, providing alternatives to frustration, relieving stress and tension, and avoiding overreactions on the one hand; and by deterring, monitoring, and even compelling disputing militaries on the other.

Virtual peacemaking allows intermediaries to "use forces" instead of the use of force. The military is a power with coercive capabilities that create pre-conditions for peacemaking. That is, the use of forces can serve a preemptive role and prevent the use of force. Virtual peacemaking can also support the rules of engagement for the forces called upon to prevent conflict.

The difficulty with virtual peacemaking is convincing governments without IT capabilities that IT is serving international and not national interests. Yet virtual peacemaking offers the opportunity for those with extra concerns and anxieties (whether they are, or are not, part of the conflict or conflict-prevention process) to "monitor the monitors." However, at times the national approaches to conflict prevention are so diverse, due to national attitudes or the participation of peoples and movements instead of states and nations in national decision-making processes, that it is impossible to keep everyone satisfied.

Virtual peacemaking is not a call for virtual presence. Troops are still required although in smaller numbers. Virtual peacemaking merely strives to control disputes and prevent them from moving to open conflict by taking

---

[200] Ibid., pp. 1, 3.

advantage of contemporary technology. Virtual peacemaking is a transparent process that offers five areas to assist conflict prevention: it **explains** the nature or causes of a conflict, or measures taken by the international community; it **demonstrates** simultaneity of effort, or the impotence of those involved in the conflict; it **compels** compliance by simulating consequences of actions taken by the participants; and it can **monitor** and **review** actions for the satisfaction of the participants and the international community. If the end goal is served, the value of virtual peacemaking cannot be overestimated. Such a process can even help promote the creation of a global civil society through the development and use of common values, something long-sought-after but deemed unattainable.

What Is the Relationship between Military Methods (Combat and Peacetime) and Virtual Peacemaking?

An important report by the Carnegie Commission, completed in 1996, recommended several ways to nurture conditions to prevent conflict from occurring. Although these recommendations were not necessarily military in orientation, they suggested other uses for virtual peacemaking. For example, the list included conflict prevention recommendations such as promoting intercommunal confidence and developing programs to open up and maintain cross-cultural lines of communication.[201] Since militaries are called upon to assist in implementing these recommendations, their application to virtual peacemaking should be considered.

The military has at its disposal a list of mechanisms to prevent conflict that are applicable to virtual peacemaking scenarios. Michael Lund, author of Preventing Violent Conflicts, listed several of these mechanisms.

Restraints on the Use of Force:
- Arms control regimes, to include their monitoring
- Confidence-building measures
- Nonaggression agreements
- Arms embargoes, blockades
- Non-offensive defense force postures
- Military-to-military programs
- Preemptive peacekeeping forces for deterrence and containment
- Demilitarized zones, safe havens, peace zones.

Threat or Use of Armed Force:
- Deterrence policies
- Security guarantees

---

[201] Second Annual Progress Report, Carnegie Commission on Preventing Deadly Conflict, New York, 1996, p. 8.

- Maintaining or restoring local or regional "balances of power"
- Use or threat of limited shows of force.[202]

Virtual means can also help explore the relationship between military power and police power, or the use of forces under extreme conditions, to prevent conflict. The use of force under extreme conditions could also be simulated if necessary. Yet another vital simulation worthy of exploration is the impact of "information friction" on the situation—the impact of media bias, language difficulties, and cultural barriers and prisms on the force.

There is a huge civilian aspect of virtual peacemaking that works hand in glove with the military component and helps prevent conflict by defusing and alleviating risk factors.[203] These civilian mechanisms include the ability to:

- Alert international bodies (use of the Internet or satellite communications).
- Secure reliable information (through access to reliable databases).
- Identify and strengthen moderate leaders (use of TV/news/radio).
- Establish channels of communication, both formal and informal (mobile phones or Internet).
- Develop coordinated political, economic, and social contingency plans; encourage and reward nonviolence; limit the spread of violence; penalize aggressors (by integrating many of the IT uses noted above).
- Follow up political support and economic engagements (virtual diplomacy and economic IT).
- Establish regular consultations (hot lines, satellite communications, and Internet).
- Increase readiness of forces (measure a unit's preparedness via simulations and use remotely piloted vehicle flights over formations and territories).
- Prepare nonmilitary measures and actions (use of virtual diplomatic, judicial, and communication assets; economic and information blockades; and use of nonlethal weapons).
- Strengthen deterrence by signaling red lines not to cross (use computer teleconferencing, transparency of preparations of the international community to act, etc.).

---

[202] Michael S. Lund, Preventing Violent Conflicts, United States Institute of Peace Press, Washington, D.C., second printing 1997, p. 203.

[203] Carnegie Commission, p. 7. The commission also recommended developing an "information index," based on comparing the logic of warning (sooner one acts the better) versus the logic of policy (put off hard choices as long as possible).

- Communicate commitments to take stronger action (demonstrate ability to conduct system override and interference in all communications activities).
- Prepare citizens to accept courses of action (use of public affairs assets and organizations along with TV/radio/Internet, and other IT capabilities).
- Initiate formal negotiations (teleconferences, virtual diplomacy, etc.).[204]

Preventive actions help control early reactions to signs of trouble, identify and resolve the underlying causes of the potential violence, and offer a balanced approach to alleviating pressure and risk that may result in violence.[205] Nongovernmental Organizations (NGOs), for example, have become one the most important indicators of the potential rise of conflict. They are often the first to penetrate crisis areas and have a wealth of information regarding the conditions and grievances that give rise to potential violence. Governments often do not have direct contact with the population, but NGOs do.[206] In this limited sense, non-state actors are replacing governmental agencies as a means for integrating and coordinating cross-border issues. It is important to be cognizant of their IT means and coordinate them with those of state actors and militaries, ensuring some compatibility and a means through which to communicate. Whatever course is taken, governments, NGOs, and militaries must keep in mind that prevention will require actions, actions will involve costs, and costs will involve tradeoffs.[207]

Is Virtual Peacemaking Applicable to the Current International Environment?

An air of optimism regarding IT's assistance to the conflict control process existed after the Dayton Accords. IT fostered both confidence and a positive attitude among the sides at Dayton (the Bosnian Serbs were not part of that process). Can virtual peacemaking responses be tailored to handle the different (race, religion, culture, etc.) causes of conflict, no two of which may be alike?[208]

---

[204] Ibid., p. 10. The uses of information technology suggested next to each item were not listed in the original, but added by the author.

[205] Ibid., p. 6.

[206] Ibid., p. 7.

[207] Ibid., p. V.

[208] Nearly a decade ago the Carnegie Commission completed a study that outlined factors in today's world that eventually can lead to war. The report cited the following as some of these causes: (1.) political and economic legacies of colonialism and the Cold War, (2.) illegitimate governmental institutions, (3.) problematic regional

What is new about the international environment to which these considerations must be applied? Some of the most prevalent though not always obvious characteristics are:

1. Modern methods for controlling crises utilize very slow decision-making processes although progress in streamlining their effectiveness has been noted.
2. Crises areas may require military action with humanitarian support or military support of a humanitarian action. That is, nothing is predictable or traditional.
3. Crises today, in contrast to the Westphalia system of the past, often require states to consider intervening and violating a country's sovereignty in order to stop military action.
4. Some crises today require intervention in an area where no legitimate government is operating.
5. Many crises today are far from America's shores, do not threaten our national interests, and consequently engender little public support.
6. Crises often encourage manipulation of the force through "mission creep".
7. Many modern crises require close coordination between many different organizations, which has required new organizational techniques to handle military interaction with both governmental and nongovernmental (NGO) agencies.
8. Contemporary crises require governments to decide if they will support the international peace process, a national interest, or a humanitarian cause.

---

relationships, (4.) social cleavages derived from poorly managed religious, cultural, or ethnic differences, (5.) widespread illiteracy, (6.) disease and disability, (7.) lack of resources such as water and arable land, (8.) patterns of political repression, cultural discrimination, and systematic economic deprivation, (9.) location of minority populations in economically depressed areas along borders with kindred states, (10.) despotic leaders, (11.) weak, corrupt, or collapsed regimes, and (12.) the exacerbation of these problems by new global political and economic forces.

The commission offered recommendations to get at the root causes of conflict produced by these circumstances. Finding ways to control conflict is crucial to world stability since local hostilities can become international ones, not in the nuclear sense as in the past, but in the sense that conducting quarrels no matter how deadly is an outdated idea. Second Annual Progress Report, Carnegie Commission on Preventing Deadly Conflict, New York, 1996, p. V.

9. Crises can demonstrate the power of national will of a country, such as has occurred when a high-tech force is faced by an opponent with a "warrior" mentality.
10. Major powers are often impotent to act in crisis situations, even with a high-tech force at the ready.
11. Regional organizations are sometimes impotent to act in crisis situations, even if they have multinational rapid reaction forces at the ready.
12. Crises can develop due to the breakdown of the laws of society and methods for obtaining pay and goods, or for religious or ethnic reasons, making use of military force a last option.
13. The multidimensional nature of crises makes it difficult to identify the center of gravity of forces involved in a conflict, especially among paramilitary forces.
14. Some crises involving irregular or paramilitary forces have demonstrated little regard for standard warfare procedures or international law.
15. Crises can spread within or between countries not initially involved in a conflict, simply over which side to take in the struggle. Any border issue usually involves military forces, however.

The greatest challenge, according to one author, in applying IT to these characteristics will be as follows:

The information "center of gravity" will vary from conflict to conflict, from level to level, and from dimension to dimension. The greatest challenge for the policymaker will be to manage a national intelligence architecture, which can rapidly identify the information center of gravity, prepare the information "battlefield", and deliver the appropriate (nonlethal) information "munitions" to carry the day.[209]

In spite of such difficulties, US armed forces leaders support ideas that directly relate to virtual peacemaking and thus offer potential momentum to the concept and encourage its integration. For example, former Chief of Staff of the Army, General Dennis J. Reimer, believes "our analysis for the future points out that we need a capability called 'strategic preemption'. Strategic preemption is the ability to halt or prevent a conflict or crisis before it becomes debilitating

---

[209] Robert Steele, "Virtual Intelligence: Conflict Avoidance and Resolution through Information Peacekeeping," http//www.oss.net/Paper...VirtualIntelligence.html, as downloaded from the Internet on 14 July 1997. Quote is on p. 26 of 28 pages.

or protracted—before it spreads out of control."[210]   Shaping the international environment is a pillar of our national security strategy. Concepts such as virtual peacemaking should compliment these visions. Obviously, virtual peacemaking will also require international legal sanction and support plus a great deal of foresight and intelligence about the military situation.

During the Cold War, it was more difficult to influence a potential conflict situation and to clear up misunderstanding, since many societies operated as closed systems. Government agencies, local business, the mass media, elites, and particularly the special organs of intelligence directed a specific flow of information at both principal actors within the system (presidents, prime ministers, general secretaries, etc.) and at society at large. Control of this flow of information from the top down formed the outlook and attitudes of the populace.

This situation was directly influenced by limited access to signals; human, photo, and electronic intelligence; and the manipulation of such information for policy formation and policy execution. Now, this position has changed dramatically as a result of IT and the end of the Cold War. While the intelligence systems still impact on policy formation and execution, public opinion also matters since many countries, previously bound by pacts of solidarity with closed societies, opened up to the global information market. An entire system known as the Global Information Environment (GIE) developed, mainly through the auspices of businesses and systems designed to monitor various situations (arms control, weather, the environment, etc.) offering an explosion of communications and other information technologies that have saturated societies worldwide. There is also a greater ability to manage open-source information from sources around the globe. Electorates at home and abroad may now question even official sources due to access to alternative and comparative forms of information.

On a positive note, IT has penetrated and evaporated some of the opaqueness that surrounded many countries and made them more transparent to both the outside world and their own citizens. The GIE includes individuals, organizations, or systems that collect, process, and disseminate information to national and international audiences. The GIE is composed of national, global, and defensive information infrastructures[211] and impacts on all countries,

---

[210] General Dennis J. Reimer, "The Army and the Cyberspace Crossroads," Defense Issues, Volume 12, Number 33, http://www.dtic.mil/defe...nk/pubs/di97/di1233.html, as downloaded from the Internet on 4 August 1997.

[211] FM 100-6, Information Operations, August 1996, pp. 1-2.

whether they realize it or not, through their use of satellites or other IT sources. Satellites and cables offer outsiders or observers the opportunity to see inside and talk with members of a closed society (such as North Korea). Satellites monitor troop mobilizations and deployments, measure the local harvest to ascertain if people will starve or not, allow ordinary citizens to communicate via the Internet with people on the other side of the world, and afford businessmen the opportunity for instantaneous communication with financial and industrial centers all over the globe without government interference. The sovereign, on the other hand, has lost control of much of what people can see and hear, making it more difficult to "form" the consciousness of the populace than in the past. If the essence of sovereignty is the power to exclude others from interfering in one's affairs (personal or governmental), then IT is eroding that concept.

Virtual peacemaking offers the international community and individual states the capability to mobilize world opinion and put pressure on government's intent on initiating conflict. The advanced countries are being transformed fastest and in the process are transforming others due to their impact on economic activity. Now, even the most backward societies are touched by the revolution in computing technology and global connectivity. Virtual peacemaking also offers the opportunity for the international community to "signal" what is and is not acceptable norms of behavior, and it can isolate a government if the need arises. This is especially effective due to IT's instantaneous impact. Now, the opportunity exists to utilize virtual diplomatic and economic means or to use virtual information blockades or information overloads outside or within a country, respectively. Access to outside information also allows the local populace to influence the decision-making processes of a nation through the exertion of public opinion more than ever before.

Walter Wriston, former chairman and CEO of Citicorp, speaking at the Conference on Virtual Diplomacy in Washington, D.C. in April 1997, highlighted several intriguing aspects of the new IT environment that military planners must keep in mind. These included the impact of virtual peacemaking methods on sovereignty, on the destiny of people, and on the development of what he termed an "information standard." His message must be considered and measured by the military as it attempts to fit its methods and hardware to the virtual peacemaking concept.

Wriston noted that the entire political process is magnified and sometimes distorted by the images on our TV screens produced instantaneously by IT, especially by the 24-hour international reporting offered by stations such as CNN. This has also impacted on the way nations communicate with one

119

another as special interests (both national and transnational) bypass official foreign ministry channels. But IT enhances the effectiveness of conflict prevention measures, if Wriston's comments are on the mark, via the same TV images and access to the Internet. In Bosnia, for example, a legal web page was developed that had a virtual library and electronic publishing format, helping to build the rule of law. Bosnian judges used the system to access ways others handled similar problems. The system tied together not only judges but also attorneys, clerks, and defendants. It may offer a symbiosis of the rule of law, the press, and the people for the not too distant future.[212] However, problems of language, different legal systems, and methods of legal input must be overcome first.

More important, Wriston added, IT offers people a say in their own destiny. The formation of an information global village implies that denying people human rights or democratic freedoms no longer means denying them an abstraction they have never experienced. Instead they are being denied the established customs of the village, which they may have seen on TV or read about over the Internet. Wriston also noted that if the economic market is viewed as a giant voting machine recording in real-time the judgment of traders all over the world about our diplomatic, fiscal and monetary policies, then we must be aware of the creation of an "information standard" which is more draconian than the old gold standard and operates more swiftly.[213] The information standard changes the way we solve problems, impacts on how we do our jobs, and most important of all changes the way we view and interpret events. Through the phenomenon of instantaneous IT, the information standard loosens the hold of the sovereign and projects the individual as the object of events and information as much as the state.

That is, those possessing IT must learn how to use its consequences. Transparency issues and institutional methods offered by international participants such as the Organization for Security and Cooperation in Europe, the UN, local academies, and institutes must also be studied. According to one Russian information warfare expert, S. A. Komov, IT can be used to distract, pacify, appease, intimidate, provoke, immobilize or pin down, wear out, confuse or weaken, suggest, or mislead.[214] This is an important list of uses,

---

[212] Henry Perritt, Villanova University School of Law, comment made during his presentation at the Conference on Virtual Diplomacy in 1997.

[213] From a speech by Walter Wriston, "Bits, Bytes, Power and Diplomacy," presented at the Conference on Virtual Diplomacy in Washington, D.C., 1- 2 April 1997. All of Wriston's comments noted in the paper come from his presentation at the conference.

[214] S. A. Komov, "On the Methods and Forms of Conducting Information War," Military Thought, July-August 1997, p. 19.

since many can help slow or prevent the use of force. These uses may also affect force projection, mobilization, and movement, thus affecting the capability to conduct actual conflict.

Another virtual peacemaking use is to energize the diplomatic language of treaties. For example, any treaty utilizing the words "develop, plan, train, or engage in" has a use for virtual peacemaking. "Develop" can refer to the ability to expand on existing capabilities through, for example, new satellite links; "plan" can refer to the construction of an Internet capability or the laying of fiber optic cable; "train" can refer to the use of simulations to learn how to use preventive techniques, or to follow logic trees that would demonstrate the negative impact of some decisions; and "engage" can refer to IT methods to conduct negotiations through the use of information technology means (communication systems, etc.)

Governments can use virtual peacemaking tools as well. They can use IT as a deterrent or a confidence-building measure to contain or block access to other information or technology. As a deterrent, IT can help explain an action, put pressure on people or organizations, help instill fear over potential actions, and even find expression as an information saturation operation. IT can also deter by threatening to expose a leader's state secrets, by demonstrating the impotence of a nation to offer a credible threat, or by exposing troop deployments or other forms of military buildups, thereby uncovering blatant lies or military plans designed to manipulate public opinion.

A final virtual peacemaking use by governments is to help achieve economic leverage over potential combatants through inducements and incentives to be brought into the Information Age or, failing complicity, by using IT to establish economic blockades and affect indicators of stability and vitality, among other measures. Virtual peacemaking relies heavily on images and communications, with words and visuals becoming a currency of sort.

The military must learn to integrate virtual peacemaking mechanisms into its preventive deployments and defensive postures. The military can fool potential combatants about the actual situation before them, gain information on potential combatants, and exert pressure. It can also take preventive steps by planning ahead to control the consequences that might develop. In the final analysis, virtual peacemaking complements General Reimer's strategic preemption concept.

Thus, the balance of power in the world is no longer simply about bi- or multi-polar issues. Nor is it simply about balancing issues of diffuse, profound, and ancient collective-memory problems (race, religion, history, national interests) or balancing diffuse force-on-force problems. The balance of power also hinges on images and the use of IT that can tilt the balance one way or the other. This makes virtual peacemaking an inviting idea to explore further since it offers enhanced understanding of all these issues through transparency in the diplomatic, economic, and military areas. Virtual peacemaking also enables the concept of strategic preemption.

What Information Technology Will Assist Us?
"Technology empowers people."[215]

The next era of peace operations and conflict resolution will be strongly influenced by the relationship between humans and things virtual if the Bosnian experience is any indicator. Designers will have to make software that can relate to soldiers, diplomats, and people, some of whom will have more influence than others. Software must also fit cultures and expectations. This requires that software manufacturers interact with academicians, religious and cultural leaders, and others who understand international sensitivities. It is a significant challenge seldom recognized and one worthy of future study.

This realization comes at a time when consumer electronics, Hollywood, military planning and peacetime actions, and society all have access to integrated IT systems. The military is buying off the shelf technology from the consumer sector, and Hollywood is amazing society with its ability to put the results of this convergence on the big screen. For those third world societies where access to IT is limited, it is still likely that decision-makers have access to some IT systems which might alter or limit the use of virtual peacemaking (if conflict were imminent) but would not eliminate its use.

The next era of peace operations may also witness the capability to customize or tailor IT to fit the contractor (a multinational force, the UN, etc.). This will make IT potentially useful for peacemaking, peace enforcement, and peace building operations. To "customize" means to select new developments according to their applicability to one of the types of peace operations. IT, of course, could just as easily be adopted for wartime use. For example, Bill Gates, Chief Executive Officer of Microsoft, described three ideas the consumer can expect to see in the not too distant future. They are the wallet personal computer (PC), electronic books that offer readers the opportunity to participate in writing the conclusion to the story, and advanced software that records each person's "documented life."[216]

---

[215] Chester Crocker, Georgetown University, comment made during his presentation at the Conference on Virtual Diplomacy in 1997.
[216] Bill Gates, "The Road Ahead," Newsweek, 27 November 1995, p. 61.

Superimposing these three ideas on a military scenario allows one to envision, in the first case, an electronic wallet in the pocket of each peacemaker that offers instant information on the treaty being implemented or the international law about to be broken, supply and refugee routes available, location of NGO support groups, telemedicine information, local phone numbers of influential people, rules of engagement, cultural sensitivities, and other types of civil-military information. The electronic wallet also could be equipped with read-outs from built in radar detectors and have the ability to place calls for help that designate both location and real-time images.

An electronic book could be used by commanders to access the electronic operations order of a higher level of command in one's own armed forces in order to help write the operations order based on the situation in his locale. Or it might be used to offer conflicting parties a chance to dialogue alone or with a mediator if all three parties were electronically connected. Access to one's documented life, in this case the documented steps leading up to a crisis, would allow the participants to review the steps that logically brought them to their conclusions in the first place.

If potential combatants wanted to talk over the phone or via a computer in complete anonymity, this is also possible with the help of IT. Camo-voice, a communications technology offering such anonymity to the caller, is available. Another communication method is a software package called Lotus Domino, which allows a mediator control over who sees who or what on a monitor. Through such devices of anonymity, presidents or secretaries of state could utilize the IT tools and conduct the negotiations personally while appearing to simply be a "representative" of the state in question.

There are many other high-tech tools and software that can be customized for military use as virtual peacemaking instruments. These include such common everyday items as electronic mail, statistical analysis, graphical illustrations, use of indicators and warnings (or flagging specific words or concept variations), and the use of computer-generated overlays or maps. It also includes such simple devices as a video camera.

Americans are very familiar with the power of images caught on video cameras. Prison guards report that one of the greatest fears of a prisoner, who has no civil rights, is to be videotaped during a disturbance because it will hurt the person's chance at parole. Some prison officials have even stopped a prisoner from further acts of harm by simply pulling out a camera and pointing it at the individual. They know that the video record will speak for itself at any hearing. Monitoring the outside of military garrisons or sensitive border regions with unmanned aerial vehicles (UAVs) could have a similar impact in recording the actions of countries that violate agreements and presenting them to international tribunals. Again, however, there are legal issues to overcome, in that countries are not prisoners and have no cause to expect violations of their sovereignty or privacy. They have rights **not** to be spied upon. But if the international legal community agrees that such monitoring is in the cause of preserving peace and eliminating bloodshed, then such "big brother" activity may have a chance, especially since nations observe one another from afar in peacetime through satellites. UAVs may not be as large a problem as they appear.

Simulations have real value for virtual peacemaking. Their adaptation for use in conflict prevention scenarios is quite simple. For example, societies about to become involved in a conflict could be shown a simulation (on local TV if the desire was to mobilize the entire populace) of the good and bad consequences of their deeds. Such a simulation may not necessarily show their destruction but only the path leading to war and its consequences for the economy versus the path leading to peace. This would offer everyone the opportunity to sit back and consider the consequences of their actions and to develop ways to interact and find solutions. Again, the problem will be cultural, finding a method to affect different parties in the same way.

Simulations can also be used to prepare the peacemaker. If human behavior can be properly modeled, to include its irrational aspects, then computer exercises would be more realistic instead of the preprogrammed responses we have come to expect over the years. These simulations could even be designed for specific locations and environments. As a result, peace operations personnel would enter into an area with a much more realistic appraisal of the situation. Thus, simulations are vital because they:

1. Provide greater visual realism. Sensations of motion, temperature, and sound are important but visual imagery is best especially if put in helmet mounted displays.
2. Offer better and less expensive databases. 3D databases are available as well.
3. Provide a broad spectrum of capabilities. They allow planners and individual soldiers and pilots to participate and offer a chance to train en route or on site.
4. Are more deployable and offer mission-specific training.

5. Offer improved upgradeability for lower lifetime costs. They can be changed easily so users can rehearse various geostrategic settings and rapidly changing scenarios.[217]

Obviously, simulations work for both wartime and peacetime operations.

Speakers at the Conference on Virtual Diplomacy mentioned earlier offered other examples of how IT can be applied to military peacemaking efforts to enhance the effectiveness of these mechanisms. Wriston, for example, noted that IT enables airborne mine detector systems to locate mines or minefields. These mines can be exploded by drone tanks that are IT equipped which demonstrates how information devices can save lives. Locating and clearing minefields makes them useless, and it demonstrates the impotence of those who planted them to influence the situation. Other panelist observations impacting on virtual peacemaking processes were:

- IT affects the way we conduct military affairs, in that we move faster to react/act than in the past due to instantaneous communications and data transfers.[218]
- IT helps us conduct "navigation warfare" (determining where things are). It also is a "negotiation weapon" in that precise information in real-time offers an advantage in decision-making. Unpiloted remote vehicles are an example of technology that can provide this information.[219]
- IT enhances a diplomat's understanding of the history, training, biological processes, and learning techniques of a nation, not just their thoughts and the things they want today. We need to learn to connect data perceptual systems.[220] This lesson should be studied by psychological operations (PSYOP) personnel.
- IT can also allow one to look at the roots of conflict associated with geography, such as natural resources, land, food, water, high ground, space, the environment, movement corridors, strategic locations, or cultural objects. A Geographic Information System (GIS) exists that can help resolve conflict by offering a number, quality, and diversity of global databases (routing, crime analysis,

---

[217] Jim Oyler, "The Battlefield in your Brain," Military Training Technology, June/July 1997, summary of pp. 8-11.
[218] Anita Jones, Defense Research and Engineering, the Pentagon, comment made during her presentation at the Conference on Virtual Diplomacy in 1997.
[219] Ibid.
[220] Mark Weiser, Xerox Palo Alto Research Center, comment made during his presentation at the Conference on Virtual Diplomacy in 1997.

line of sight, monitoring) which have peace keeping/peacemaking implications for combatants (where is the bread, the mine, the ammo, and so on). It also shortens the time lag between collecting and using data, relates available information, and can put any factor of reality in a reference base.[221]

- IT has assisted the mapping industry to enable us to communicate intuitively, since maps offer a framework for compromise and tradeoffs (they can show flood plains overlaid on property, buffer zones around rivers, line of site for communication sites, and so on).[222]
- IT can model biological processes, hydrological processes, and the movement of animals or humans, among other things; and offers a framework for cooperation between academia, business, nongovernmental agencies, government/military, and citizens.[223]
- IT enhances TV coverage, influencing measures of military success.[224]
- IT is heightening our view of the unusual (the "Rodman-Madonna" effect), which is making us more tolerant of "different" thinking about an issue.[225]
- IT should discourage us from thinking in terms of platform versus platform. Adversaries won't build pieces like that. We can't predict events due to change, chaos, and complexity, but we must be ready for all contingencies.[226]
- IT has created greatly flattened bureaucratic structures to implement conflict prevention processes. How to work with this apparatus must also be learned by diplomats and the military.

Limitations and Problems

"The Internet may develop a conscience. It appears to be evolving on its own without a mandate."[227]

---

[221] Jack Dangermond, Environmental Systems Research Institute, comment made during his presentation at the Conference on Virtual Diplomacy in 1997.
[222] Ibid.
[223] Ibid.
[224] Lieutenant General Anthony Zinni, US Marine Corps, comment made during his presentation at the Conference on Virtual Diplomacy in 1997.
[225] Arno Penzias, Bell Labs/Lucent Technologies, comment made during his presentation at the Conference on Virtual Diplomacy in 1997.
[226] Lieutenant General Paul Van Riper, US Marine Corps, comment made during his presentation at the Conference on Virtual Diplomacy in 1997.
[227] Dangermond.

How nations learn to manage or leverage the consequences of the Information Age may greatly determine their power or influence on world affairs much like the influence of great state diplomacy and nuclear weapons in the past. Yet while virtual peacemaking shows great promise as a new means to prevent or control conflict, there are also limitations and problems with its use. For example, there is an imbalance in the capacity to store, process, and use information among nations, another reality of the new world order. This means that virtual peacemaking might work in some areas with developed information infrastructures but be limited in others. Another aberration is that the attainment of IT allows some smaller countries to possess a greater ability to conduct these operations than former superpowers (i.e., Japan versus Russia). And the mere thought of using IT as an intervention tool to prevent conflict raises serious questions about the need to fix responsibility for its use and misuse under law. Legal decisions will play a major role in the use of IT, and these decisions must be studied closely. They will help decide whether IT use represents interference in state or human rights affairs or whether IT use violates a nation's sovereignty.

Another problem for virtual peacemaking methods is one that has been with us for years. It is the historical, cultural, logic, and religious frames of reference used by different nations to measure IT developments. What may be an acceptable use of IT for one nation may be extremely limited in another. For example, in societies dominated by religion, the Internet may be forbidden due to its ability to access information especially about other religious movements or access to negative information about their own. In America, the restrictions the Amish place on their people represent an example close to home.

Yet another limitation or problem may be the use of virtual peacemaking as a psychological operations (PSYOP) weapon. PSYOP offers many uses for one's benefit, whether in the diplomatic, economic, or military arena, but it also offers several dangers since it can act on the limited understanding of the gap between reality and a human's ability to comprehend things virtual. For example, TV's transformation from pixel to digital systems may offer an enormous opportunity for the moving, editing, and transforming of visual information and subsequent manipulation of a populace. Another example concerns the ability of software to recognize vehicles or other objects. The software could be manipulated, misinformed, or penetrated, perhaps even by other virtual images, to fool a monitor or an adversary about intentions or movements. Even the mass media can, wittingly or not, play a huge role here through the images it displays on the evening news.

Another problem is the attention paid to processing technology at the expense of developing doctrine, training, and an infrastructure to support virtual peacemaking. This was also one of the conclusions from the study by Kenneth Allard on the use of information operations in Bosnia: namely that advances in information technology are valuable "only to the extent that they are accompanied by coherent doctrine, organizations, equipment, and people—to say nothing of the time needed to make them function as a team." That is, we can't forget the fundamentals.

There is also the problem of excess attention focused on the "get rich quick" schemes of information technology at the expense of virtual peacemaking and other, more humanitarian uses of IT. For example, Ismail Serageldin of the World Bank is adamant about ridding the world of some of its most obvious disparities, frustrations, and tensions. He noted that while we are more interdependent and environmentally conscious, connectivity is better, and democratic principles are winning the globalization battle as are human rights, we still have an abject demographic mess all over the globe. Globalization appears to be only for the minority, since 20% of the world's population gets 83% of the world's income, and some 40,000 people die of hunger each day, a moral outrage. What a contradiction we have in the era of the information revolution as a result, Serageldin concludes.[228]

In addition to problems, there are also dangers associated with the use of IT. For example, the use of IT not only allows small groups to mobilize quickly, but it also allows them to influence or even shut down political processes. The US Congress has recently felt the pressure of this "participatory democracy." In the past, the US electorate stayed at home and was content to vote every few years for a president and to vote in local, state, and national congressional elections. In extreme cases, letters would be written to congressmen to bring attention to an issue. Today the situation is entirely different. With Internet access and email links to senators and representatives, the electorate not only votes, but offers opinions merely by sending email. The danger is that the electorate can also send multiple messages that overload and shut down systems. In this fashion the Internet is developing a conscience of its own.

In an associated danger relative to small groups, small countries possessing the right kinds of IT can become as powerful as large countries overnight. This situation can become dangerous if the country having access to the right types of IT is a nation such as North Korea. Terrorist groups of any kind, for that matter, can threaten the entire world with the correct IT in their hands.

---

[228] Ismail Serageldin, World Bank, comment made during his presentation at the Conference on Virtual Diplomacy in 1997.

There are various scenarios through which terrorists can use information to become dangerous, such as through the use of computer viruses, a terrorist home page to unite causes, or simple destruction or vandalism of vital IT equipment. Terrorists can access IT cheaply as well. Their goal will be conflict escalation, not prevention. Nothing could provide terrorists with more opportunity to demonstrate or exploit their causes than their ability to knock out the communications of governments.

Conclusion

"Computers exchanging video calls as commonly as email. Three-dimensional windows that open into virtual worlds instead of virtual scrolls...and everything, from our medical records to our office files to the contents of our refrigerators, hypertextually linked via the great global network."[229]

The future promises excitement and opportunity to those who capture the ability to work with IT. Will concepts such as virtual peacemaking be part of that future? Hopefully, this chapter has demonstrated that the capability to do so exists and that it is a worthwhile cause. First, there is a wealth of ideas, technologies, and software applications with direct applicability to conflict prevention practices and theory. Some are as common as email and the Internet, others as specific as computer programs like MapLinx and Lotus Domino. Just as Bill Gates adapts these concepts to the life of the consumer, soldiers and diplomats should begin exploring their application to conflict prevention mechanisms.

Second, these technologies enable "strategic preemption." This means that the concept of virtual peacemaking is applicable to conflict prevention theory not just on the tactical but the strategic scale. It can offer a new tool to political scientists, soldiers, and diplomats to develop their models and uses of technology (of course, IT preemption has a purely aggressive military use as well [escalation domination to protect US interests]; this is not its virtual peacemaking intent). Far too little time has been devoted to this topic to date. While we have examined and used IT as a crisis management mechanism, rarely have we looked at it as a conflict prevention mechanism. Virtual peacemaking is in need of further elaboration, especially since the military and consumer sectors are converging, implying one can assist the other in helping to prevent conflict.

---

[229] Gibbs, p. 82.

Third, it is important that software manufacturers be made aware of the crucial role they can play in this effort. Academicians, religious and cultural leaders, and others who understand international sensitivities need to work closely with software producers to develop the products that take into consideration the terminology, cultural specifics, and concepts associated with international negotiation processes. For example, just between Russia and the US, peace operations terminology can have varying interpretations that must be taken into account as well as cultural and political peculiarities. Only talented people with the proper guidance can develop the software required of such specificity.

Fourth, virtual peacemaking can take advantage of a phenomenon of the new world order, namely that many formerly closed societies are now, like it or not, more transparent due to IT. Whether it be email, the Internet, or cellular phone linkups (it is hard to forget the striking image of the African warrior in the field with a spear in one hand, a cellular phone in the other), the world is more integrated than at any other time in history, offering opportunities to use virtual peacemaking tools to assist in deterring, blocking, pacifying, and controlling conflict.

Fifth, there are as many dangers as there are advantages to the use of IT, and we must remain aware of them. Some believe that we, the IT tool makers, have made the tools so simple that now anyone can use them, even to destroy the tool makers. We must work to limit a terrorist's access to particularly powerful IT applications, and we must work to limit a group's ability to employ IT in a virtual PSYOP operation (use of morphed images, etc.) against individuals or states. One PSYOP example in America involved an email of a speech delivered by author Kurt Vonnegut at a commencement address. Filled with pearls of dry wisdom, it was passed around the country. However, the message was a fraud, written by a journalist and not Vonnegut. It demonstrated how vulnerable everyone is in the age of information technologies. And this analysis has not mentioned the dangers of hackers nor the friction and fog of information war.

Sixth, in Dayton it was demonstrated that the US was able to use IT (linked to simulation and mapping capabilities) to demonstrate in a benign form its potential military power. This was the finest hour to date in preventing conflict through virtual means. The Dayton process added credibility to virtual peacemaking's potential to become an important conflict prevention tool in the future. It also must be kept in mind, however, that the management of this effort was possible because the agreement was in place before US troops were deployed to the field.

There remains an entire series of questions that indicate other problem areas to address in future papers on this subject. These include the following concerns about controlling conflict: Whose interests are served through the use of virtual peacemaking (a country's national interests, black market interests, the U.N., etc.)? Who will be in charge of the global information infrastructure? Can virtual peacemaking be used to predict as well as stop conflict? Can cultural sensitivities be included in virtual peacemaking methods and technology? How can virtual peacemaking support humanitarian assistance? How does bureaucratic stupor, cultural psyche, clans, tribes, or Mafias affect virtual peacemaking? How does the composition of society affect the use of virtual peacemaking? What is the impact of virtual peacemaking on diplomacy? What is the role of the mass media in this effort? When does virtual peacemaking become a violation of a nation's sovereignty? What determines elite consensus for virtual peacemaking (information or personal interests, power, or clan input)? Can virtual peacemaking be used by a potential enemy or apparent "friend" against you? How do we distinguish between PSYOP, persuasion, the truth, and vested interests such as the black market during the conduct of virtual peacemaking? Can a "participatory democracy" be mobilized to support virtual peacemaking or will it be an obstacle?

In spite of the problems, limitations, and dangers associated with virtual peacemaking listed above, it must be a subject of further exploration simply because we live in the IT age and we must learn how to control it. Better now to start studying the positive uses of the information revolution to prevent conflict and find ways to monitor potentially dangerous groups or gangs before it is too late. This includes groups and gangs on the Internet who invade personal privacy, invite you to participate in illegal behavior, or ask you to complicate police investigations and criminal cases. Child pornography is a huge problem in which law enforcement invests thousands of hours every year.

Some reports indicate that, on occasion, citizens are taking it upon themselves to impose their own version of law and order on the largely unregulated Internet. There is even a group called Cyberangels, an offshoot of the New York City Guardian Angels, seeking out potential offenders and those who would take advantage of other "netizens." In the past year, web pages such as Women Halting Online Abuse were developed, as well as hundreds of others.[230] And these problems arise at a time when we are already slipping away from silicon technology to DNA, molecular, or quantum computing. Time is of the essence.

---

[230] Bill Golden, wgolden@psrw.com, with more information available at:
http://headlines.yahoo.com/thirdage/stories/8731019242.html

CHAPTER EIGHT: KOSOVO AND THE CURRENT MYTH OF INFORMATION SUPERIORITY[231]

The Pentagon's March 1999 brochure on information operations begins with a few words from the Chairman of the Joint Chiefs of Staff, General Henry H. Shelton. He notes that "information operations and information superiority are at the core of military innovation and our vision for the future of joint warfare. . . . The capability to penetrate, manipulate, and deny an adversary's battlespace awareness is of utmost importance."[232] The Pentagon's brochure adds that "the chief concern of information superiority is the human user of information. Without knowing when, where, why, with what, and how to act, warfighters cannot perform mission-essential tasks efficiently and effectively."[233]

Kosovo, unfortunately, exposed problems with this concept. First, in spite of NATO's near total information superiority, its battlespace awareness was manipulated by the Serbian armed forces more often than expected. When human and software interpreters of intelligence information were fooled, it resulted in munitions wasted on fake or incorrect targets and in bad assessments of the actual situation on the ground. It also affected both mission-essential tasks and battle damage assessments. In the latter case, it meant different estimates by NATO and Pentagon officials of the number of armored vehicles destroyed.

Second, testimony indicates that both NATO planners and the human users of information were not adequately prepared to conduct information operations. For example, in their lessons-learned testimony before the Senate Armed Services Committee on 14 October 1999, Secretary of Defense William Cohen and General Shelton noted that "the pool of personnel available to perform certain key functions, such as language translation, targeting, and intelligence analysis, was limited" and that "the conduct of an integrated information operations campaign was delayed by the lack of both advance

---

[231] This article was published under the same title in <u>Parameters</u>, Spring 2000, pp. 13-29.

[232] US Joint Chiefs of Staff, "Information Operations," March 1999, p. 1. Information superiority is based on dominance in three areas: intelligence (with surveillance and reconnaissance support), C4 (command, control, communications, and computers), and information operations.

[233] Ibid., p. 6.

planning and strategic guidance defining key objectives."[234] But planning had started in earnest in the summer of 1998, Cohen and Shelton testified, some nine months before the start of the conflict on 24 March 1999. Did initial planning not include information operations?

Finally, General Wesley K. Clark, Supreme Allied Commander Europe, reportedly stunned a recent session of the Senate Armed Services Committee when he called for a complete rethink of Western strategy and questioned the need for the aerial assault on Serbia. General Clark noted that NATO could have used legal means to block the Danube and the Adriatic ports, and could have used "methods to isolate Milosevic and his political parties electronically."[235] If implemented and augmented with other measures, Clark added, *the military instrument might have never been used.*[236] These and other issues demonstrate that, for the present anyway, information superiority is a goal to be achieved and not a given that US forces can assume as their birth right.

This article will look at the conflict between NATO and Yugoslavia not from the standpoint of the intent or success of the air campaign (although these issues will be touched upon) but rather through the prism of information superiority. Information superiority allowed NATO to know almost everything about the battlefield, but NATO analysts didn't always understand everything they thought they knew.

What Is Information Superiority?
Information superiority, the cornerstone of Force XXI, is a capability (not a proven condition) that the US armed forces are trying to develop. Once the concept becomes robust it will help to reduce uncertainty, provide a more complete intelligence picture of the battlefield, and assist precision-guided missiles in obtaining and destroying targets. Much of this capability was on display in the recent conflict in Kosovo.

Information superiority is defined by US Joint Publication 3-13 as "the capability to collect, process, and disseminate an uninterrupted flow of

---

[234] "Joint Statement on the Kosovo After Action Review," presented by Secretary of Defense William S. Cohen and General Henry H. Shelton, Chairman of the Joint Chiefs of Staff, before the Senate Armed Services Committee, 14 October 1999. Downloaded from the Internet, DefenseLINK news,
http://www.defenselink.mil:80/news/Oct1999/b10141999_bt478-99.html.
[235] Julian Borger, "Cyberwar Could Spare Bombs," The Guardian, 5 November 1999, p. 17.
[236] Ibid.

information while exploiting or denying an adversary's ability to do the same."[237] According to this definition, NATO's forces entered the Kosovo conflict with near total information superiority. It appeared that NATO was able to collect, process, and disseminate military information at will while denying the Serbs the same capability. However, NATO forces did encounter intelligence and information problems, including instances of the Serbs using nontechnical methods to manipulate NATO analysts' perceptions, resulting in misinterpreted information. Joint Publication 2-01 warns about this phenomenon in a discussion of the "intelligence cycle." The publication notes, "Time constraints and the demands of modern battle tend to make the processing and production phases indistinguishable."[238] This in turn limits "evaluating, analyzing, and interpreting information from single or multiple sources into a finished intelligence product."[239]

In addition, Serbian civilian and military personnel were able to use civilian telephone and radio links to pass military information. Such nontechnical offsets either thwarted information collection or corrupted NATO information superiority. That is, the human link in the NATO analytic process was less successful in interpreting information, reducing uncertainty, and providing a clear intelligence picture of the battlefield than expected. For example:

- Some six months after the conflict, NATO and the Pentagon still did not know how many tanks and armored personnel carriers they destroyed, in spite of supposed total information superiority during the conflict, the ability to monitor Serb forces leaving the area after the conflict, and the presence of their own people on the ground to inspect targets that were hit.
- NATO pilots were forced to drop millions of dollars of ordnance in the Adriatic and on open countryside because they could not find their targets or engage them properly due to bad weather and the aerial rules of engagement (ROE) imposed by politicians. (The planes could not land with the unexpended ordnance on board.) Since the ROE were imposed by politicians, this means that politicians affected information superiority, too.
- NATO after-action reports stress that Milosevic may have intercepted NATO communications and warned targets that they

---

[237] US Joint Chiefs of Staff, Joint Publication 3-13, <u>Joint Doctrine for Information Operations</u> (Washington: GPO, 9 October 1998), p. GL-7.
[238] US Joint Chiefs of Staff, Joint Publication 2-01, <u>Joint Intelligence Support to Military Operations</u> (Washington: GPO, 20 November 1996), p. III-2.
[239] Ibid.

were about to be hit. The testimony of Secretary Cohen and General Shelton supports this thesis. They indicated that NATO lacked interoperable secure communications, forcing reliance on nonsecure methods that compromised operational security.[240] This speaks poorly about the progress of communications technology, compatibility, and information superiority in NATO after 50 years of practice (and in this case with no enemy radio-electronic opposition of any consequence).

- NATO had almost perfect intelligence about the intentions, goals, and attitudes of President Milosevic through a multitude of personal discussions with him over the previous four years by representatives from scores of nations (and possibly from communications intercepts), yet could not get him to the negotiating table, foresee his ruthless ethnic cleansing campaign in time to stop him, or predict his asymmetric responses to NATO technological and bombing prowess.

Further, NATO did not process information quickly enough to enable aircraft to strike mobile targets. This was because of the reaction time required to pass data from EC-130 (airborne command, control, and communications) aircraft to NATO's Combined Air Operations Center at Vicenze, Italy, and then on to strike assets. Total information superiority did not prevent the most technologically advanced air armada in the world from mistakenly striking trains and convoys, schools and hospitals, and Bulgaria with missiles. Yes Bulgaria, the wrong country, although that incident was the result of a weapon system malfunction, not an error in the application of information.

Two important qualifiers are missing, but implied, in the Joint Publication 3-13 definition of information superiority: "accurate" and "timely." Information superiority requires the "accurate and timely" collection, processing, and dissemination of information. Battle damage assessments on armored vehicles indicate that the accuracy of hits on mobile targets, for example, was much lower than originally stated. Such inaccurate information can lead to wrong conclusions and assumptions. For example, NATO claims that 99.6 percent of the bombs dropped hit the intended target are difficult to fathom.[241] Undoubtedly the percentage differed for stationary and for mobile targets. And does this figure reflect that some bombs hit fake targets and that many bombs had to be jettisoned into the Adriatic due to bad weather or because a target had moved? Only after illuminating the data with such criteria

---

[240] "Joint Statement on the Kosovo After Action Review."

[241] Phillip S. Meilinger, "Gradual Escalation," <u>Armed Forces Journal</u>, October 1999, p. 18.

can a real assessment of accuracy be made. A lower figure—perhaps 80 percent—might be a more realistic assessment but still a perfectly acceptable measure of success.

Strikes on fake targets indicate that the Serbs let NATO daytime reconnaissance flights see real targets and then replaced them at night, or that US target analysts misinterpreted the information furnished them. Processing information is one thing, interpreting it is an art. Serbian civil and military officials improvised and developed low-tech offsets that limited the effectiveness of NATO's information superiority and misled NATO collection assets. Put another way, they fooled our information interpreters. Their offsets included deception, disinformation, camouflage, the clever use of radar, spies within NATO, helicopter movements NATO couldn't detect, and the exploitation of NATO's operational templating of information-dominance activities (e.g., satellites, reconnaissance flights). As Lieutenant General Michael C. Short, NATO's air operations chief, noted, "NATO placed its own air crews at increased risk by taking certain steps to reduce civilian casualties, such as bombing bridges only on week nights between 10 p.m. and 4 a.m.—a regular schedule that made NATO planes more vulnerable to antiaircraft fire."[242]

Additionally, Serbia exploited the strict rules of engagement to protect or move certain target sets. This further limited the effectiveness of NATO's information technology. For example, NATO aerial ROE stated that pilots could fire only on visual recognition, diminishing the value of targets obtained by other methods. Finally, political statements that no ground campaign was planned allowed the Serbs to hang on longer against an opponent with total information superiority and attempt to exploit any cracks in NATO's solidarity. One can conclude there are ways to manipulate total information superiority.

Digital interpreters of data differ from the old intelligence analysts who worked with photos and captured documents to interpret data. The former must be aware of and study nontechnical offsets in addition to technologically produced intelligence, and constantly review the methods they use to interpret data. There is much to learn from Kosovo about the current myth of information superiority, particularly that simple human innovations can severely degrade digital dominance and that human interpretation of data is a science worth reinvigorating.

---

[242] Dana Priest, "Air Chief Faults Kosovo Strategy," The Washington Post, 22 October 1999, p.14.

NATO's Information Superiority

The conditions were right for NATO to achieve total information superiority. There was virtually no air force flying against NATO's 37,000 sorties (Serbs flew only some 10 air intercept or fast-mover missions). NATO faced antiquated, minimal enemy air defense artillery assets developed in the 1950s through the 1980s that couldn't reach above 15,000 feet. No real counter-radar challenge was offered since the air defense assets that could reach higher levels were not turned on. NATO possessed the ability to pinpoint targets using Predator and Hunter unmanned drone aircraft as well as satellite and JSTARS intelligence links, yet made mistakes. There was a huge assortment of intelligence products on hand concerning Belgrade and Serbia based on several recent field exercises. There were elements on the ground to assist in the effort, including personnel from the Kosovo Liberation Army. There was no Serb jamming of communication or radar assets. Total NATO information superiority was at hand. Yet errors were made in the selection of buildings to be hit, most notably the Chinese embassy.

In spite of this superiority, a ground operation was almost launched. The Washington Post described top-secret talks among NATO countries' defense ministers at the end of May to plan a ground invasion. That is, flying with impunity, grounded only by bad weather, NATO mounted a 78-day air campaign (Desert Storm's lasted 43 days), and this still wasn't enough. NATO was forced to stand down a last-minute scramble to mount a ground campaign. (Planning for such an operation had taken place much earlier. The reference here is to moving forces into position to cross the Kosovo border in an underdeveloped theater, where the force in place was attending to the needs of thousands of refugees, and to conduct operations before winter.) It took a combination of an underrated assist from President Martti Ahtisaari of Finland and former Prime Minister Victor Chernomyrdin of Russia, the threat of a ground operation, and the air campaign to actually achieve a negotiated settlement and later a capitulation to stop the air war. General Wesley Clark, Supreme Allied Commander Europe, noted that Milosevic probably caved in simply because he ran out of options.[243]

The air campaign, however, was the signal event of NATO's strategy. The pilots and support personnel should rightly receive nearly all the credit for making Milosevic blink. On the other hand, what did the air campaign eventually achieve? Achievements should be viewed in accordance with both political and military measures. A logical political expectation would be that the Milosevic government would sign Rambouillet Two or some other

---

[243] Wesley K. Clark, "The United States and NATO: The Way Ahead," Parameters, 29 (Winter 1999-2000), 11.

agreement less acceptable to Yugoslavia, since Serbian reluctance to sign this document was the motivation for going to war. But Rambouillet Two was not signed and the Belgrade Agreement that was signed delivered something far less. That is, the prosecution of the air campaign did not lead to NATO getting what it originally wanted. The question must be asked, was the air campaign unsuccessful in the political respect because NATO's initial demands were too high?

On the other hand, military planners state that the intent of the air campaign was to negate the effective use of Yugoslav forces in Kosovo and ultimately eject those forces from Kosovo. This was accomplished by the use of air power, and no one can dispute this. Simultaneously, however, Yugoslav paramilitaries and police began their ethnic cleansing operation which the air campaign could not target. The air campaign was unable to target individual policemen or other ethnic cleansers unleashed by Milosevic. Was a ground operation needed to prevent the ethnic cleansing? Did the successes of the international negotiators and the threatened ground force intervention at the time that Milosevic threw in the towel mean that the air campaign "was successful because it failed"?[244] That is, the air campaign was not able to deliver an end game by itself without the combined threats of a ground attack and the negotiating prowess of the Russian and Finnish participants.

There is much to ponder and learn from the conflict in Yugoslavia. However, Kosovo should not be considered a typical future conflict on which to base subsequent contingencies. NATO and US leaders cannot plan on always flying without opposition (or having unimpeded communications). Kosovo and, to a certain extent, Desert Storm were aberrations in that regard. Another danger is the tendency of some officials to spout euphoria about the "matchless" NATO force and its unrivaled capabilities. "Matchless" when pitted against what—the air defense forces of Iraq and Yugoslavia? Neither NATO nor the United States has fought a modern, up-to-date power. Finally, another lesson to be learned is that even without information superiority, a thinking opponent can take actions that must be countered. Clausewitz noted this lesson in his own century.

Battle Damage Assessment: What Do We Believe?
One of the major indicators of the myth of information superiority is the ongoing examination of battle damage assessment. This is particularly the case with official figures offered by the NATO Supreme Allied Commander

---

[244] Discussion with a British defense analyst. The comment is his, not the author's.

and the Department of Defense versus those of foreign defense departments and independent reporters.

The Views of General Wesley Clark, Supreme Allied Commander, NATO
It is important to note that this analysis is simply an attempt to express the concern generated by sets of figures that do not correspond to one another. It is not an attempt to cast doubt on General Wesley Clark, who has received far less credit than he deserves for keeping the alliance together during the conflict. General Clark does not count tanks; he relies on figures provided by others. It is fair to examine the figures he is being provided, however, and to consider how he chose to use them.

On 12 July, one month after the end of the bombing, the Navy Times discussed General Clark's testimony before the Senate Armed Services Committee. Relying on information provided by his staff, Clark stated that reports about NATO warplanes striking decoys and failing to destroy tanks and personnel carriers was a concerted disinformation campaign. Rather, he chose to underscore the virtual invulnerability of NATO aircraft and the fact that Kosovo set a new standard for warfare. He did not mention that there was no air force flying against NATO nor that the 15,000-foot limitation was set to ensure there would be no damage to NATO's "virtually invulnerable" fleet. Battle damage assessment, according to Clark, included the destruction of 110 Serb tanks, 210 armored personnel carriers, and 449 guns and mortars. He also noted that NATO was aware the Serbs were using decoys and were able to recognize them. Department of Defense estimates of battle damage were slightly higher than Clark's estimates (120 tanks, 220 armored personnel carriers, and 450 artillery pieces).[245]

Clark later offered a reason why the battle damage may not have been as high as initially expected—there was a spy within NATO giving targets away to Belgrade. The Pacific Stars and Stripes quotes Clark on 13 August as saying the leak "was as clear as the nose on your face."[246] That is certainly one form of asymmetric offset to information superiority, and again it involves the human dimension. Even with complete information superiority, one can't destroy the target if the enemy knows an attack is coming and simply moves it or replaces it with a dummy target. NATO officials were reportedly tipped off that a spy might be among them by the fact that certain targets appeared to be vacated after appearing on target lists but before NATO planes attacked.

---

[245] William Matthews, "Clark: Kosovo Attack Set Standard for Waging War," Navy Times, 12 July 1999, p. 13.
[246] Hearst Newspapers, "NATO Chief: Targeting Goals Leaked to Yugoslavia," Pacific Stars and Stripes, 13 August, 1999, p. 1.

In September, a Pentagon review of the war was delayed by one month in order to fill in gaps in the number of armored vehicles and artillery batteries actually destroyed. One report noted that General Clark told a Pentagon officer that analysts verified only some 70 percent of the reported hits. Clark then ordered the US European Command to prepare a new estimate as well.[247] In a later report, Clark lowered his battle damage assessment, noting that in all likelihood only 93 tanks and 153 armored personnel carriers were destroyed.[248] The difference—17 tanks and 57 armored personnel carriers—is close to two reinforced infantry battalions. That obviously would be an extremely significant difference to a ground commander preparing for an attack. Accurate damage assessments are crucial to a ground commander's maneuver requirements.

Even with total information superiority, it was not possible to verify battle damage with any accuracy some two months after the conflict ended, despite having NATO forces on the ground and overhead coverage of departing Serb vehicles. Since DOD and NATO still have not produced a compatible set of figures to this day, there clearly is a faulty methodology or other problem here as well. All of these hits were cockpit recorded and many were shown on TV. There should be near compatibility between NATO and Pentagon findings in the age of information superiority.

The British Press and Other Reporters on Battle Damage Assessment
Independent accounts from reporters covering the battle for Kosovo offered an entirely different set of battle damage statistics from those offered by either General Clark or the Pentagon. Their perspective is interesting for it is offered from firsthand, on-the-ground analysis, just like the latter NATO and Pentagon estimates.

The first newspaper reports on battle damage appeared at the end of June. Indications were that only 13 Serb tanks and fewer than 100 armored personnel carriers had been destroyed. Reporters noted the ruins of many different types of decoys hit by NATO forces (e.g., rusted tanks with broken parts, wood or canvas mock-ups). Carlotta Gall of The New York Times, a veteran war correspondent from the first Russian war in Chechnya, saw little damage. Newsweek reporter Mark Dennis found only one destroyed tank after driving around Kosovo for ten days. Did the Serbs manage to extricate all of their destroyed vehicles during their publicly filmed withdrawal, did they hide

---

[247] Bradley Graham, "War Review Extended a Month," The Washington Post, 15 September 1999, p. 23.
[248] "Airstrikes Hurt Serb Military Less than Initially Believed," The Kansas City Star, 17 September 1999, p. A16.

them, or did they really experience much less damage than NATO sources declared?

In late July, <u>Aviation Week and Space Technology</u> reported that NATO had dropped 3,000 precision-guided weapons that resulted in 500 hits on decoys, but destroyed only 50 Yugoslav tanks. Deputy Defense Secretary John Hamre also reported that all 30 (other sources use the figure 20) incidents of collateral damage would be studied (the trains, convoys, schools, hospitals, and Bulgarian strikes).[249] What types of bombs actually hit the decoys is known only by Pentagon insiders, so they are the only ones capable of calculating the amount of money wasted on these targets. This is an important issue, however, because early in the war NATO and US stocks of precision weaponry ran very low, a fact that undoubtedly was noted and highlighted by other nations with hostile intent toward the alliance. They received a yardstick measurement of how long an air campaign can proceed using certain types of high-tech armaments against specific targets before stocks run low.

<u>US News and World Report</u>, in its 20 September 1999 edition, stated that a NATO team visited 900 "aim points" targeted by NATO in Kosovo and found only 26 tank and similar-looking self-propelled-artillery carcasses. This would again throw NATO's revised number of 93 tanks out the window. However, how many tank carcasses were in Serbia, where the NATO team did not visit, is not known, making this figure less provocative and contradictory than it originally appears. The article also reported increased friction between General Clark and his NATO air operations chief, Lieutenant General Michael Short, over target selection and strategy (mobile targets such as tanks versus infrastructure, respectively). The article concluded that it was not air power but Russia's withdrawal of support for Serbia that probably brought an end to the air war in Kosovo. The article noted that in future conflicts, the most merciful way to end them may be to conduct them swiftly and violently instead of by the trial-and-error, phased approach used in Kosovo.[250]

Finally, several British officers, both retired and serving, also noted that damage was much less than originally stated. One newspaper report, citing British Ministry of Defense sources, stated that the damage done to tanks was perhaps even less than the lowest quoted figure of 13 tank kills.[251] But the most

---

[249] David A. Fulghum, "Pentagon Dissecting Kosovo Combat Data," <u>Aviation Week and Space Technology</u>, 26 July 1999, p. 68.

[250] Richard J. Newman, "The Bombs that Failed in Kosovo," <u>US News & World Report</u>, 20 September 1999, pp. 28-30.

[251] Andrew Gilligan, "RAF Admits Failings in Kosovo Inquiry," <u>The London Sunday Telegraph</u>, 25 July 1999.

damning comment could prove to be from an <u>International Herald Tribune</u> article on 1 October. Written by Frederick Bonnart, the editorial director of the independent but highly authoritative <u>NATO's Nations</u>, the article discusses how NATO "propaganda" was used against the West. He notes:

> In democracies, it is the duty of the public services to present the truth even in wartime, and particularly when they are in sole control of the information. If it is deliberately designed to engender fear and hate, then the correct term is propaganda.[252]

In particular, Bonnart believes the armored vehicle totals did not properly represent the vehicles actually destroyed, and that NATO deliberately used the West's reputation for truth and fairness to carry out a highly charged information policy against the Serbs. This made NATO's information policy rife with propaganda, Bonnart contends, and he points out that recommendations are being prepared to create a future NATO crisis information organization to keep this from happening again.[253] When did we ever think that a NATO-oriented publication's editor would be publicly accusing SACEUR's organization of propaganda and disinformation?

Assessing the Results of Information Superiority

One danger of the air campaign over Yugoslavia is overestimating NATO and US capabilities. All of the systems did not function all of the time with perfection. For example, some of the high-tech systems were unable to operate under poor weather conditions, as underscored in the daily Pentagon briefings during the campaign. Certainly it was an exaggeration to say:

> A vast number of intelligence, surveillance, and reconnaissance systems allowed for the rapid collection and collating into a single system the vital battlefield intelligence that we sent to our shooters. Taken together, all these innovations allowed our pilots to hit any target, any time, day or night, in any weather, accurate to within a few feet.[254]

Secretary of Defense William Cohen, in a November speech in California, listed several extremely important qualifiers regarding capabilities.

---

[252] Frederick Bonnart, "NATO Has a Duty to Be Truthful," <u>International Herald Tribune</u>, 1 October 1999.

[253] Ibid.

[254] William S. Cohen, International Institute for Strategic Studies, Hotel del Coronado, Coronado, California, 9 September 1999, downloaded from the Internet (OSD/PA news release), http://www.defenselink.mil:80/news/Sep1999/b09101999_bt409-99.html.

He noted that even the most advanced technologies have limits and that a precision-guided weapon can only hit the coordinates it is given. Moreover, "our vast intelligence system can create such a haystack of data that finding the one needle that will pinpoint a target in the right time frame is difficult, indeed."[255]

Hitting the right target on time requires sorting out the right coordinates from a pile of information (interpreted correctly) at the right time, a degree of data management that is difficult to achieve. Yet that, most believe, is just what information superiority was designed to do. It is clear from the Secretary's comments that much work remains. His "technologies have limits" qualifier requires our attention. This is perhaps a recognition that our systems still cannot, as evidenced by Kosovo, determine if a target is a fake, and this in an environment where we were not confronted by opposing information technology systems to disrupt friendly systems. As a result, NATO and the United States lost untold resources each time we expended ordinance on impostor targets.

Does a count of destroyed tanks matter? When counts are off by such a margin, they do. A comparison of these figures causes the average American to shake his head in confusion and frustration. Worse yet, these figures affect American lives. The interpretation of data by analysts at the lowest level also directly affects the credibility of our leaders and commanders who must stand before service members and the American public to relate the data. The problem is analogous to that encountered with counting SCUD missiles during Desert Storm. Coalition assets often hit gas or trailer trucks instead of missile launch vehicles for the same reasons. We haven't corrected this problem, and maybe it is simply beyond our ability to do so with current technologies. But we must face up to our shortcomings if we want to do better. Concern over battle damage assessment is not analogous to the Vietnam era's "body count" fixation, as some try to imply. Rather, the battle damage assessment debate is over just how much of our battlespace awareness was manipulated, and that does matter.

Another problem with disputes over battle damage assessment in Kosovo is that focusing on that aspect loses sight of the actual war that Milosevic fought (and not the template war that NATO assumed he would fight). Milosevic's real war was the ethnic cleansing offensive against the Albanian civilian population of Kosovo. Milosevic had two objectives. The first one was immediate, to rob the Kosovo Liberation Army (KLA) of its medium

---

[255] Ibid.

of support. The second objective was the campaign against NATO's center of gravity, its political stability. Milosevic confronted the United States and its allies with the grave risk of expanding instability throughout the "target" countries of Albania and Macedonia, and extending into the entire Balkan region. His instrument in this campaign was primarily paramilitary and police formations which left little information signature. This made targeting armored vehicles and artillery systems largely irrelevant to countering Milosevic's offensive. Additionally, targeting the Yugoslav infrastructure offered only protracted operations with significant economic damage to all of southern Europe, whereas the refugee problem was immediate and catastrophic. Milosevic proved he was a master at playing chess while his NATO counterparts played poker.[256] This made General Clark and General Short's arguments over targeting at best tangential to the war Milosevic was imposing on his opponent.

Asymmetric Offsets to Information Superiority

Admiral James Ellis, Commander-in-Chief of NATO's Allied Forces Southern Europe, noted in an interview on Kosovo in early September 1999 that too much information has the potential to reduce a military leader's awareness of an unfolding situation. Too much data leads to sensory overload: "Information saturation is additive to the 'fog of war' . . . uncontrolled, it will control you and your staffs and lengthen your decision-cycle times."[257] Admiral Ellis extended this problem to video teleconferencing as well, since it can become "a voracious consumer of leadership and key staff working hours."[258] This is probably the most interesting and underrated lesson learned of the entire war, that information superiority overload can actually hurt mission performance. Whether this fact influenced the tank count is unknown. Secretary Cohen also mentioned this problem in his speech in California. The point to make is that perhaps this flood of information in its own way manipulated the human interpreter's evaluation of the situation on the ground. Technical systems provided "proof" that a tank had been destroyed, when in fact the target hit wasn't a tank.

Admiral Ellis also recounted some of the asymmetric Serbian responses during the conflict, sighting the following: sporadic use of air defense assets; deceptive media campaigns; deliberately increasing the risk to NATO pilots of collateral damage; and developing political cleavages between NATO allies. To

---

[256] Paragraph is based on a discussion with Dr. Jacob Kipp, Foreign Military Studies Office, 30 September 1999.
[257] Elaine Grossman, "US Commander in Kosovo Sees Low-Tech Threats to High-Tech Warfare," Inside the Pentagon, 9 September 1999, p.1.
[258] Ibid.

prevent its air defense assets from being neutralized, the Serbian armed forces turned their assets on only as needed. They therefore presented a "constant but dormant" threat. This resulted in NATO using its most strained assets (e.g., JSTARS, AWACS) to conduct additional searches for air defense assets and forced NATO aircraft to fly above 15,000 feet, making it difficult for them to hit their targets. Ellis noted that NATO achieved little damage to the Serbian integrated air defense system.[259]

Admiral Ellis also spoke about not being able to counter Milosevic's state-controlled media and his attempts to gain international sympathy. As Milosevic's forces killed hundreds of people, NATO was always responding to its collateral damage problem. This is another lesson that must be addressed, how to prevent the press from becoming an asymmetric asset for the enemy.

Regarding the media, the US military's airborne psychological warfare machine, "Commando Solo," was unable to affect the Serb state media. Its use was hampered by the unknown air defense threat in the area. NATO officials were unwilling to risk flying the plane over Belgrade in fear that Milosevic would trade an air defense site in exchange for shooting down the slow-moving platform. As a result, Commando Solo flew far away from the Serb capital and was unable to affect TV coverage. One report during the bombing campaign asserted that NATO had proposed a moratorium on the bombing if Milosevic would just give NATO three hours of air time on TV and radio each evening. This indicates how unsuccessful the psychological warfare plan had become. All the while Milosevic maintained information superiority over his own people.

The expectation that the air campaign would last only a short time also was a detriment to the NATO psychological operations effort, since those assets were not included in the initial plans. It took two weeks to start delivering products and some 30 days to develop a campaign plan. Serbia started its psychological operations campaign days earlier and won the early initiative. The Serbs were initially successful on two fronts. First, they instituted the "target" campaign among their own people, in which citizens adorned themselves with bulls-eye targets, as if daring NATO to strike them personally. This idea greatly enhanced Serb morale and resistance at the start of the conflict. Second, they used the Internet to spread various campaign themes and claims, an effort the former US Information Agency (USIA) worked hard to control. One USIA analyst believes the conflict was the first Internet war, with both sides using the electronic medium to fight one another in a war of words

---

[259] Ibid.

and logic. But the point to again be made is that at the start of the conflict Serbia maintained information superiority over the minds of its citizens.

Another asymmetric offset, one not noted by Admiral Ellis, was the ability of Milosevic's air defense personnel to template US and NATO air operations based on their performance during the Gulf War and in Bosnia. Knowing when reconnaissance flights would be conducted, or when satellites would fly overhead, the Serb military would preposition armored vehicles to be picked up as targets. Then the Serbs would move the actual targets; in some instances they put in the target's place an old tractor with a telephone pole attached to make it look like a tank from 15,000 feet. At night it was difficult to tell the difference. And, it must be remembered, NATO pilots still had to contend with the possibility that air defense assets could be turned on and fired at a moment's notice, reducing their target focus.

In hindsight, NATO did not handle the political side of information superiority well either. The alliance had the combined assets and knowledge of its 19 nations to draw on in composing a psychological and negotiating profile of President Milosevic. From this background, political analysts around the world should have been able to draw a reliable profile of Milosevic's intentions, goals, and desires. In addition, NATO had the negotiating edge at Rambouillet. Some believe, however, that a mistake was made in the form of an ultimatum to Milosevic that ended the talks. Many diplomats apparently expected the ultimatum to result in a quick capitulation or a Milosevic retreat.[260] That did not happen. Instead, look at the results: at Rambouillet One, Albanian moderates signed the agreement; at Rambouillet Two, the KLA signed in the expectation that elections for Kosovo would be held in three years, and that NATO transit in Serbia would be allowed; and at the final moment when the Belgrade Agreement was signed, neither of those two conditions survived.

One hopes that State Department analysts are studying in depth these negotiating shortcomings and the inability to persuade Milosevic, just as the military should be studying the shortcomings in its information superiority approach. For example, did diplomats and military representatives alike make the wrong assessment of the projected length of this conflict based on Milosevic's behavior following NATO's air campaign in August 1995? The 1995 concessions were likely the result of the combination of the air campaign *and* the simultaneous ground force offensive that was under way in Croatia, not just the bombing campaign alone. Did planners overlook this? Undoubtedly,

[260] Mark Danner, "Kosovo: The Meaning of Victory," New York Review of Books, 15 July 1999.

Milosevic was to some extent irrational, but we also knew him well and should have been able to foresee his responses with some degree of certainty based on previous conversations and actions.

Technological and Political Fixes

Of course attempts are being made to correct some of the technological problems encountered during the conflict in Kosovo. NATO technical weaknesses included an inability to identify moving targets and to find armored or other equipment that was well camouflaged. The director of the Defense Advanced Research Projects Agency (DARPA), Frank Fernandez, is trying to solve both of these problems. He noted, "You had to put a human eyeball on [a] target before you could give the command to shoot because we don't trust our identification systems."[261] Again, the human dimension is stressed. Initial areas of intensified DARPA research include:

- Improving a sensor's ability to identify targets and see through camouflage. Reducing the size of space radars and their antennas to more accurately sense moving targets.
- Finding better methods to combine and pass target data through networks to aircraft or weapons.
- Developing techniques to find underground facilities and see what is happening inside.
- Establishing tactics for accurately striking moving targets in bad weather.[262]

The efforts to identify moving targets are focused on multi-, hyper-, and ultra-spectral (optical) sensors that take electromagnetic spectrum slices to identify targets. Technologies to uncover camouflaged equipment will take advantage of operational sequencing of various types of targets to uncover them, as well as low-frequency radars and computer programs designed to see through foliage. Finally, Fernandez noted that future attacks will be based on a piloted vehicle operating in tandem with two or three pilotless vehicles: "That's what we learned in Kosovo—to strike these targets that are hidden took two people, one to fly and release the weapon and another to look for and designate the targets."[263] Fernandez's desire to have human assisted pilotless vehicles is important because it indicates that DARPA may not fall prey to an American tradition—trying to just find technological answers to problems.

---

[261] "DARPA Tackles Kosovo Problems," Aviation Week and Space Technology, 2 August 1999, p. 55.
[262] Ibid.
[263] Ibid.

It also will be interesting to watch the explanation of political lessons learned over the next few months. For example, there should be a serious effort at the State Department and in the National Security Council to right some apparent wrongs in our decision-making process. Wouldn't it be wise to study why we failed to develop a campaign plan beyond the first five days? And shouldn't we study why we put our operational art in the hands of politicians who tried to dictate the pace, scope, and rules of engagement, and perhaps even the target selection process? Wouldn't it be advantageous to find new ways to persuade the Milosevics of the world to negotiate, allowing NATO and the United States to withhold the use of their war machine in the first place and thus not having to deal with the technological problem sets of such a conflict? Wouldn't this be better than simply developing new technological solutions?

Conclusion

Why is information superiority a dangerous myth? Primarily because we don't interpret what we collect as well as we might. It is not that we are doing poorly, just that we aren't doing as well as we think we are. Consider, for example, the shortcomings sighted above of NATO's use of total information superiority:

- Total information superiority did not allow us to achieve a political or diplomatic victory. Like Saddam Hussein, Milosevic is still in power, and the Belgrade Agreement was a far cry from what was sought at Rambouillet.
- Total information superiority did not enable NATO to locate the Serbian armed forces' center of gravity, the police and paramilitaries doing the killing.
- Total information superiority did not counter rumor nor prejudiced reporting. For example, to cite an instance not covered in this analysis, information superiority did not allow NATO to know, even approximately, how many Kosovo civilians were killed before the bombing started. Instead of 100,000 Kosovo victims, as rumors suggested, 10,000 now appears to be closer to the truth. Would NATO have gone to war over 10,000 people? To date, only some 2,500 bodies have been discovered.
- Total information superiority was affected by politicians, who demanded that pilots fly above a certain height to minimize casualties, thereby degrading the effectiveness of information systems.
- Total information superiority was manipulated, if the debate over the total number of tanks destroyed is any indicator, by asymmetric offsets (e.g., fake tanks, other decoys) and by a study of NATO air operation templates.

- Total information superiority did not result in NATO communications working without serious problems, even after years of practice and in the face of no radio-electronic counterattacks.

During the air campaign over Yugoslavia and Kosovo, NATO had information superiority. But as the discussion above demonstrates, if analysis is inadequate, then information superiority is not enough. One danger in information superiority, then, is in assuming knowledge. Another danger, as the 99.6 percent figure demonstrates, is in overestimating our abilities.

If applied against the major criteria of reducing uncertainty, providing a more complete intelligence picture of the battlefield, and assisting precision-guided missiles in acquiring and destroying targets, information superiority passed many but failed some critical tests in Kosovo (as battle damage assessment showed). We may possess information superiority, but we often fail to exploit it because we can't always correctly interpret what we gather. As a result we are unable to lower uncertainty.

Three problems deserve to be highlighted. First, the methodologies we are using to evaluate data appear to have minor shortcomings which sometimes result in horrific mistakes that directly affect our credibility at higher levels. That is, incorrect assessments by low-level data interpreters eventually diminish the credibility of those officials who have to stand before the public and explain the facts and figures. Sometimes this is a result of consumers who press too hard for answers. But had NATO ground troops been inserted into Kosovo before the Finnish-Russian negotiations ended the conflict, two more reinforced mechanized infantry battalions were awaiting them than expected. This miscalculation was due to the inability of information technology systems and analysts to properly assess and interpret what their "total information superiority picture" of the battlefield really showed (and there were cockpit recordings to study). If open-source reports are correct, we destroyed mockups and decoys in many cases, not working armored vehicles. The cost-effectiveness of air power was greatly diminished as a result. Clearly, more emphasis needs to be placed on the art of battlefield visualization.[264]

Second, we are not realistically assessing the conditions under which our military capabilities are being employed. What was "combat" directed against in Kosovo? Stationary objects, such as buildings, civilian infrastructure,

---

[264] The subject of battlefield visualization is addressed in the pamphlet "Information Operations" produced by the US Army Information Operations Division, 1999, p. 11.

press and police headquarters, and military garrisons; and mobile targets that moved mainly at night if at all, such as tanks, armored personnel carriers, and artillery units. It was not face-to-face combat, but combat conducted from afar. Perhaps "engagement" would have been a better choice of words than combat, although no pilot would agree! We can do better in realistically assessing and describing the conditions under which our forces are engaged.

Third, the US military must rid itself of a degree of self-deception that occasionally appears. The US and NATO forces are good, and they know it. But they must do better in their estimates of success, for manipulated figures could lead to unrealizable goals or expectations. This attitude can lead military planners to draw false conclusions about Kosovo, previous conflicts, and consequently future operations. A sober assessment of what went wrong is just as important as seeing what went right. No better example could be offered than the expectation of a repeat of the August 1995 "quick concession" from Milosevic, which left planners unprepared beyond the first few days of the conflict in 1999. Our air power is magnificent, but we are becoming its captive because of exaggerations such as those enumerated in this article. Let air power's success speak for itself; even without exaggeration it is without peer.

Drawing the wrong conclusions, as was pointed out with battle damage assessments, can have dramatic and lethal effects on any intervening force. There is a lesson in this, namely that the human in the link still plays a very important role even in the age of information operations, perhaps a more important one than we recognize. Automated warfare is still a long way off if the problems that developed in the nearly empty skies over Kosovo are any indicator. US analysts must hone their methodologies to quickly and correctly interpret the cascading amounts of information that confront them in a conflict situation. They must consider asymmetries in information-age conflict. Improvements in the art of battlefield visualization or conceptualization, including the vital element of interpretation, must be made. The human interpreter of information is every bit as important as the human user of information.

Future conflicts may be very different from NATO's experience in Kosovo. Future enemies could possess some or all of the following: an adept air force; up-to-date air defense sites; precision-guided cruise missiles that can do to our air bases and planes from standoff positions what we can do to theirs (to include destroying AWACS); and the ability to reach the United States with weapons of mass destruction, precision missiles, or terrorist acts. When these threats confront US and NATO systems, what will information superiority do for us? Will it be even more unreliable when stressed by both nontechnical offsets and technological counters? How reliable will those new estimates be? What will happen when a real information warfare system confronts ours? Will our capabilities be degraded by a quarter, a third, or more?

The Pentagon's top civilian leaders evidently plan to produce an official report on Kosovo, breaking their study into three parts: a deployment-employment group, an intelligence support for operations group, and an alliance and coalition warfare group. It is important that the intelligence support group study the current information superiority dogma to correct some of the faulty data and impressions being generated by both analysts and leaders from the Kosovo conflict. We have to stop ourselves before heading down the wrong "yellow brick road," and instead inculcate the wisdom that people like Admiral Ellis are revealing. NATO and the United States did almost everything right in Kosovo. Now it is time to assess the little that was done wrong. As the Chinese might say, you can lose in contemporary war in two ways: if you fail to defend your information superiority, or if you become trapped by false information. It is the latter to which we should now pay attention.

CHAPTER NINE: "POLICEKEEPING" AND THE NEED FOR INFORMATION TECHNOLOGIES[265]

Introduction
      Traditional peace support operations differ by degrees of consent, force, and impartiality. Peacekeeping operations require the consent of the belligerent parties, the use of force only in self-defense, and the maintenance of impartiality. Peace-enforcement missions do not require absolute consent; force can be used to compel or coerce, and impartiality is usually strained.

      Today, peace support operations are caught between these two extremes. Peace support personnel deal more often with crowds than armies and with questions of ownership of houses and pigs rather than buffer zones. Population resource control is as important as equipment control. Missions are increasingly intrastate with a police mission overtone. These missions do not fall neatly into either the peacekeeping or peace-enforcement categories but approach "police-keeping" performed by "policekeepers."[266]

      Luckily for peace support personnel facing these new missions, there has been a rapid proliferation of information technology (IT). If properly understood, these new technologies can help policekeepers prevent or control conflict.

New Peacemaking/Peacekeeping Model
      On 7 September 2000, the United Nations Security Council voted unanimously to overhaul its peacekeeping operations. There was strong support in the Council for a more professional, high-tech UN force that would work harder at conflict prevention. Former US Secretary of State Madeleine Albright agreed with this reassessment. She had stated earlier that

      Old models of peacekeeping don't always meet current challenges. Peace operations today often require skills that are neither strictly military nor strictly police but, rather, a combination of the two. The

---

[265] This article was originally titled "IT Requirements for 'Policekeeping.'" It was published in <u>Military Review</u>, September-October 2001, pp. 29-35. This is a slightly expanded version of that article. The editors of <u>Military Review</u> inserted the term "policekeeper" in many places where the term "peacekeeper" would normally be found.
[266] Author's term to describe the current situation. No such term actually exists in the peace support operation lexicon. It has been brought to the author's attention that Graham Day used this term in the past when he described another peace support operation.

international community needs to identify and train units that are able to control crowds, deter vigilante actions, prevent looting, and disarm civilian agitators while, at the same time, winning the trust of the communities in which they are deployed.[267]

In the past, a peacekeeper's job was to deploy between two opposing militaries at their invitation to serve as a buffer between the forces, usually in interstate operations. Albright noted that today's mission is more intrastate, with more attention directed toward crowds, vigilantes, and civilian agitators than to separating traditional military forces. As a result, militaries are in direct contact for long periods of time with the people of a region; they are exposed to local nuances and traditions.

IT, which was seldom available to peacekeepers before, is addressed in the Brahimi Report, which discusses the need for a new peacekeeping strategy and organization to support these efforts. It recommends that an executive information and strategic analysis secretariat (EISAS) be formed and composed of information system specialists, military analysts and criminal network experts. The last category reflects the UN's increased focus on police matters. Further, the report noted that the UN presently has no IT center responsible for user-level strategy and policy in peace support operations. The Brahimi Report also recommends developing a peace operation's extranet with access to the EISAS and other databases.[268]

This resolution for change and new technology could not come at a better time. Although currently engaged in fourteen peacekeeping operations worldwide that employ more than 37,000 troops, UN policekeepers have had numerous failures over the past few years.[269] Part of the reason is that peace support forces are underequipped for the changed nature of the mission since IT has traditionally gone to the warfighter. This emphasis needs adjustment.

The US Army appears to understand this dilemma and is developing US Army Field Manual (FM) 3-07, Stability and Support Operations, to address peace operations. The new FM is a compilation of FM 100-23, Peace Operations; FM 90-29, Noncombatant Evacuation Order; FM 100-19, Domestic Support Operations; and FM 100-20, Military Operations in Low-Intensity

---

[267] Madeleine Albright as quoted in Jason Sherman, "Middle March," Armed Forces Journal International, August 2000, p. 8.

[268] See http://www.un.org/peace/reports/peace_operations/, the Brahimi Report.

[269] "UN Council Votes to Improve Forces," The Kansas City Star, 8 September 2000, p. A9.

Conflict.[270] It is still a year or so away from publication (in 2001, when this article was written) but shows the complexity of peace support operations today.

IT Databases and Policekeeping

IT can look at the geographic roots of a conflict, such as natural resources, land, food, water, high ground, space, the environment, movement corridors, strategic locations, or cultural and historical objects, in ways more comprehensive and descriptive than ever before. These methods are of tremendous use to diplomats and policekeepers. The Geographic Information System (GIS) offers a number, quality, and diversity of global databases (routing, criminal analysis, line of sight advantages, monitoring, etc.) that have peacekeeping/policekeeping implications for combatants (where is the bread, the mines, the ammo, and so on). Such IT databases shorten the time lag between collecting and using information, and they both share available information and put a factor of reality in a reference base.[271]

From an international perspective, the United Nations may have the best IT databases available to diplomats and policekeepers to help in their planning process associated with conflict management. Two of the most popular are the Integrated Regional Information Network (IRIN) and ReliefWeb sites developed by the UN Office for the Coordination of Humanitarian Affairs. The sites are designed to provide the kind of detailed information necessary to accurately predict the likelihood that chaos and violence will break out in a country or region. IRIN focuses on in-country issues, especially populations at risk (who's who, where are people going and what are they doing, etc.). The network produces reports on political, economic, and social issues affecting humanitarian efforts (information on washed-out roads, bombed airfields, landmines, disease-infested water, epidemics, or civil unrest). IRIN's initial focus has been Africa, although plans for exporting the model to Asia and the Caucasus are under consideration. It is a value-added product since it does not duplicate or distribute current news output but enhances it with further analysis and details, to include the use of email contacts with the population. In the age of blogging, this could be a very

---

[270] US Army Field Manual (FM) 100-23, Peace Operations (Washington, DC: US Government Printing Office [GPO], 30 December 1994); FM 90-29, Noncombatant Evacuation Order (Washington, DC: US GPO, 17 October 1994); FM 100-19, Domestic Support Operations (Washington, DC: US GPO, 1 July 1993); FM 100-20, Military Operations in Low-Intensity Conflict (Washington, DC: US GPO, 5 December 1990).

[271] Jack Dangermond, Environmental Systems Research Institute, comment made during his presentation at the Conference on Virtual Diplomacy, 1-2 April 1997, Washington, D.C..

important element to ascertaining the situation. IRIN is a noncommercial venture that is totally dependent on donor government or institutional financing. The website is http://www.reliefweb.int/IRIN.[272]

ReliefWeb aids decision-making through updates on disasters and the consolidation of information from numerous sources. This information is designed to allow relief agencies and governments to respond quickly when needed. ReliefWeb lists reports from nongovernmental organizations (NGOs) and news agencies. It has a searchable database of over 50,000 documents dating back to 1981, updated every half-hour from locations in New York, Geneva, and soon Asia. It was launched in 1996 and entrenched by General Assembly resolution 51/194 on 10 February 1997. The site receives up to 50,000 page requests per day (with a staff of only five in New York and four in Geneva), and it has handled nineteen complex emergencies and over 1,100 natural disasters. The August 1999 earthquake in Turkey produced over 50,000 hits a day on ReliefWeb's site.[273] As the site notes

> Impartiality and transparency are cornerstones of our policy and we maintain them by meticulously sourcing and dating all documents we put up, allowing ReliefWeb to provide balanced coverage. We post the information as is. No editing, no rewriting, no tampering. What you see is what the information providers give us.[274]

ReliefWeb's Internet site is http://www.reliefweb.int/. Its email site is comments@reliefweb.int. The UN has recommended the creation of a Humanitarian Extranet to provide global access to authorized users. This would allow situational analysis without prejudicial input from the combatants out of the eyes of the press.[275]

IT also impacts on issues of law in international conflicts. The "sovereign" has lost control of much of what people can see and hear, making it more difficult to "form" the consciousness of the populace than in the past. If the essence of sovereignty is the power to exclude others from interfering in one's affairs (personal or governmental), then IT is eroding that concept. In Bosnia, for example, Villanova University developed a legal web page that had

---

[272] Information listed here on IRIN was taken from the IRIN website on 18 October 2000.
[273] Information reported here on ReliefWeb was taken from the ReliefWeb website on 18 October 2000.
[274] Ibid.
[275] "Information Technologies Can Help Prevent, Manage, and Resolve Conflicts Internationally," downloaded from the U.S. Institute of Peace website, June 1997.

a virtual library and electronic publishing format. The web page helped judges in Bosnia to build the rule of law.[276]

IT impacts on conflict management in other ways. For example, some view media coverage of conflicts as a form of military pressure, while others view the media as a means of subtle diplomacy. Communications technologies (the Internet, websites, etc.) serve selected audiences or regional or specialized markets. Groups can communicate with one another nearly instantaneously and simultaneously, sending messages, photos, or other website links at any time. Still, diplomats claim budgetary constraints, security concerns, and organizational culture as blockades to their ability to access these technologies. This results in an environment in which individuals and groups are sometimes empowered by information processing and communications to a greater extent than foreign relations departments.[277] Information is so easily transmitted and influential today that in 1997 author Warren P. Strobel entitled his book Late Breaking Foreign Policy.

Potential IT Military Uses

If Albright is correct in her analysis that a new peacekeeping model is required today, then IT is poised to play a significant role in developing the capabilities to assist that model. One of the facilities involved with accelerating the availability of tools and techniques to develop training applications for policekeepers is the Institute for Creative Technologies (ICT) located in Marina Del Ray, California. These efforts are the result of a $44.5 million contract between the US Army and the University of Southern California that concluded in August 1999. The Institute is charged with creating a system adaptable enough to provide the correct virtual environment for policekeepers, such as the proper terrain, culture, and situational context.[278] Policekeeping forces trained by facilities such as ICT learn how to resolve disputes on city streets or in crowded market squares before they become conflicts.

ICT's first product has met these expectations. The Institute constructed an interaction simulation vignette that depicts a peacekeeping operation in Bosnia. It demonstrates how squad leaders and other noncommissioned officers can learn "through simulation to deal diplomatically

---

[276] Henry Perritt, Villanova School of Law, comment made during his presentation at the Conference on Virtual Diplomacy in 1997.
[277] Margarita S. Studemeister, "The Impact of Information and Communications Technologies on International Conflict Management," ASIS Bulletin, Feb/Mar 1998.
[278] Jim Starling, "Soldiers Help Create Cultural Training Vignette," Defense News, 4 September 2000, p. 14.

with people from differing cultures, and without relying on firepower."[279] During a mission rehearsal exercise for a battalion preparing to deploy to a peacekeeping mission, a writer for the <u>Christian Science Monitor</u> observed:

> A hostile crowd confronts the US Army commander. His troops are supposed to be on a peacekeeping mission. Instead, they're now trying to rescue a local child who has been injured by a U.S. Humvee [high-mobility, multipurpose wheeled vehicle (HMMWV)]. Gunfire erupts over a hill. A helicopter circles deafeningly overhead. What should he do? Teams of soldiers run up and demand orders. He barks out commands. Units disperse in three directions about to carry out the operation when…someone turns on the lights. The soldier—though in fatigues—is standing in a small room surrounded by a 180-degree screen. This is no regular movie or video game. It's the Army's latest high-tech tool to train tomorrow's soldiers.[280]

The military can use IT to guide or force (when necessary) militaries and civilians of disputing nations away from conflict. IT can be used to distract, pacify, appease, intimidate, provoke, immobilize or pin down, wear out, confuse or weaken, suggest, or mislead.[281] This is an important list of uses since many can help slow or prevent the use of force. An IT difficulty is producing software that can reflect cultural sensitivities and expectations. If software developers interact with academicians, religious and cultural leaders, and other with experience in regional sensitivities, then such computer developments stand a chance. Remember that IT cannot replace troops.

IT supports peace operations at both the operational and tactical levels. It can demonstrate simultaneity of effort. A simulation capability known as Spectrum simulates the actions of several interagency groups all working together in a peacekeeping environment. Policekeepers could develop a synchronization matrix to monitor this process and keep it under observation. It might demonstrate where help is needed, what combinations of agencies are most effective, and so on.

IT can also demonstrate the vulnerabilities of those involved in the conflict. Bahktar Associates has reportedly developed radar that gathers intelligence on hidden or underground weapons facilities, enemy bunkers and

---

[279] Ibid.

[280] Gloria Goodale, "Army Enlists Hollywood to Help Harden Its Soldiers," <u>The Christian Science Monitor</u>, 2 October 2000.

[281] S. A. Komov, "On the Methods and Forms of Conducting Information War," <u>Military Thought</u>, July-August 1997, p. 19.

other hard-to-find structures. Known as Ground Penetrating Radar (GPR), it can provide three-dimensional images up to 45.7 meters below the surface of land or sea. GPR's Doppler radar uses very little power, thus reducing its probability of detection. The system can also identify unexploded ordnance, find utility lines or mass graves, and help map minefields.[282]

Another development is the Discoverer II satellite system. The House Appropriations Committee recently delayed accepting the satellite system but did not cancel it outright. Discoverer II offers warfighters and policekeepers affordable, continuous and contiguous coverage of the battlefield in all weather, day or night. Discoverer II detects camouflage, concealment, deception, and movement by combining synthetic aperture radar, moving target indicators, and digital terrain-elevation data. Designed for the theater commander, the entire system involves twenty satellites and could be in place by 2005 if approved.[283]

IT enables compelling compliance by simulating actions and consequences. The best example of compelling compliance through simulations is still the use of digital mapping at the Dayton Peace Accords. As one participant noted

> Digitized map information (points, lines, and areas in vector form), names data, elevation data, scanned map images, and imagery could be pulled into the PowerScene terrain visualization systems and presented to negotiators as still screen shots, fly-through videos, or dynamic fly-throughs under joystick control. PowerScene also supported dynamic annotation and visual assists such as flooding, slope computations, and intervisibility exploration. Any realignment of real or negotiated boundaries between the factions could be reflected in automated recompilations of areas and in adjustments of buffer zones.[284]

Digital mapping allows policekeepers to intimidate negotiators by showing detail, displaying the instantaneous ability to change the format from peacekeeping to war, providing absolute consistency and offering flexibility and responsiveness of support. The technology intimidated the negotiators by

---

[282] Bryan Bender, "Radar Breakthrough Could Help DOD See Underground," Jane's Defense Weekly, 22 December 1999.
[283] Kenneth Israel, "Space-Based Radar Essential in Future Conflicts," Aviation Week and Space Technology, 25 September 2000, p. 98.
[284] Richard G. Johnson, "Negotiating the Dayton Peace Accords through Digital Maps," United States Institute of Peace, 25 February 1999.

giving them a sense of loss of control and privacy since they had to work with computer operators who were not on their team.[285]

IT can assist policekeepers by monitoring and reviewing actions for participants and the international community. For example, unmanned aerial vehicles provide situational awareness and locate unauthorized equipment. Commercial imagery is now available for UN policekeepers and can revolutionize the way they do business. For example, the imaginative policekeeper can look for refugees, artillery positions or arms control storage sites, or he can search for conventional terrain imagery. A US company called Orbimage offers 1-meter imagery applications for resource deployment, mission planning, targeting, battle damage assessment, intelligence gathering and trend analysis. While some of these do not apply to peacekeeping, it is important to know the capabilities available because potential combatants have the same access to this cost-effective combat multiplier. This capability offers continuous monitoring of any area for less than the cost of operating a reconnaissance aircraft.[286] Money and download capabilities are the only limitations. Imaging technology also enables defensive uses of information technology. Imagery also allows the peacekeepers to view their positions and uncover any vulnerability to their perimeters.[287]

For the policekeeper the most important uses of imagery at the operational level are:

- Verifying claims by potential belligerents.
- Observing terrain that can be inspected by ground forces.
- Searching for refugees or mass graves.
- Building confidence and security measures between disputing parties.
- Destigmatizing intelligence use in UN peacekeeping operations.
- Providing hard evidence to confirm or deny claims made by disputants.[288]

IT Policekeeper Needs at the Tactical Level
A November 1997 issue of Time magazine was devoted to IT issues. In one example, there was a picture of a Home and Garden calculator capable of producing 4,000 pages of tips and gardening hints for the horticulturist.

---

[285] Ibid.

[286] Mark Stout and Thomas Quiggin, "Exploiting the New High Resolution Satellite Imagery: Darwinian Imperatives?" Commentary No. 75, Canadian Security Intelligence Service, Summer 1998.

[287] Ibid.

[288] Ibid.

Policekeepers would benefit greatly from the same type of simple technology, a calculator containing over 4,000 pages of "tips and hints" such as rules of engagement, specifics of the treaty being enforced, cultural and religious information on local customs and traditions, uniforms and equipment of the sides, and so on. Casio now produces a watch capable of taking 100 digital photos. Why not affix the watch to a corner of the calculator so the policekeeper has both a timepiece and camera to take pictures of crowds or troublemakers? Clearly there are many ideas available for the soldier to enhance his policekeeping skills. And these same technologies could also have warfighter use later—simply change the 4,000 or so pages to the ranges of tanks and artillery or photos of enemy planes or other vital information.

Discussions with policekeepers who have served in Bosnia, Kosovo, Haiti, and Somalia reveal the need for other specific types of IT. A partial list includes:

- **Electronic Tagging** – One of the most difficult problems policekeepers face is tracking troublemakers. Tagging troublemakers or opposition leaders to follow their movements would significantly help peacekeeping forces; however, this may not be possible due to legal constraints. By tagging friendly troops, commanders could follow their subordinates' whereabouts in cities and in the countryside. If one were taken hostage, the commander would immediately know the hostage's location.
- **Electronic Informants** – Any type of device that could provide information to improve situational awareness would be of great assistance. This could include electronic monitoring devices, tape recorders, sensors, or other devices.
- **Satellite Monitoring** – On the sidelines at National Football League contests are satellite dishes designed to pick up sounds from the game. Similar systems could be invaluable for policekeepers trying to monitor crowds or troublemakers.
- **Search and Seizures** – Drug-detection, pulse, or x-ray devices to help with searches for contraband would be invaluable.
- **Language Decoders** – Hand-held instantaneous language translators would relieve tension between policekeepers and soldiers where hand signals are sometimes the only communication. These devices are presently undergoing testing and will offer some relief from the conundrum of foreign languages.
- **Flying Transport Discs** – It is difficult to cordon off an area or chase someone through a city, forest or countryside. A flying disc that could hover above the ground and move at speeds up to 15 miles per hour would be invaluable to policekeepers.

- **Vector Technology** – This includes cameras, the Remotely Monitored Battlefield Sensor System or other types of sensors, including global positioning systems (GPS) that get policekeepers to the proper place quickly and precisely.
- **Intimidating Technologies by Culture** – Different cultures are coerced by different degrees of intimidation. In Haiti, a club was enough to get someone moving. In Somalia, it took something much more intimidating—weapons. In Bosnia, a tracked recovery vehicle was often more intimidating than a tank.[289]
- **Crowd Control** – Various items such as rubber sting balls, foam grenades, and foam batons can disperse a crowd without causing fatalities.[290]
- **Observer Support** – The plethora of readily available commercial observation equipment can provide observers with more remote viewing, sensing, and listening capabilities.
- **Transparency** – Communication technologies are being touted as a confidence-building measure to demonstrate to all parties that everyone is adhering to agreements in a similar fashion.
- **Separation Zone** – Sensors and GPS can be used to locate or establish zones of separation and security. Linking this information with the peace process in real-time is key to developing a mandate.[291]

The use of time and space can be enriched and enhanced through access to concepts such as the University After Next (UAN). This concept envisioned a virtual library and virtual access "phone book" through which a peacekeeper in the field could call back to the US via the Internet or a hand held device to get subject matter experts to answer pressing questions. These experts might be in universities or federal agencies. A whole host of cultural, religious, language, norms, or procedural questions or problems could be answered in this manner—issues that require further explanation than the peacekeeper initially has at his or her fingertips.[292]

---

[289] Based on talks with US officers LTC Mike Chura, Major Rick Nussio, Major John DeJarnette, and Captain John (Clay) Mountcastle. The author would like to thank these officers for their policekeeping and IT ideas.

[290] Jon R. Anderson, "Nonlethal Weapons Pack Powerful Punch," European Stars and Stripes, 9 April 2000, p. 3.

[291] Author's discussion with retired Colonel William Flavin, US Army Peacekeeping Institute, 10 October 2000.

[292] For more on the UAN concept, see http//call.army.mil/call.

IT also offers systems that create time and space to give other courses of action a chance. Using IT to manage time and space can help policekeepers when they handle potential conflicts. For example, if a crowd confronts a policekeeping force at a roadblock, soldiers must know how to manage the space between the checkpoint and the policekeeper's backup to ensure the backup has access to the checkpoint. The same scenario applies to VIP safety in a crowd. It can also depict how a policekeeper handles time and space before deployment. For example, time and space parameters are enhanced for the policekeeper who trains while en route to an area or in theater and immediately before a mission. This helps hastily assembled joint or multinational teams to reach a common understanding of a mission.

The University of Houston's Virtual Environment Research Laboratory, which is part of a joint venture with the National Aeronautical Space Administration's Johnson Space Center, is developing such technology for the US Army and Marines. They have developed software that creates virtual crowds and opposing forces for policekeepers to confront. Perhaps most important, policekeepers can train on simulated rules of engagement before deploying. The software also demonstrates how to deal with other cultures and situations where verbal communications will not work. The idea

> Is to be able to provide crowd scenes, for example, that behave as crowds behave: that may run at the sound of gunfire, that may provide hiding places for opposing forces…we want to enable people who are planning a mission of this type to rapidly examine the alternatives. What if this happens? What if that happens? What would I do in this situation? Without having to go to the real environment, which is often at times impossible, or do it basically as a mental exercise with the obvious limitations you would have without having a detailed copy of the environment to work with.[293]

Identifying those responsible for vigilante activities, agitation, and looting is a huge problem for policekeepers. In the Balkans this process also involves finding armed individuals. Early identification puts time and space between these people and the policekeepers. The military can use IT as a deterrent or confidence-building measure to contain or block the actions of vigilantes or crowds. As a deterrent, IT can put pressure on people or organizations, instill fear over consequences of potential actions, threaten to expose a leader's state secrets, demonstrate the impotence of a nation to pose a credible threat, or expose troop deployments or other forms of military

---

[293] Peter La Franchi, "Going Virtual to Get the Rules Right," Simulation and Training Technology, October 1999, pp. 7, 10.

buildups. These activities can uncover blatant lies designed to manipulate public opinion.

The policekeeper, however, has always been the neglected soldier when it comes to new and exciting technology. It was assumed in the past that policekeepers could use IT developed for combat soldiers. That was and is true, especially for peace enforcement missions, but the tables have also turned somewhat—past peacekeeping models do not apply. Intrastate conflicts are now more common than interstate conflicts. Peacekeeping missions are now more oriented toward police actions and require new IT, as interviews with US policekeepers demonstrate. Today's policekeepers request language encoders, satellite dishes, electronic informants, crowd control devices and drug detection or x-ray technologies. The warfighter can use these technologies as well, especially in urban combat.

Many technologies policekeepers want are still in the US Army's procurement system. Some potential opponents, if they have sufficient financial assets, can purchase commercial off-the-shelf high technology products faster than the US military can procure them. The procurement cycle for equipment can thus put US forces at a disadvantage. Potential opponents might use these technologies to prejudice troop-contributing countries through media or situation manipulation.

Conclusions

Peace support personnel should benefit from IT more than they have in the past, especially if the UN expects them to confront IT-enhanced criminals and insurgents. IT can explain, pressure, instill fear, uncover manipulation, expose deployments or plans, threaten, and demonstrate impotence. It can contain and recover, and it offers certainty of punishment in an invisible, anonymous manner that ignores sovereignty. In addition, IT enhanced policekeeping can deter conflict by:

- Coercing by demonstrating potential military power in benign form.
- Building confidence, mustering support, saving time, explaining visually complicated processes, offering to reach people or places directly with speed, providing accurate and timely information, eliminating mistrust and disinformation, and compelling compliance.
- Developing common values for the world community.
- Offering a virtual show of force and potential outcomes.
- Modeling information friction or those areas needing special attention.
- Signaling acceptable behavior.
- Offering a preemptive strategy.
- Capitalizing on the transparent world.

164

- Developing an information blockade or overloading to compel behavior.
- Integrating all assets such as law, people, and technologies.
- Reverting to a react-act mode due to its speed.
- Offering precise information on a variety of issues for decision-makers.
- Helping connect data perceptual systems.
- Enabling nations to learn to manage or leverage consequences of actions.
- Allowing smaller nations to dominate larger ones.

These issues require intense doctrinal, policy, and legal review. IT can prevent conflict by manipulating, interrupting or interfering with information systems and infrastructures, areas where there are serious legal questions. IT needs to be regulated under such circumstances. IT remains a national issue. It is not a focal point for the UN, which remains inundated with more pressing issues. States must develop their own peace-support IT within international guidelines. But, the issue is crucial. Without such support, peace operations may indeed lose their effectiveness and ability to keep the peace. Give IT-supported policekeepers, not criminals and insurgents, a chance to succeed.

CHAPTER TEN: INFORMATION WARFARE IN THE SECOND (1999-PRESENT) RUSSIAN-CHECHEN WAR[294]

During the past ten years, the Russian military has attentively studied the subject of information war (IW). The main catalyst for this interest was the successful use of IW by the coalition forces during Desert Storm. Russian military theorists watched coalition planes bomb Iraqi targets in real-time with precision and understood that warfare had entered a new phase, one dominated by information-based equipment and resources. Two further motivators were the poor use of IW by the Russian armed forces during the First Russian-Chechen War (1994-1996), which contributed to the loss of Russian morale, and the successful use of IW by NATO during the conflict over Kosovo.

The success of the coalition forces in both Desert Storm and Kosovo indicated that military reform would be bankrupt if the technical aspect of reform did not include information-based technologies. These technologies must be imbedded into new military equipment, from sensors and radars to jet fighters and cruise missiles. However, Russia was also concerned about the impact of information technologies on the brain and, consequently, Russian morale. These technologies included the rapid distribution of information via the mass media and Internet. Military reform would also have to take this element into consideration.

Russia's Understanding of IW and the Information Weapon

This rather detailed discussion of Russia's concept of information war and information weapons is necessary so that the reader can construct the correct prism through which to view Russian information operations in Chechnya. Relying on a US or British definition of the term will not suffice, because the parameters included by the Russians are so different.

Russian military theorists divide the concept of information warfare into two distinct fields: information-technical and information-psychological. If an information warfare element under consideration is a machine-driven, data-processor component (computers, sensors, satellites, reconnaissance-strike systems, etc.), then the category under consideration is information-technical. Electronic warfare also would be an element in this field. If the IO element is a

---

[294] This chapter was previously published as "Information Warfare in the Second (1999-) Chechen War: Motivator for Military Reform?" in Russian Military Reform: 1992-2002, Anne C. Aldis and Roger N. McDermott, editors, Frank Cass Publishers, 2003, pp. 209-233. This version includes several paragraphs that Aldis and McDermott were unable to add due to the manuscript's length.

human-based, data-processor component (the brain, which can be influenced or manipulated by propaganda, psychotronics, nonlethal weapons, or special pharmaceuticals according to the Russian paradigm), then the issue under consideration is information-psychological. Thus, psychological operations (PSYOPs) are an element of this field.

This division of labor for IW theory has been constant throughout the past several years. For example, instructors at the Russian General Staff Academy in 1995 defined information war (using the Russian phrase informatsionnoe protivoborstvo [information struggle]) in a technical-psychological sense. Their definition reads:

> Information warfare is a means of resolving a conflict between opposing sides. The goal is for one side to gain and hold an information advantage over the other. This is achieved by exerting a specific information/psychological and information/technical influence on a nation's decision-making system, on the nation's populous, and on its information resource structures, as well as by defeating the enemy's control system and his information resource structures with the help of additional means, such as nuclear assets, weapons and electronic assets.[295]

In 1999 Vitaliy V. Panov, first vice president of the Russian Academy of Missile and Artillery Sciences, stated that divisions between military operations and economic or political forms of warfare were very distinct. However, he found it more and more difficult to separate strictly military aspects from the entire set of techniques (to include economic and political) that guide the information area. He felt it imperative to interpret the essence and forms of IW. He stated that its content "includes both software-hardware as well as information-psychological components...in contrast to conventional warfare, information warfare has not only overt, but also covert threats and purposeful hostile actions."[296]

Russia's military doctrine of 22 April 2000 noted that hostile information-technical and information-psychological information operations were the main external threats to Russia. Thus, these dual themes appear to be

---

[295] Discussion with a Russian officer in Moscow, 1995.
[296] Vitalii Valerianovich Panov, "New Technologies and Their Influence on the Development of the Means of Warfare," Vooruzhenie, Politika, Konversiia [Equipment, Politics, Conversion], No. 1 (January 1999), pp. 22-26 as translated and downloaded from the FBIS web page, 6 July 1999.

the main prism through which Russia views the topic of information war and information threats.

Russian military officers as well as civilian intellectuals note that in order to have an information war, one needs information weapons. Dr. Vitaliy Tsygichko of the Institute of Systems Analysis has provided the best description of the information weapon from a Russian perspective. He wrote that information weapons could be classified by a number of attributes. These include single and multimission/universal purpose; short- and long-range operation; individual, group, and mass destruction capabilities; various types of carriers; and destruction effect. He and some Russian colleagues, in the pamphlet Information Weapons—New Challenges to International Security,[297] further classified information weapons as belonging to one of six forms:

1. Means for the precision location of equipment that emits rays in the electromagnetic spectrum and for the destruction of that equipment by conventional fire
2. Means for affecting components of electronic equipment
3. Means for affecting the programming resource control modules
4. Means for affecting the information transfer process
5. Means for propaganda and disinformation
6. Means for using psychotronic weapons.

The pamphlet then discussed the significance and potential types of these weapons.

The first form, the means for precision location, includes the effective detection of individual elements of C2 information systems, to include identification, guidance, and physical destruction (by firing for effect). The second form, the means for affecting electronic equipment components, includes the temporary or irreversible disabling of individual elements of electronic systems. Weapon types include means of forcible electronic suppression (such as generators of super-high frequencies) and means to disable equipment (such as the head resonance of hard disks), burn out monitors, erase RAM, and affect reliable power sources.

The third form, the means for affecting programming resource control modules, disables or alerts the operating algorithm of control systems of

[297] V.N. Tsigichko, D.S. Votrin, A.V. Krutskikh, G.L. Smolyan, and D.S. Chereshkin, Information Weapons—New Challenge to Information Security, Moscow 2000, pp. 20-21. The description in the next seven paragraphs is taken from this pamphlet.

software by using special programming means. These weapon types include the means for defeating information security systems; penetrating the enemy's information systems; disabling all of, or a specific portion of, an information system's software, possibly at a very specific point in time or when a specific event occurs in the system; making a covert, partial change in an operational algorithm of a piece of software; collecting data that is circulating in the enemy's information system; delivering and inserting certain algorithms into a specific place in an information system; and affecting the security systems of facilities (with viruses, worms, etc.).

The fourth form, means for affecting the information transfer process, can stop or disorganize the functioning of subsystems for the exchange of information by affecting the signal-dissemination environment and operating algorithms. Types of weapons belonging to this class include electronic equipment, especially ground and air stations (helicopters, unmanned airborne vehicles, etc.) that interfere with radio communications; disposable, air-droppable interference transmitters; means that affect the protocols of data transmission by communication systems and the data transmission itself; means that affect algorithms used for addressing and routing; means for intercepting and disrupting information as it passes through the technical channels of its transmission; and means for causing system overload by making false requests of a communications system.

The fifth form, means for propaganda and disinformation, can change the information component of C2 systems; create a virtual picture of the situation that differs from reality; change the system of human values; and damage the moral-psychological life of the enemy population. Types of this weapon include means for causing disinformation in secure systems and means for modifying navigation systems, information and meteorological-monitoring systems, precision-time systems, and so on.

Finally, for the sixth form, psychotronic weapons, Tsygichko and his colleagues describe weapons that affect a person's psychology and subconscious in order to reduce will, suppress and or temporarily disable the person, or zombify the person. These weapon types include:

- Psycho-pharmacological substances
- Psycho-dyspeptics
- Tranquilizers, anti-depressants, hallucinogens, and narcotics
- Specially structured medicines
- Special-beam generators that affect the human psyche
- Special video graphic and television information (25th frame effect, elevating blood pressure, inducing epileptic seizures, etc.)

169

- Means for creating virtual reality that suppresses the will and induces fear (projecting an image of "God" onto clouds, etc.)
- Technologies of zombification and psycholinguistic programming.[298]

Information technologies can also be utilized as information weapons, the pamphlet notes. Those information technologies that are integral components of high-precision ammunition are used to guide missiles via position finding and reconnaissance as well as by visual, electronic, and other factors. These functional subsystems can also be treated as information weapons in that they gather, process, and disseminate information. The pamphlet defines information war as "actions taken for securing information superiority by damaging information, information-based processes, and information systems of the enemy along with protecting one's own information, information-based processes, and information systems." This definition is very much like the US definition and contradicts many other purely Russian definitions. It is unknown why Tsygichko and his associates chose this definition.

Tsygichko and his colleagues, of course, are not the only Russian scientists who write profusely about information weapons. One of the first (and still most outstanding) Russian articles to define and discuss the information weapon was published in 1996 by Major S. V. Markov in the journal Bezapasnost' [Security]. Many of his thoughts and definitions are still quoted word-for-word by leading specialists today. Markov defined an information weapon as

> A specially selected piece of information capable of causing changes in the information processes of information systems (physical, biological, social, etc.) according to the intent of the entity using the weapon.[299]

This understanding of the information weapon and its impact on the information-psychological and information-technical activity of Russia produces a much different national will and language of dialogue than the West is accustomed. Markov is convinced that it is imperative to develop international and state control over the creation and use of information weapons.[300]

---

[298] Ibid., pp. 20-21.

[299] S. V. Markov, "O nekotoryk podkhodakh k opredeleniyu sushchnosti informatsionnogo oruzhiya" ["Several Approaches to the Determination of the Essence of the Information Weapon"], Bezopasnost [Security], No. 1-2, 1996, p. 53.

[300] Ibid.

The information weapon can be used in the following ways according to Markov:

- To destroy, distort, or steal data files.
- To mine or obtain the desired information from these files after penetrating defense systems/firewalls.
- To limit or prevent access to them by authorized users.
- To introduce disorganization or disorder into the operation of technical equipment.
- And to completely disable telecommunications networks and computer systems and all the advanced technology that supports the life of society and the operation of the state.[301]

The Use of the Information-Technical IW Aspect in Chechnya
The Russian armed forces utilized several types of information-technical devices during the fight for Chechnya. Three stand out. They are the use of remotely piloted vehicles (RPVs), the electronic warfare battle between the two sides, and the first use of the reconnaissance-strike system (not the reconnaissance-strike complex) to direct precision-guided weapons.

Remotely Piloted Vehicles
An August 1996 article in the journal Armeyskiy Sbornik [Army Journal] discussed the US, Israeli, and British use of remotely piloted vehicles (RPVs) in Vietnam and Grenada, Lebanon, and Argentina, respectively. It was noted that RPVs provided detailed information about the situation in a zone where a strike was planned. In the same journal in December 1996, Colonels Grigoriy Budzinskiy and Vladimir Platonov wrote that reconnaissance drones, equipped with television cameras, were very successful in carrying out real-time reconnaissance missions in Chechnya. The colonels advised including a squadron of reconnaissance drones in future combined-arms army reconnaissance forces.[302]

At the very start of the most recent Russian-Chechen conflict, journalist Nikolay Novichkov wrote that the Stroy-P remotely piloted reconnaissance system was deployed in one of the areas adjacent to Chechnya at the end of September 1999, and it had been added to the list of military equipment shipped to the combat operations area. Used in Chechnya in 1995 as well, the system

---

[301] Ibid., p. 56.
[302] Grigoriy Budzinskiy and Vladimir Platonov, "Don't Look Down on Reconnaissance, Otherwise You Will Lose any Battle before it Begins," Armeyskiy Sbornik [Army Journal], December 1996, p. 39.

consists of two ground mobile remote command and control facilities with launchers mounted on them, and ten Pchela-1T remotely piloted rescue aircraft, each with TV equipment and designed for ten flights. The RPV flies at speeds of 110-130 kilometers per hour, has an operating altitude of 100-3,000 meters, and has a flight duration of two hours with a combat operating radius of 50-60 kilometers. The Pchela has no night vision capability which is required if round-the-clock artillery strikes are to be used. Three Stroy-P systems were in the inventory in 1999, with a fourth planned for 2000, and there were forty Pchela-1T RPVs by 2001, but no current figures are available. If additional money is allocated, flight-technical specifications could be increased by an order of magnitude (flight time will increase from two to four and a half hours).[303] Such support is vital since Russia has admitted on more than one occasion that its space intelligence is insufficient, and that the Stroy-P can make up for this shortcoming in a land as small as Chechnya.

The missile and artillery forces also foresee a vital need for more RPVs. Missile and Artillery Chief Colonel General M. I. Karatuyev, in a lessons-learned article in 2000, noted that the fighting in Chechnya demonstrated the need for remotely piloted reconnaissance vehicles with optical and infrared bands to see enemy territory in day or night, to carry out laser illumination of individual targets for laser-guided precision shells, and to support artillery fire corrections. The fighting also demonstrated the need for a reconnaissance complex allowing reconnaissance of the local area conducted from a portable, elevated platform in the optical and IR bands, and also in radar mode.[304]

Electronic Warfare
In the opinion of journalist Andrei Soldatov, writing just before Russian troops surrounded Grozny in November 1999, Russia's chances of winning the second Russian-Chechen war ultimately depended on the outcome of the radio electronic struggle. Soldatov wrote that Chechnya, however, was at a real disadvantage since its radar stations, cellular and trunk-line communications, and relay points were bombed in the first weeks of the war. But other systems such as satellite telephones and field commanders' radios

---

[303] Nikolay Nikolayevich Novichkov, "The Stroy-P System is Once Again in Chechnya: The Russian Army is Overcoming the Lag in the Use of Remotely Piloted Aircraft," Nezavisimoye Voyennoye Obozreniye [Independent Military Review], 5 November 1999, p. 2 as translated and downloaded from the FBIS website on 23 November 1999.
[304] Yu. D. Bukreyev, M. I. Karatuyev, and L. S. Zolotov, "The Counter-terrorist Operation in the Northern Caucasus: the Main Lessons and Conclusions," Voyennaya Mysl [Military Thought] No. 3, May-June 2000, pp. 5-21 as translated and downloaded from the FBIS website on 16 June 2000.

were available to the Chechen commanders, and this equipment appeared to be sufficient. The low number of Russian units capable of conducting such warfare also offset this disadvantage.

Colonel Vasiliy Gumeniy, Chief of the Russian North Caucasus Military District's radio-electronic warfare service, supported this view that, in spite of all the disadvantages, the Chechens had developed an extensive reconnaissance communications system by 1999. In April 2000, he and coauthor Colonel Vladimir Matyash noted that the Chechens had acquired the following reconnaissance communications equipment by the start of the war: a network of NMT-450 standard cellular communications (connected to a cellular communications system in Ingushetia, allowing field commanders to have 20-60 "correspondents"[305] in their radio network, and 60-80 correspondents in the reconnaissance information network of short-wave range); a trunk-line communication system using Motorola and Kenwood products, among others; radio relay communication lines; stationary and mobile tele-broadcast stations; short-wave communications from international organizations like the Red Cross; radio networks based on amateur short-wave radio transmission resources; cable communication lines; and portable and mobile radio communications equipment (operating in the ultra short-wave spectrum of 136-74, 300-50, and 390-470 megahertz) and radio telephones operating in the 860-960 megahertz range. Satellite communications in Chechnya were conducted via INMARSAT and IRIDIUM systems, offering access to both intercity and international communication nets and the Internet.[306] Further, they noted that Chechen reconnaissance was conducted with optical-electronic, acoustic, radio-technical, and radar means. Chechen "front" commanders had mobile TV transmitters that could transmit 20-30 kilometers. These broadcasts were sometimes used to show Russian atrocities against Chechen civilians or to engage in visual deception. Authors Gumenniy and Matyash concluded that the Chechens had professionally prepared for information war with their reconnaissance communications assets.[307]

But new equipment also was on hand for the Russians this time. According to the Main Intelligence Directorate (GRU), the Russian army already was equipped with new Akveduk-type communications assets to assure confidentiality in tactical communications. New Vega radio-technical reconnaissance systems were in radio-electronic units as well. Russian concerns

---

[305] Correspondents were radio amateurs acting in the interest of the Chechens.

[306] Vasiliy Gumenniy, Vladimir Matyash, "War in the Airwaves," Krasnaya Zvezda [Red Star], 5 April 2000, as translated and downloaded from the FBIS website on 4 April 2000.

[307] Ibid.

were that the Chechens would obtain equipment from Arabic countries to test these systems, in some cases from Western governments.[308]

In addition to the armed forces electronic warfare (EW) units, two other Russian groups, the GRU of the armed forces and FAPSI (Federal Agency of Government Communications and Information), conducted radio espionage. The Tselina-2 is the most widely used radio electronic reconnaissance satellite in Russia, and the Kosmos model satellites are also used for the same purpose.[309] Russian intercept operators reported finding 49 enemy radio transmitters in the battle zone around Grozny in January of 2000. In order to "take out" a transmitter, radio interceptors first ascertained the location of a target. A reconnaissance group then went out to discover the precise location of the enemy and to ensure that the "intercept" is real and not set up to ensure unacceptable collateral damage to the civilian population. Once the target was verified, the information was passed to the fire control command post, and a strike was launched.[310]

The Russian command created groupings of radio-electronic combat (REB) forces designed to work at the tactical control level. During the first Chechen war, REB forces experienced a narrow frequency range for their equipment and an insufficient level of automation. Additionally, REB units lacked equipment for radio-electronic suppression of trunk-line, cellular, and satellite communications systems.

In the second Chechen war, REB forces conducted tests of the radio network and developed an understanding of the radio-electronic situation confronting them. They determined the coordinates of communications centers, control points, and Chechen concentrations of forces and firing means. The Russian commanders called these REB groupings the eyes and ears of the forces. Their system's ability to supply real-time enemy emission sources that were used for target reconnaissance and target data served, in essence for the first time, as prototypes of reconnaissance-strike systems on the tactical and operational levels. This was especially true for the "Arbalet-M" portable radio direction-finding and radio suppression systems:

---

[308] Andrey Soldatov, "Probing Action. Chechnya has become an Electronic Battleground between Russian and Foreign Special Services," Segodnya [Today], 1 November 1999, p. 2 as translated and downloaded from the FBIS website on 2 November 1999.

[309] Ibid.

[310] "The Eyes and Ears of the War," section of the "Telespetsnaz: Duty Unit" TV program, 27 January 2000 as translated and downloaded from the FBIS website on 28 January 2000.

The course of the counter-terrorist operation shows us convincingly that the effectiveness of the disorganization of the enemy's control system in many ways determines the results of interfering with his radio electronic equipment and information database. He who controls information, and he who is able to reliably destroy the communications and control systems of the enemy and to provide for the uninterrupted operation of his own automated troop command and control system (ASUV) will be the victor in modern wars.[311]

The Russian journal Voyennaya Mysl [Military Thought] also discussed deficiencies in the EW force at the start of the second Chechen-Russian war. One officer noted that Chechen capabilities were underestimated, enabling the Chechens to continue the operation of their information-reconnaissance networks. Russian soldiers did not do a good job of concealing methods used to command and control their troops (as they had failed to do in the first conflict), and consequently the Chechens were able to ascertain where Russian troops would regroup and the locations of their positions, both firing and rear sites.[312]

Lieutenant-General Valeriy Volodin, Chief of the Electronic Warfare Directorate of the Russian Federation Armed Forces General Staff, highlighted the growing importance of electronic warfare still further by celebrating the first ever Electronic Warfare Specialist Day on 15 April 2000. He noted on this occasion that the purpose of the directorate is to use electromagnetic emissions to compromise useful information and introduce false information; and to protect Russian radio-electronic systems and reduce the likelihood of destruction by precision weapons from missile systems, aircraft, and ships. Future combat systems will be based on reconnaissance equipment, precision direction and fire destruction, and joint automated control systems. Volodin added that the development of EW equipment is efficient and of minimal cost. According to his calculations, expenses to maintain EW equipment are only 5-8 percent of other types of arms. More importantly, EW resources increase combat capabilities of ground troops by one and a half times, and decreases the loss of aviation by four to six times, and of ships by two to three times.[313]

---

[311] Ibid.

[312] Yu. D. Bukreyev, M. I. Karatuyev, and L. S. Zolotov.

[313] Oleg Falchev interview with Valeriy Volodin, "The Battlefield—The Airwaves," Krasnaya Zvezda [Red Star], 15 April 2000, as translated and downloaded from the FBIS website on 18 April 2000.

A year later Volodin noted that EW was growing from a support to a new, independent, specific form of military operation. This indicates that the communications struggle in the war in Chechnya had demonstrated to the Russian military the increased importance of the service. Volodin noted that the struggle for superiority of control mechanisms includes not only electronic suppression of an enemy's communications means but also their electronic destruction. Further, he noted that success in combat depends on the "stability of the state and military command and control system and other information systems against the information-psychological, software and electronic influence of an enemy." In Chechnya, Volodin pointed to Russian successes in helicopter and portable electronic reconnaissance and suppression systems, specialized automated jamming systems, and automated equipment systems which permitted operational-tactical computations with the use of modern information technologies, including electronic terrain maps.[314]

These maps made a significant difference by providing Russian forces with an accurate display of the land before them. During the first Chechen campaign, maps in the troops' hands were made years before in Soviet days. Commanders were extremely critical of the 1980 maps they received before the first Grozny battle, which resulted in many leaders getting lost. Entire "microrayons" were absent from some maps. Those used by the troops in 1999, according to General G. Troshev, commander of Russian troops during the second Chechen campaign, were not any better at the start of the operation.

As a result, the Topographic Service rushed into publication both paper and electronic maps. To the Russians, the system of topogeodetic support is now an element of the side's information conflict or confrontation. Now

> ...electronic maps were being used successfully for accomplishing tactical missions, assessing terrain properties, determining the disposition of friendly battle formations, determining target coordinates, selecting assault landing sectors and so on. This required not only electronic topographic maps, but also electronic photomaps and digital ortho-photomaps that were highly detailed and corresponded to the real condition of the terrain to the maximum extent.[315]

---

[314] Oleg Falichev interview with Valeriy Volodin, "Electronic Warfare Chief on State, Prospects of EW Service," Krasnaya Zvezda [Red Star], 14 April 2001 as translated and downloaded from the FBIS website on 13 April 2001.
[315] Valeriy Yelyushkin, Viktor Sedov, and Yevgeniy Dolgov, "Electronic Maps—Capabilities and Prospects: Troop Use of Information Technologies Will Depend on the Status of their Topogeodetic Support," Nezavisimoye Voyennoye Obozreniye

A Russian TV report on 15 December 1999 noted that the General Staff is using electronic map technology. The technology allows one to find minute details in both Grozny and in Chechnya's mountains. The electronic maps can also create simulations of military actions and offer flight paths for helicopters.[316]

In April of 2002, EW was again highlighted, this time by Major General Andrey Osin. Osin, who also works in the EW Directorate, stated that systems and complexes make it possible to suppress radio, radio relay, satellite communication lines, and radar and radio navigation systems; to conduct reconnaissance; to control jamming stations; and to protect troops and installations from strikes and reconnaissance.[317] These items reflect the essence of the Russian effort in Chechnya in locating and destroying the Chechen resistance.

The Reconnaissance-Strike System
Without a doubt, combat operations in Chechnya have underscored the need for Russia to devote more attention to the development of integrated space and precision-guided systems, and space-based intelligence-gathering systems. According to one report, Russia only has one electronic intelligence (ELINT) and one naval intelligence-gathering satellite in space and not a single optical electronic or photo reconnaissance asset. With three times fewer satellites in orbit than required, Russia is experiencing gaps of up to six hours a day in monitoring areas posing missile threats to Russia. Troops in Chechnya are forced to use a system similar to the US global positioning system (GPS), since Russia's Global Navigation Satellite System (GLONASS) is on its last legs with only nine of twenty-four satellites operational.[318]

Informed sources report that the GRU's Space Reconnaissance Directorate has put several Tselina-2 satellites over Chechnya.[319] These satellites, and others with similar functions, were used in the first Chechen war as well. A satellite signal intercept was used by Russian forces to direct a precision-guided weapon to kill former Chechen President Djokar Dudayev in

[Independent Military Review], 26 January 2002, as translated and downloaded from the FBIS website on 25 January 2002.
[316] Russian "Vesti" TV newscast, 1000 GMT, 15 December 1999 as translated and downloaded from the FBIS website on 15 December 1999.
[317] Andrey Osin, "War of the Airwaves," Krasnaya Zvezda [Red Star], 12 April 2002, as translated and downloaded from the FBIS website on 11 April 2002.
[318] "We No Longer Make Rockets," Kommersant [Business], 28 January 2000, page 2, as translated and downloaded from the FBIS website on 28 January 2000.
[319] Soldatov, "Probing Action."

1996. Other satellite uses have been less successful. For example, Russia's Intelligence Service, when asked "with purported great satellites, why can't you find Shamil Basayev?" answered that the GRU's main reconnaissance satellite only crosses Chechnya for twenty minutes every twenty-four hours. Thus, it is impossible to find Basayev in such a short period of time. At such speeds, the representative noted, it is not possible to align the objective lens on a moving vehicle column.[320]

The Russian General Staff recognized the impact of new-generation weaponry on military art several years ago and began to work diligently to adapt to it. For example, a former chief of the Main Operations Directorate of the Russian General Staff, Colonel General Viktor Mikhaylovich Barynkin, wrote in 1996 that operational goals are now achievable just by the use of reconnaissance-fire operations (battles).[321] These changes have caused an evolution in Russian reconnaissance-strike and fire planning. In the past, this activity was called either the reconnaissance-strike complex (razvedyvatel'no-udarnnyy kompleks or RUK) or the reconnaissance-fire complex (razvedyvatel'no-ognevoy kompleks or ROK). Today, Russian theorists are discussing the reconnaissance-strike system (razvedyvatel'no-udarnaya sistema or RUS), the reconnaissance-fire system (razvedyvatel'no-ognevaya sistema or ROS), and the reconnaissance-fire operation (razvedyvatel'no-ognevaya operatsiya or ROO) as additions to the RUK and ROK concepts.[322]

One of the earliest definitions of both RUK and ROK was in a 1985 issue of the journal Voyennyy Vestnik [Military Herald]. Information in the article was attributed to foreign sources, a common Soviet practice to avoid revealing tactical-technical characteristics of their own systems:

> If the strike element destroys the target by fire (for example with conventional or rocket artillery), the complex is called a reconnaissance-fire complex (razvedyvatel'no-ognevoy kompleks or ROK), while if it does so by a missile strike (tactical or army aviation, tactical and operational-tactical missile launchers), it is called a reconnaissance-strike complex (razvedyvatel'no-udarnyy kompleks or

---

[320] Andrey Soldatov, "Spy Satellites," Versiya [Version], 27 February 2001, p. 7, as translated and downloaded from the FBIS website on 9 April 2001.

[321] Viktor Mikhaylovich Barynkin, "Effect of Precision Weapons on the Nature of Combat Operations and on the Evolution of Military Art," Vooruzheniye, Politika, Konversiya [Equipment, Politics, Conversion], 1996, No. 4 (11), pp. 17-21, as translated and downloaded from the FBIS web page on 2 May 1997.

[322] Some are the author's abbreviations. They were not used in the original Russian. The terms RUS and ROS were used by the Russians.

RUK). Therefore reconnaissance-fire complexes are more of a tactical command resource while reconnaissance-strike complexes are operational command resources.[323]

A strike as used by the Russian military refers to a massive, simultaneous attack that is like a hammer and carries strong psychological overtones due to its destructive nature. Fire, on the other hand, is more rhythmic and takes place over a period of time. Thus ROK appears as a conceptual stepchild to RUK, with the latter much more mature and massive in nature.

Two catalysts that catapulted the RUS ahead of the RUK were the performance of the coalition forces in Desert Storm, their use of C4ISR (Command, Control, Communications, Computers, Intelligence, Surveillance, and Reconnaissance) systems; and the Revolution in Military Affairs under discussion at the time. Russian analysts saw the revolution as transforming warfare from a struggle of forces and means into a contest between systems of systems. The term "military systemology," in wide use among Russian military systems analysts, was used to describe the super-large, dynamic, complex systems under consideration. The method of systemology, in fact, stands traditional analysis on its head, emphasizing complexity and the need for models based on dynamic, evolving, self-organizing systems, and emphasizes a shift from modeling combat as force-on-force to system versus system.[324] Asked to mathematically demonstrate the relation of processes that lead from "detection to kill" in near real-time, one Russian scientist offered the following: destruction capability = exposure of an object (via satellite or reconnaissance asset) x strike assets precision and speed of its components.[325]

Even a cursory look at Russian military writings underscores the importance placed on the acquisition of the location of the enemy, followed by fixing him through fire means. As one analyst noted:

> The increase in fire capabilities of the troops, the appearance of high-precision weapons, and the development of various types of guided missiles are objectively increasing the role of reconnaissance and command and control systems. In conditions when the likelihood of hitting targets with the first shot or salvo is approaching 1, reaction

---

[323] M. Belov and V. Shchukin, "Reconnaissance-Strike Complexes of the US Army," Voyennyy Vestnik [Military Herald], No. 1, January 1985, p. 86.
[324] Comments provided by Dr. Jacob Kipp, Foreign Military Studies Office, while reviewing this article.
[325] Discussion with Russian officer in Moscow, January 1999.

speed is becoming a paramount factor. The main targets of battlefield reconnaissance are enemy artillery and armored equipment.[326]

Acquiring and fixing the enemy in a manner compatible with this formula is a priority item, and it explains why Russia cannot employ the system in Chechnya to its total satisfaction and thus effectiveness. Satellite systems are outdated and are being replaced slowly.

Major General (retired) Vladimir Ivanovich Slipchenko, writing on future war in 1999, noted that any state unprepared to wage "new-generation war" will be forced to absorb the impact of an integrated precision-weapon strike and electronic-warfare operation.[327] The precision strike represents a combination of reconnaissance and command and control weapons whose target kill effectiveness, according to Slipchenko, sometimes can surpass that of tactical nuclear weapons.[328] This system has found limited, though good, use in the fight in Chechnya.

The integration of satellites, command and control assets, and precision-guided weapons into reconnaissance-strike complexes became an area of added interest immediately after the end of the first Russian-Chechen conflict. In an article in Armyskiy Sbornik [Army Journal] in October 1996, Lieutenant General Yuriy Merkulov and Colonel Igor Golovanev discussed the value of destroying targets with precision non-nuclear means. The authors noted that new systems were similar to RUK in principles of organization for combat, but surpassed them in capabilities. These systems use a heterogeneous mix of weapons from strategic aircraft and precision weapons to tube artillery, and are called inter-branch reconnaissance-fire delivery systems (ROS). Merkulov and Golovanev noted that the creation of reconnaissance-fire delivery systems with space systems can drop the requirement for precision weapons fivefold. The depth of space reconnaissance is limited only by the range capability of offensive weapons. Intelligence updates should not exceed two hours for the operational echelon and twenty minutes for the tactical echelon with such systems in place.[329]

---

[326] Sergey Grigoryev, "Who Will Fire First? The Eyes, Ears, and Nervous System of the Ground Troops," Nezavisimaya Gazeta [Independent Review], 22 August 1996, No. 16 (20), p. 6.

[327] Vladimir Ivanovich Slipchenko, "Future War," found at Internet site http://users.mos.ru.boris/vb.htm, 1 January 2000, as translated and downloaded from the FBIS website on 13 March 2000.

[328] Ibid.

[329] Igor Golovanev and Yuriy Merkulov, "Space Nerves of Reconnaissance-Fire Delivery Systems," Armeyskiy Sbornik [Army Journal], October 1996, pp. 12-13.

Naturally, Russia does have satellite assets in Chechnya. The 42nd Motorized Rifle Division, stationed in Chechnya in 2000 on a permanent basis, reportedly has a Ministry of Defense satellite communications station co-located with it. The network of portable stations can communicate with city networks of any city in the world. A protected modern computer network is used in the division's command and control system. The computers communicate with the GLONASS navigation system, and the computers are installed at mobile command and control points of all links.[330]

In August 2001, Colonel A. A. Petrov and Lkeutenant Colonel A. L. Safronov wrote in the journal Military Thought that satellite communications had improved command and control immeasurably. They noted that over fifty satellite communications stations attached to units and subunits were used effectively in Chechnya to organize communications. Yet even this number of sets did not completely satisfy troop needs, as they lacked light, mobile, and armor-protected stations. The satellites were also a problem due to their low traffic capacity.[331]

Ground Forces Commander and Deputy Defense Minister Nikolay Kormiltsev noted that in Chechnya up to 80% of the firing missions were accomplished by missile troops, artillery, and aviation in the immediate tactical depth of the enemy. Missile Troop Commander Lieutenant General Vladimir Nikolayevich Zaritskiy added that the direction of future arms development would be the creation of combined-arms reconnaissance-fire delivery systems based on the missile-artillery reconnaissance-fire delivery system.[332]

The Russian military has used precision-guided ammunition for artillery and mortars.[333] Ammunition was of the Krasnopol and Smelchak varieties. A complex of guidance systems is used to fire these munitions, with a laser target designator-range finder and synchronization instruments. These

---

[330] Vasiliy Fatigarov interview of Vladislav Gekov, "The Nervous System of a Division," Krasnaya Zvezda [Red Star], 2 June 2000, as translated and downloaded from the FBIS website on 2 June 2000.

[331] A. A. Petrov and S. L. Safronov, "Features of Organizing Communications in Conducting Combat Operations in the Mountains," Voyennaya Mysl [Military Thought], 15 August 2001, pp. 13-17, as translated and downloaded from the FBIS website on 29 October 2001.

[332] Vladimir Nikolayevich Zaritskiy, "The 'God of War' at the Crossroads," Armeyskiy Sbornik [Army Journal], 1 November 2001, pp. 3-7, as translated and downloaded from the FBIS website on 5 February 2002.

[333] Moscow Agentstvo Voyennykh Novostey [Military News Agency] WWW-Text, 1141 GMT, 15 November 2001, as translated and downloaded from the FBIS we site on 15 November 2001

munitions reduce the number of conventional projectiles and shells by a factor of ten.[334]

The use of precision-guided weapons is a key tactic used in the fight with the Chechens. According to the head of the Combined Arms Academy of Russia, Colonel General L. S. Zolotov, to counter a guerilla's trump card (that is, the use of surprise and direct confrontation), it is necessary to attack the guerilla with long-range or remotely controlled fires.[335] This thinking is similar to what the coalition forces used in Afghanistan to take out guerilla concentrations with "Hellfire" missiles mounted on "Predator" unmanned aerial vehicles.

Space troops experts noted that the GLONASS increases the efficiency of missile troops and artillery units by 40 percent. Munition consumption is cut four or five times and artillery munitions by 1.7 to three times. The air force and navy could also use GLONASS, and its use would reduce the inaccuracy of long-range cruise missiles to 10 or 15 meters. As a result, the Defense Ministry has requested for delivery some 9,000-10,000 navigation units before 2005.[336]

Thus, RPVs, EW, and the reconnaissance-strike systems are three IW means to strike from afar and observe and listen in on the enemy 24 hours a day. While they are not perfect, the systems are providing more timely intelligence and accurate strikes on the Chechen positions.

The Use of Information-Psychological IW in Chechnya
There were three areas of interest related to the information-psychological aspect of IW in Chechnya. First was the manner in which Russian and Chechen officials fought one another verbally to win the media or "information war" for public opinion. As the Russians found out, in the Information Age, it is more difficult than ever to control the flow of information to a population. A second area of interest was the intense information-psychological atmosphere of the war, where deception and manipulation were used extensively and the impact on the soldier's moral-psychological condition was great. Finally, there was widespread use of the Internet for the first time as an agent of influence, manipulation, and organization for combat in a local war.

---

[334] Orlov Aleksandr's interview of Vladimir Zaritskiy, "As Before, Artillery Remains the Main Weapon of the Battlefield," Strana.ru National Information Service, as translated and downloaded from the FBIS website on 19 November 2001.
[335] Yu. D. Bukreyev, M. I. Karatuyev, and L. S. Zolotov.
[336] Agentstvo Voyennykh Novostey, 1201 GMT, 7 March 2002, as translated and downloaded from the FBIS website on 7 March 2002.

Information-Psychological Activities and the Media

There were several important military lessons that the Russian government and military learned from their first experience in Chechnya during 1994-1996. Perhaps none was more important to long-term Russian success than the battle for public opinion. In the first war, for example, Russian journalists would fly into Dagestan's Makhachkala airport (Dagestan is the Russian republic next to Chechnya) and get free taxi rides into Chechnya. The Chechens would pay for the taxi ride once the journalist arrived at his or her destination, give interviews, and remunerate the journalists for articles. Federal forces, on the other hand, avoided journalists, a remnant from the Soviet days of avoiding the press. The military media did less than 5% of the reporting in January 1995 of the news coming from Chechnya. Army journals came out some three months into the fighting, and policy for the mass media came out some six months later. Nor was there a "musical score" that the military followed. As a result, Russia's citizens only saw what was important from the Chechen point of view on the evening news. This situation went on for weeks with each journalist printing his or her own truth.[337]

The Russian military learned that information support to an operation can play a key role in the operation's success or failure, can protect government interests, and can achieve military-political objectives. Major General V. A. Zolotarev noted in 2000 that "the Chechen campaign of 1994-1996 by military definition was three-quarters won by the Russian Army by August 1996, but by that time it had lost 100% in infospace."[338] Military information specialists needed support from other professionals such as the mass media and propaganda experts. But this support was not available. The Chechens, on the other hand, had created a Ministry of Information by February 1995, and they maintained the use of several mobile television complexes to report to the Chechen people from the mountains after being kicked out of Grozny.

The Chechen newspaper Ichkeriya was the main backer of the concept of separatism and continued resistance to Russia's armed forces. Local publications such as Respublika and Vozrozheniye did their part as well.

---

[337] Gennadiy Alekhin and Timofey Borisov, "Distinctive Feathers of National Hunt for 'Canards.' We No Longer Lose Media Wars, but We Have Not Learned to Win Them Thus Far," Moscow Rossiskaya Gazeta [Russian Newspaper], 26 June 2001, taken from HTML version of Source, as translated and downloaded from the FBIS website on 27 June 2001.

[338] V. A. Zolotarev, editor-in-chief, Russia (USSR) in Local Wars and Military Conflicts in the Second Half of the 20th Century, Kuchkovo Polye Publishing, Moscow, 2000, p. 317.

Zolotarev considered the greatest effect of this effort to be the 30,000-40,000 volunteers that supported the initial small group of Chechens opposing the Russian intervention. Two radio stations in support of the Chechen cause were opened abroad—Radio Free Caucasus in Latvia and a Chechen information center opened in Krakow, Poland. Chechen President Dudayev made requests to the United Nations through other countries, and he even requested NATO assistance. Zolotarev concluded that the Chechen use of information support demonstrated a corresponding influence on the course of the conflict and was a contributor to creating contradictions leading to the end of combat operations.[339]

In November 1999, while reporting on the Second Chechen-Russian War, Andrey Soldatov noted that

> Whereas during the first Chechen campaign the majority of television reports and newspaper articles were couched in terms of sympathy with the rebel republic, this time the situation is the absolute opposite. Ruthless censorship is not letting Wahhabist propaganda get through...battle reports from Basayev, Khattab, and their minions, interviews with guerrillas—items given high-profile coverage on all channels during the last war—are now banned.[340]

Russian authorities initially shut off independent reporting during the second war in Chechnya, and did everything possible to insure that official TV and newspaper reporters carefully reported their facts from the battlefield. The Chechens had unwittingly aided the Russian's information campaign. In September 1999, Russia obtained a film of a Chechen fighter cutting the head off a Russian prisoner. This film was shown unedited on Russian TV, which did two things: first it warned Chechnya not to employ military-propaganda capabilities against Russia, and second the film caused many of the TV stations that reported Chechen news during the first campaign to take a Russian slant this time around.[341] That is, the Chechen atrocities and their incursion into Dagestan in August 1999 exhausted any sympathy the Russian populace had toward the Chechens. It was easier for them and the journalists to swallow only an official version of events. At the same time, Russian memories were still fresh of NATO's bombing of Kosovo. This translated into permission to apply force in Chechnya, since Russia faced problems with Chechens similar to Kosovo's problems with the Serbs, from a Russian perspective. There were increased Chechen activities such as a wave of kidnappings, raids on republics

---

[339] Ibid., p. 320.
[340] Soldatov.
[341] Zolotarev, p. 322.

bordering Chechnya, and the outbreak of additional criminal activities in Chechnya that supported, however tangentially, this line of thinking.

Russian demographic expert Emil Pain, in a January 2000 speech, described the changed atmosphere in detail. He noted that the press was met with bayonets when they tried to go into Chechnya with the Russian troops in 1994, but in the second war there was only the official, Kremlin version of events coming from the press. The army was "working" in Chechnya, and the assault on Grozny was a "special operation" and "cleansing." There was also a significant increase, as compared with the first war, in the amount of censorship, and journalists were restricted in their access to events. In December 1999, Resolution No. 1538 of the Russian president created the Russian Information Center (RIT). The Center filtered information from the theater of military operations and selected information from foreign publications to be disseminated in Russia.[342]

Pain also noted how subtle changes in the goals of the military campaign continued to develop, which helped guarantee society's support. The first goal was to repulse Chechen aggression; then the goal was to establish a sanitary cordon to protect Russian regions from Chechen raids; and by November 1999 the goal had become the complete annihilation of the "terrorists." Putin changed that goal once more on 1 January 2000 when he noted that the operation was designed to "protect the integrity of Russia."[343]

Finally, Pain noted that Russia's strategy was to "reprogram the mass consciousness" by introducing a number of information-propaganda clichés into it. These included the development of "models" that included the terrorist and aggressor model; the "new war" model (this time the army is ready); and the "Free Chechen" model (convincing Russian society that Chechens are simply waiting for the Russian armed forces to liberate them). Pain concluded by stating that Russia, unfortunately, did not learn the real lesson of the first war, that controlling territory does not signify victory in a partisan war. Victory can only happen when one gains the trust of the population, not territory.[344]

In July 2001, an NTV reporter from Russia reported on the new travel restrictions affecting journalists attempting to work in Chechnya. In order to travel in Chechnya outside the Khankala airport next to Grozny, one had to

---

[342] Emil Pain, "The Information Component in the Second Chechen War," paper presented at the US/Russia Information Warfare Seminar, Washington, D.C., 26 January 2000.
[343] Ibid.
[344] Ibid.

obtain a permission slip from the staff of the Interior Ministry and be accompanied by a member of the military press center. There are three press centers in Khankala: the press center of the Russian joint task force, the military; the press center of the Interior Ministry; and the press center of the Internal Troops. And between them are only three cars to take people places. The Chief of the General Staff, Anatoliy Kvashnin, offered the rational for this treatment. He told the journalists that they were not doing a very good job and therefore it was decided to set up two military media outlets. Kvashnin added, "we will have a military television studio broadcasting here. You are working for the sake of war and we are working for the sake of peace. This is what it appears to be."[345]

As time progressed, however, and as the Chechens were able to bypass the Russian-imposed information blockade via the Internet and via access to cellular phone hook-ups with foreign correspondents, Russia's information advantage began to slip away. As the conflict drags on it is becoming more difficult for President Putin's government to maintain public support both from Russians and from pro-Moscow Chechens living inside Chechnya. This is particularly true with regard to casualties, as the Organization for Security and Cooperation in Europe (OSCE) and other international organizations investigate claims from both sides. Pain noted that it was inevitable that:

> The current support of Russian societal opinion for the second Chechen War will not be very strong, and in the case of many people, will bring about an investigation of the domination of myths and illusions in Russian infospace created to manipulate the mass consciousness of the people.[346]

Initially, however, Russia's control of and access to information was very successful, making the armed forces appear much more effective and capable than they were. This kept public opinion strongly behind the effort to subdue the "terrorists." When this control began to wane after two years of fighting, the Russian Duma, in December of 2001, changed the law on mass media and prohibited Russian media from publishing interviews with Chechen separatists. In addition, part of the blame for the gradual loss of public opinion can be placed on Russian tradition. The Russian government demonstrated little accountability to its people in both Afghanistan and WW II over casualty numbers. In both Chechen conflicts, it took public pressure applied by the Soldier's Mothers Committee finally to force the government to account for its

---

[345] Natalya Zabuzova, "Moscow NTV," 1000 GMT, 26 Jul 2001, as translated and downloaded from the FBIS website on 26 July 2001.
[346] Pain.

soldiers. This public pressure group demonstrated how, in the Information Age, contradictory information could rise and escape the clutches of state control. Therefore, while it might be possible to win the IW struggle by controlling public opinion in the early going, it was demonstrated that the press or public pressure can nullify this control later on or control can be affected negatively by outside events.

President Putin alluded to this in March of 2002. He warned his staff that they were beginning to lose the information war in Chechnya and must correct this situation. He was referring to the effect of a multitude of negative media events that had taken place in March. Among them were: the public showing of a film by Boris Berezovsky that implied Russia's security forces might have played a role in the bombing of Moscow apartment buildings that began the Chechen war; statements by Chechen special representative Akmed Zakayev in the Hague where he stated that Russia's leaders, like Milosevic, should stand trial for their "crimes" in Chechnya; the appearance of Chechen Foreign Minister Ilias Akmadov before the United Nations, where he called for a tribunal on Russian actions in Chechnya; and the initiation of Radio Liberty reporting into Chechnya in Chechen (which actually took place on 3 April, but was heatedly discussed in March). In response, Russian Minister of Internal Affairs Boris Gryslov announced in mid-April that a "counter-propaganda" agency would broadcast to Chechnya to counteract Radio Liberty.

Information-Psychological Activities and the Impact on the Soldier
Psychological operations are a key element of information-psychological operations. Information-psychological measures are "those that change the conduct and emotional state of service members and the civil population of the opposing side, neutral and friendly countries to a desired direction during the determination of military-political questions."[347] One of the key lessons of the war in Chechnya is that the psychological climate of small-scale operations is equally as complicated and stressful as large-scale operations such as Desert Storm. Correspondingly, there will be an important role for psychiatrists/psychologists to play at or near the front. It was clear from the fighting in the first Russian-Chechen conflict that the moral-psychological stability of a soldier could be easily upset and then manipulated by the side with the best information support devices.

War always invokes fear in man. But the psychological climate for Russian forces in Chechnya was exacerbated by specific conditions. For example, the toughest fighting during both interventions, the combat in and around Grozny, took place under horrible weather conditions. Additionally,

---

[347] Zolotarev, p. 429.

this was a civil war in which Russian forces were asked to perform police functions among their own population who resented their presence. The situation could not have been worse for combat-stress-related injuries and for manipulation.

The Chechen fighters had been a part of the Soviet armed forces. Therefore most of them spoke Russian fluently and had an excellent knowledge of Russian tactics and military culture (staffing procedures, logistics, etc.). Acts of subversion and terrorism also kept Russian forces on their guard and in a high state of readiness and anxiety. This increased stress, making Russian forces tentative in their planning since Chechen forces appeared able to predict their every move. Rumors easily became facts. In addition, the Russian force was not fighting for the survival of their ethnic identity, as were the Chechens.

This environment persuaded the Russian force to look at everyone as their potential enemy. Was it the old man (need to check his arms for powder burns) or the young child (look under his coat for a grenade) or the nongovernmental organization (NGO) worker (is he a Chechen posing as a Red Cross worker simply to get inside Russian defenses)? Or was it the good-looking female, or the Russian officer (who was really a Ukrainian dressed in a Russian officer's uniform)? Such continuous uncertainty allowed the Chechens to exert intense psychological pressure on the Russian force. This point was always kept in view by the Chechens, and they manipulated it to their benefit whenever possible. Also, much of the fighting in Chechnya was hand-to-hand or at close range, and mutilations or torture were commonplace practices against those captured. This further increased stress and battle fatigue. The Chechens were easily able to provoke, intimidate, persuade, and deceive Russian soldiers on many occasions.

Not surprisingly, the first Russian-Chechen conflict caused several moral-psychological problems for the Russian armed forces. The main problem was the impact of the mass media on a soldier, and the lack of material support during the initial winter months of the operation (when a quick victory was sought). The focus for moral-psychological support to the troops, according to Zolotarev, should be educating service members on their patriotic duty, formation of hatred for the enemy, the development of both moral character and fighting qualities in the soldier, the timely detection of psychological injuries in their subordinates, and ideological and moral-psychological protection from enemy propaganda. This was not accomplished in the fight for Chechnya. It was also noted that informing personnel about the situation, together with propaganda to improve the fighter in battle (dissemination of combat experiences, etc.) and preventing the dissemination of facts that damaged civil-military relations, was not conducted.

In the second conflict, from October 1999 to the present, the Russian armed forces did much better in preparing the moral-psychological condition of soldiers. The Main Directorate for Educational Work and corresponding structures in the North Caucasus Military District published a newsletter on a periodic basis. It was clear that the command wanted to prevent Chechens from developing an information and psychological influence on soldiers, especially through Russian and foreign mass media outlets, as happened the first time.[348]

The military publication Morskoi Sbornik [Navy Journal] published a long article on the moral-psychological conditioning of soldiers in Chechnya, and Voennaya Mysl [Military Thought] did the same. The latter article highlighted the activities of a naval infantry battalion fighting in Chechnya.[349] The article noted both group and individual tasks. For the former, "indoctrination" personnel offered a rundown on the propaganda machine of the Chechens and how their psychological operations impacted on the consciousness and psyche of servicemen. Instruction was provided on how to act during contacts with the population, and how to use weapons in areas where combatants were present (training which didn't seem to do much good in light of the need to issue a special order to stop "cleansing" operations amongst civilians). Servicemen were also taught the importance of interacting with representatives of the local population and with religious figures. Finally, servicemen were taught not to allow civilians to feed them false information and win them over psychologically.[350]

On an individual basis, much morale and psychological support (MPS) training was available. The main aim of such training was to teach how to achieve moral and psychological superiority over the enemy; how to maintain discipline during combat; and how to inculcate feelings of self-confidence and certainty of mission. The main forms of MPS were: twice-daily 15-minute combat briefings; a weekly political hour; weekly combat news sheets about soldiers who displayed gallantry; daily listening to radio news; agitator's conversations with personnel; and regular delivery of newspapers. MPS tasks included psychological preparation of servicemen for close support of combat operations and psychological aid to servicemen when it was needed. Psychological preparation included practice in specific combat situations and

---

[348] Aleksandr Dyankonov, "From the Experience of Hot Spots. Honoring the Naval Infantrymen," Armeyskiy Sbornik [Army Journal], 1 June 2001, pp. 32-35.
[349] D'yakonov, A. G., "The Moral-Psychological Support Experience of the Counter-Terrorist Operation," Voennaya Mysl [Military Thought], No. 3 (May-June) 2001, pp. 41-48.
[350] Ibid.

the teaching of methods to promote psychological self-regulation and emotional mobilization in times of stress. Psychological aid was focused at the combat crew and vehicle crew level. Mobile groups of psychologists with skills in psycho-diagnostics and corrections and rehabilitation work, and psychiatrists and psycho-neurologists did consultative and diagnostic work. Psycho-correction and rehabilitation programs were provided on an as-needed basis.[351]

The article asked for better information support for servicemen. This included the supply of portable radios and small television sets to the area of combat. In addition, it was recommended that the armed forces operate a closed electronic media system. This would help create an "information field" at the troop level that was under strict control.[352]

The Use of the Internet during the Chechen Conflict

The second Russian-Chechen conflict has witnessed a much greater use of the Internet than the first conflict. In fact, the Internet shares part of the blame for Russia's loss of state control described above. Websites enabled combatants to mobilize public opinion and outside support for their cause. Use of the Internet demonstrated its importance to the weaker side in a conflict as a means for reaching public opinion and international organizations.

Websites accomplished the following main tasks for the Chechens during the second conflict. First, the Chechens used websites to gather money. One of the amino.com sites, for example, showed where to send money to support the Chechen cause, including a bank account number in Sacramento, California. Thus, any American could easily support the Chechen cause monetarily if he or she chose to do so. Second, the web was used to unite the Chechen diaspora. By conducting a search for the term Chechnya, one would stumble across related web pages that were of Chechen origin and supported the Chechen point of view. This allowed Chechens worldwide to stay in touch with the conflict and to offer support (material, monetary, personal, etc.) if desired. Third, websites offered Chechens opportunities to show the world the results of successful combat actions against the Russian military through streaming video, such as Chechen ambushes of Russian convoys. It was hard for the Russian official media to refute what the video presented, especially if it showed a Russian defeat. On the other hand, this technique backfired on several occasions, in particular when Chechen sites showed the execution of Russian prisoners losing Chechens international support. Fourth, the Internet was used by the Chechens to rally Islamic faithful worldwide against the Israelis in their conflict with the Palestinians, serving to unite a religious sector of the world

---

[351] Ibid.
[352] Ibid.

population. Fifth, the web allowed the Chechens to show the world what types of atrocities the Russians had committed against the Chechen population. Whether the Russians committed the atrocities or not was, of course, unverifiable but that is another use of the Internet—to put out one's position on an issue and not have to justify it. Finally, the Internet offered products for sale such as CDs and other items showing the Chechen position.

The situation in Chechnya is also reflected on websites in the context of the joint Russian-US fight against terrorism. Students from the Russian city of Tomsk have tried to thwart the efforts of the Chechen website Kavkaz-Tsentr by writing to US government agencies, the media, and private companies warning them that Kavkaz-Tsentr was transmitting from their territory. The Chechens have moved their Internet provider from the US to Canada, then to Georgia, and then back to the US.[353]

The Internet sites of the Russian Federation generally are not dedicated solely to the war, but contain many articles about it. The Chechen websites were more dynamic than the Russian sites and more easily accessible in the West. The Chechen kavkaz.org and Russian infocenter.ru sites are particularly good, however filtered and one-sided they might be.

A sampling of Russian Internet sites includes antiterror.ru, infocentre.ru, and kavkaz.com. The kavkaz.com site is located in Dagestan. Nezavisimaya Gazeta [Independent Newspaper] has a website that includes a "Severniy Kavkaz: Khronika Konflikta" [The North Caucasus: Chronicle of the Conflict] section that is good for current events in the area. The Infocentre site is apparently operated by the Ministry for Press, Television, Radio Broadcasting, and Mass Communications of the Russian Federation. It contains a "Chronicle of the Day" section that explains in great detail (with photos) the day's events in Chechnya, and it is recommended as an excellent site for understanding the Russian perception of the war.

Another Russian site dedicated to the war is Chechnya.ru. According to the newspaper Kommersant [Business], the site was created on 14 December 2001 by the Moscow-backed Chechen government and the Kremlin-connected strana.ru website. Presidential aide Sergey Yastrzhembsky noted that the site would provide positive information on Chechnya to the Russian populace. Sponsors of the site include three websites—utro.ru (an Internet newspaper founded by RosBiznesKonsalting), gamma.ru (Gamma Internet Service Provider), and porta.ru (Webcom Company affiliated with the porta.ru e-

---

[353] RIA-Novosti, 0632 GMT 3 February 2002, as translated and downloaded from the FBIS website on 3 February.

commerce site). The site has eleven sections: The Latest News, Maps of the Republic, The War in Chechnya, The Genocide of the Population, Opinion, Community, Anti-Terrorism, Services, Our Neighbors, Our Colleagues, and Our Sponsors.[354] The website kavkaz.strana.ru is a pro-Moscow Chechen government (recognized by Moscow) website.

The story was quite different on the Chechen side of the conflict where several websites are directed either specifically at the war in Chechnya or anywhere Jihad is taking place. These sites included, but were not limited to, chechentimes.com, kavkaz.org, and amina.com. The website qoqaz.net, another and perhaps the most popular site for showing atrocities, was renamed at some point between September 2000 and April of 2002. It is now called Assam Publications. The website has links to "azzam.com" and a section on Jihad in general that includes news, fatwa, photos, videos, and so on. Other links include "jihad in Chechnya" and "jihad in Afghanistan." Features of a download from 16 April 2002 included "Women of Afghanistan"—a section on the Chechen view of the suffering of the women of Afghanistan under the new US-propped regime and "Children of Iraq"—an exclusive feature on the children of Iraq who were being slaughtered by American terrorists, according to the website. Thus the website clearly has an anti-Russian and anti-Western tone.

Another site available is daimohk.org belonging to the Chechen news agency Daymohk.[355] Chechen President Maskhadov reportedly has opened sites called chechengovernment.com, ichkeria.com and noakhchi.com. The purpose of these sites is to distance him and his associates from some of the more violent images and activities shown on the net. Another source indicates that Maskhadov's personal site is chechenpress.com.

A newspaper that has a website used for Chechen purposes is kvestnik.org or Kavkazsky Vestnik [Caucasus Herald] from the Council of the Caucasus Journalists. In November of 2001, the Russian site Utro.ru discussed a recent edition of the paper, noting that it published a hit list of 134 Chechen collaborators. Most of those named were policemen or village administrators. Main Chechen ideologist Movladi Udugov, who reportedly also opposes Chechen President Maskhadov and believes real power lies with Shamil Basayev and Khattab, prepared the report. The latter has since been confirmed dead, so this power arrangement will undoubtedly change. Mayrbek Taramov

---

[354] "Assessment of Chechnya.ru," downloaded from the FBIS website on 8 January 2002.
[355] Internet Kavkaz-Tsentr News Agency, 0553 GMT 4 December 2001, as translated and downloaded from the FBIS website on 4 December 2001.

heads the paper. Both Taramov and Udugov fled the republic when the war started and set up shop in Georgia and Azerbaijan. The paper was initially (March 1997) called Islamskiy Poryadok [Islamic Order], a group headed by Udugov. In 1998, the paper was called Islamskaya Natsiya [Islamic Nation] and Put Islama [Path of Islam]. From January 1999, it was called Kavkazskiy Vestnik [Caucasus Herald], a supplement to the paper Kavkazskaya Konfederatsiya [Caucasus Confederation]. The paper's title came from the 1942 fascist occupation of the North Caucasus, a title used by Goebbles.[356]

Other websites with additional listings about the war are worth viewing. The Internet site www.amina.com has a series of listings worthy of consideration. These sites include not only information about the war, but also about Chechen culture. Some are from pure Chechen sources while others are from a variety of sources (Russian, Western, Chechen, etc.):

> amina.com/audio–for Chechen music and audio files
> chechenpress.com–the Chechen News Agency (Russian language)
> chechen.org–Press Center of the Chechen Republic Ichkeria (Russian language)
> groups.yahoo.com/group/chechnya-s–mailing list devoted to the current situation in Chechnya
> watchdog.cz–Prague watchdog on the crisis in Chechnya
> chechnyafree.ru–information about the Chechen Republic
> sakharov-center.ru/walk–Open Society Institute (which takes you on a walking tour through Grozny and shows you photos of the destroyed city)
> osce.org/chechnya–OSCE Assistance Group to Chechnya
> chechnya.gov.ru–pro-Russian government of the Chechen Republic (Russian language)
> google.com–listed as the best search engine on Chechnya
> time.com/time/photoessays/grozny–Time, "The City that Can't Heal"
> dailynews.yahoo.com/fc/world/chechnya–Chechnya full conflict coverage
> tjetjenien.org–Swedish Committee for Chechnya
> man.torun.pl/archives/chechnya.html–archives of Chechnya mailing list
> hrw.org/campaigns/chechnya–human rights watch
> themoscowtimes.ru–the war in Chechnya
> guardian.co.uk/chechnya–Guardian Unlimited's Special Report on Chechnya

---

[356] Oleg Petrovskiy, "Maskhadov will Find Himself on Hit List," Moscow Utro.ru, 1 November 2001 as translated and downloaded from the FBIS website on 1 November 2001.

fotograaf.com/wessel/westet.htm–Eddy van Wessel photography, Chechnya-Grozny
kvestnik.org–Kavkazsky Vestnik in Russian
kavkaz.org/russ–Kavkaz Center in Russian
infocentre.ru–Russian Information Center
achmadow.de–Shamsudin Achmadow's Art and Grozny.

The "information war" is not yet over in Chechnya. Initial Russian successes are beginning to fade, but the Chechens have not capitalized on Russian shortcomings as they did during the first conflict. As one analyst noted:

> The Russian media, like the free media in most Western countries, was for the most part willing to accept both government controls and the government's story in the name of national security for as long as that story made sense. The public, too, seemed happy enough at first with the government-released information. Over time, however, the disparities between the official line and the increasingly obvious realities, reported both by soldiers themselves and by their parents, proved impossible to ignore.[357]

How long the government's picture of the conflict can be sustained is an open question. But then again, the name of the game is access, and Russia is in the driver's seat.

Chechen Use of Information-Psychological Issues

One of the more interesting sources encountered in the preparation of this chapter was the book The Armed Caucasus. It is a view of the fighting from the Chechen side and contains a good deal of information on the information-psychological factor. According to the book, the Chechens considered their "moral-psychological" factor as extremely high. Not less than thirty percent of the population between the ages of 14 and 50 voluntarily took part in the fighting. The main characteristics of the Chechen fighters included patriotism, nationalism, religious fanaticism, decisiveness, being prepared to die, aggressiveness, strict internal discipline, the capability to continue fighting under extreme conditions, contempt for the enemy, unpredictability of actions, and revenge.[358] Information-propaganda and political support to the Chechen campaign were viewed as an independent activity, usually associated with information war in the West. This included political and psychological work

---

[357] Olga Oliker, "Moths to the Flame: Russian Urban Operations in Chechnya, 1994-2000," May 2000 publication of the RAND Corporation.
[358] Dzhangir Aras, Vooruzhenn'i Kavkaz [The Armed Caucasus], Reference Book on Military Systems of North Caucasus Nations, Volume III, 2000, p. 51.

with personnel in the armed forces and society; the use of special propaganda (PSYOPs) against the enemy and various sectors of his society; diplomatic support for the actions of Chechens, to include use of the foreign press; and legislative support of military activity.[359]

Work within the armed forces included the use of slogans, swearing allegiance on the Koran, and acceptance of the Jihad. National ideas, Islamic values, and the military history of Chechnya were often used in this regard. Islamic slogans were frequently tied to weapons and armored vehicles. Work among the population included the development of several factors: a base of social-political support for the armed forces; the galvanizing of the population against Russians operating in their areas; the conduct of mass meetings and teaching how to spread rumors; and the spread of Chechen military traditions and the ideas of Islam, using audio- and video- cassettes, leaflets, radio, TV, and the press.[360]

The Armed Caucasus noted that a Minister of Information and Propaganda, as well as offices of propaganda and external relations with the General Staff of Chechnya, information centers, agents, and the press are required to implement this work. The coordinator for Chechen PSYOPs was the Minister of Information and Press of the Chechen Republic, Movladi Udugov.

Of greatest interest to a student of military history is the book's listing of Chechen principles for organizing PSYOPs. It requires a combination of propaganda methods: a demonstration of real facts; keeping quiet about or negating real facts; specific distortion of facts for a particular use; and premeditated disinformation. These methods are aimed at Russia's armed forces, its population, and government leaders, as well as foreign audiences. Channels to spread these methods include the Internet and electronic mail, the Russian Press, lobby groups and agents of influence, political organizations and movements in Russia, the intellectual and cultural elites of Russia and other countries, the Chechen diaspora, and social organizations such as antimilitary, humanitarian, and human rights groups everywhere. Channels to spread PSYOPs among the Russian armed forces appeared to contain nothing new— agitation, leaflets, loudspeakers, and radio stations, and capturing Russian soldiers by wearing Russian uniforms as a disinformation operation. [361]

Work among the civilian population included utilizing to the maximum degree Russia's press service. It was estimated during the First Chechen War

---

[359] Ibid., p. 52.
[360] Ibid., p. 53.
[361] Ibid., pp. 54-57.

(1994-1996) that nearly 90 per cent of the information from the zone of conflict came from Chechen sources that helped formulate favorable conditions for influencing social opinion and spreading information "pictures." Missions included forming an anti-military mood and a desire to stop military activity, discredit activities and the military-political leadership of Russia, and misinform Russia's leadership about future Chechen plans. Exploiting the destabilizing psychological factor of losses among Russian forces and threatening the potential use by Chechnya of nuclear weapons helped accomplish this. The Chechens believe that work to agitate the Committee of Soldier's Mothers in Russia greatly damaged the Russian armed forces draft in 1995.[362]

Work with foreign audiences was also discussed. It included forming a positive image of the armed forces, strengthening international support, and weakening the international position of Russia. This would be accomplished by exploiting the thesis of Chechnya fighting for liberation from Russia, by accusing Russia of violating international norms and laws on the conduct of war and using banned weapons, demonstrating cruelty by Russia's forces as well as a disregard for the ecology of Chechnya, and keeping quiet about or negating similar actions by Chechnya's forces.[363] Chechens listed unofficial news outlets in the following countries: Jordan, Azerbaijan, Poland, Latvia, Saudi Arabia, Pakistan, Ukraine, Denmark, Great Britain, Byelorussia, Russia (since closed), Germany, the USA, Lithuania, Turkey, France, Estonia, Georgia, and Finland.[364]

The author of <u>The Armed Caucasus</u> listed the following websites as either Chechen or pro Chechen. Some of the sites do not appear to have anything to do with Chechnya, focusing instead on business sites:

> chechengovernment.com, the government of the Chechen Republic
> chechentimes.com, a newspaper from the US based on an alliance with American Chechens
> qoqaz.net, www/azzam.com, www.qoqaz.com, www.qoqaz.de, from the transnational Islamic movement
> naqshbandi.net, naqshbandi.org, a Suffi order
> sbcif.com, an international fund to support the people of Chechnya
> islamicsupremecouncil.org, Supreme Islamic council
> pp.clinet.fi, Chechen representation in Finland

---

[362] Ibid., pp. 57-58.
[363] Ibid., p. 58.
[364] Ibid., p. 61.

kavkaz.org, www.argun.mirror.com, www.dagestan.org, Chechen
Kavkaz sites

amina.com, Chechen Republic online

nohcy.org.ge, Georgia

ichkeria.com.ge, Chechens in Georgia

muslimmag.org/webversion/caucasus, unstated Islamic organization

geocities.com/kafkasclub, Japanese Kavkaz Club

chechenija.hypermart.net, social organization of Lithuania

postimees.ee, social organization of Estonia

alt.culture.Chechnya, unstated organization

egroups.com/group/chechnya-sl, unstated organization

pcs.ca, social organization of Canada

compiling.hu-berlin.de, social organization of Germany

hro.org/war, social organization of the Russian Federation

lviv.net/news/kavkaz.htm, private computer service of news from
Ukraine

freekavkaz.org/, UNA-UNSO

stigal.com/, unstated organization.

Conclusions

Military reform in the Information Age will strain Russia's financial resources and its conventional military thinking. Militaries are moving out of the age of huge, ponderous armies for which the Soviet Union prepared, and into armies of sensors, satellites, and space weapons. Hidden mobilizations (by electronic weapons), deep rear fights, and space as the new theater of military activity characterize the new military environment. Weapons required to participate are expensive and hard to test and detect.

Simultaneously, the Information Age is providing individuals and small groups with the power once attainable only by nation states. Armies today, while preparing for the new age, must keep a wary glance on these groups or face the probability of a surprise attack and the possible internal massive movement of populations. Much of the information to construct dirty weapons, as well as the capability to unite these disparate factions and to send coded messages between them, are present on the Information Age's great communicator, the Internet. Instead of a Global Village, the Internet may be viewed as the terrorists' greatest planning and execution mechanism of all time.

Thus, during its period of military reform, Russian planners (already strapped for cash) are going to have to confront a scalable series of scenarios from the terrorist to Star Wars. Russia will have to choose its weapons platforms carefully. Most important, it will have to organize the military to meet these multiple and simultaneous challenges.

The second Russian-Chechen conflict has provided insights into this dilemma. Russia's use of high-technology equipment (RPVs, EW capabilities, reconnaissance-strike systems for its artillery and aircraft) has been successful but not capable of ending the conflict against an opponent fenced into a small plot of land and missing these same capabilities. These observations must be incorporated into the military reform package under consideration. Russian military theorists have undoubtedly learned a lot from the Chechen conflict, including how much even a local conflict can cost. They have also been able to test new weaponry under real conditions, much like the US and Britain in Kosovo and Afghanistan. Undoubtedly this will impact some area of military reform.

Finally, military reform will have to take into consideration the moral-psychological aspect of the soldier. This might mean better housing, or higher pay, or even better equipment. Minister of Defense Sergei Ivanov noted that military reform couldn't go on indefinitely, that it is psychologically impossible to do so. Other impartial observers to the Russian process might state that the Russian armed forces cannot stall military reform any longer. The Information Age train is leaving the station, and Russia still is not on board.

Part Four

Cyber Threats to the Mind

PART FOUR: CYBER THREATS TO THE MIND

Part Four consists of four chapters. All of the chapters refer to ways that the Cyber Age affects our logic—from cause and effect to the action-reaction cycle of the military decision-maker.

Chapter Eleven considers some of the dangers of the Cyber Age for decision-makers. This chapter focuses on the dangers that can occur if machines incorrectly process data or are corrupted or manipulated by outside sources. The danger is especially great if time is of the essence and decisions need to be made based on information (or even decisions) provided by machines. The action-reaction process can be a source of immense danger if the action aspect is misinterpreted.

Chapter Twelve discusses some of the different ways that manipulation and perception management techniques are used to persuade people. The discussion includes examples of scenarios from the Bosnia conflict and of a tense standoff between the US and Soviet Union, highlighting some of the techniques utilized.

Chapter Thirteen discusses topics that are often discarded from consideration by scientists—parapsychology, subliminal messages, psychic readings and so on. It discusses these issues from the perspective of China and Russia and what they mean for future developments. These elements are included because, unlike the US, China and Russia consider these developments to have a direct bearing on IO.

Finally, Chapter Fourteen discusses the history and current application of an old Russian concept, reflexive control (RC), that is similar to the US concept of perception management. The chapter covers the development of the concept from the time of the Warsaw Pact to how RC is used in the Cyber Age by military planners utilizing satellites and computers.

CHAPTER ELEVEN: THE CYBER THREAT ENVIRONMENT[365]

Introduction

On 3 July 1988, the USS Vincennes, located in the Persian Gulf, picked up an Iranian plane on its Aegis system radar. Seven minutes later the plane (which turned out to be a civilian airliner and not an F-14 as indicated by the Aegis system) was blown from the sky. One analysis of the incident noted that "the US, and by extension other countries using high-tech weapons, may have become prisoners of a technology so speedy and complex that it forces the fallible humans who run it into snap decisions that can turn into disaster."[366]

This unfortunate incident highlighted some of the emerging problems of the Information Age. First is the inability of analysts and equipment to visualize the "intent" or identity of electronic images, often causing an inaccurate operator "perception-reaction" response. The tactical operator/strategic decision-maker works in a "perception-reaction" chain of events in the IT age, a phenomenon that is more dangerous than perception-management problems of the past. Perception-reaction is the knee-jerk impulse that operators/decision-makers feel when presented with images and warnings of an imminent attack, as happened in the case of the Vincennes. Perception-reaction can be understood as "actions based on observations of electronic images that elicit survival or other immediate response actions. Whether these images are real or artificial matters not, as both types will influence emotions, motives, or the objective reasoning of individuals or systems."[367]

A second Information Age problem is the inability of software's embedded scenarios to handle all of the anomalies and options that develop, by design or otherwise, and these anomalies can manifest as a dangerous game of digital roulette over the stability of the 0's and 1's of binary code.

Finally, there is the problem of the impact of electronic input on the human dimension of decision-making. Is a human capable of correctly interpreting what an electronic version of events means? If the past is any indicator, humans are still not capable of doing so. During the Cold War a nuclear Armageddon was avoided thanks to a Russian officer who did not believe his electronic display which indicated that a nuclear launch had been

---

[365] This article was published under the title "Infosphere Threats" in the September-October 1999 issue of Military Review, pp. 46-51.

[366] George C. Church, "High Tech Horror," Time, 18 July 1988, p. 14.

[367] Author's definition.

initiated by the US. In this sense we are living in a most dangerous and sensitive timeframe until our devices become fail-safe.

The analysis suggests the need for work on developing a "military software science" to help understand these new phenomena. Such a science would have a goal of providing a better interpretation and forecast of the scenarios that countries embed in their military software. Such software would not only improve our response posture but embed areas for human reason to overcome electronic virtual situational mistakes.

Background: Implications of the Switch to a Digitized Force

There has been a massive shift from analog to digital representations of data. Analog systems processed continuous voltage amplitudes and were costly and specially designed which caused difficulties when sharing information with other systems. Digital systems utilize rapidly switching "on" or "off" states of binary "1" or "0" representations of data. Digital technology not only permits a vast decrease in the size and cost of electronic hardware, but much of the task of processing digital information can be accomplished in software rather than hardware. This makes the digital format vastly more flexible which explains our increased reliance on it.

The underlying commonality in all digital signal processing hardware, and the ready ability to convert formats and process the information by using software, have caused an explosion in information sharing among digital systems. But it is this very ease of transmission, ease of extensive processing, ease of changing the processing software, and consequent widespread sharing of digital data that makes intrusion so scary; and so possible. If intrusion and corruption succeed, stability disappears and the software's 1's and 0's start falling into unpredictable places, much like the ball that falls unpredictably into the spinning roulette wheel. Stability could also be affected if the scenarios embedded in the software are unable to handle unexpected anomalies deliberately introduced by an opponent.[368] This is the game of digital roulette nations play with the software in their advanced warning systems, rockets, and satellites on a daily basis.

Such a game of digital roulette could result in serious mishaps or instigate some catastrophic chain reaction of events. For example, what would happen if one side develops the technology to present false radar blips on JSSTARS (or the equivalent aircraft in other countries) in a manner so realistic, extensive, and threatening that a potential opponent uses up an arsenal of cruise and other precision-guided missiles on the illusory threat? Could it result in

---

[368] Author's discussion with Mr. Jay Willis, defense scientist.

command and control decisions that put nuclear forces in a ready-to-launch status once other assets are exhausted? The world would be poised on the brink of a holocaust for the sake of false images on a computer display. There are no guarantees that all cultures/nations will be capable of including some type of "fail-safe" rules in their software to guard against such an accidental launch.

When a programmer writes code, it is written to fulfill a task. As one specialist has noted, it "is a task as a human sees it: full of unexpressed knowledge, implicit associations, allusions to allusions. Its coherence comes from knowledge structures deep in the body, from experience, memory."[369] The issue of human knowledge mechanisms, as they relate to culture, language and the means of expression, is quite complex. It is reasonable to suggest, however, that if (IF) different cultures think differently in terms of logic and perception, then there is no reason why this practice might not affect the way they program.[370] However, perhaps more pertinent at this moment, any difference in programming will be swamped by basic differences (how cultures develop and interpret computer displays, what they design the system to provide, etc.). The suggestion offered here is that cultures will specify tasks differently to solve problems (for example, the manner in which heads up displays are developed for the helmets of Russian versus American fighter pilots).

Two Russian analysts who studied the implications of the digitized age added other characteristics of the digital context, noting that:

- Collection is becoming more closely linked with the analysis and processing of data—that is the entire effort is much more integrated than before.
- Human involvement is decreasing, especially in the collection and processing phases.
- Just as virtual reality is blurring the geo-political boundaries of information space, so it blurs the enemy image—is it a state (nation, country) or transnational (drug cartel, terrorist) threat?
- Distance is not as important as time (implementation and decision-making elements).
- Software may become hostile to mankind if it replicates and gives birth to systems of growing complexity, or self-destructs.[371]

---

[369] Ellen Ullman, Wired, April 1999, p. 128.
[370] Discussion with Ms. Ullman via email, 6 April 1999.
[371] Yuriy Baturin and Sergey Modestov, "Intelligence in Virtual Reality," Vooruzheniy Politica Konversiya [Equipment, Politics, Conversion], No. 1-2, 1998, pp. 53-56.

Within this digitized context a short examination of some problems/consequences will be taken.

Problem One: Understanding "Information-Based Intent"

Intent is an amorphous concept that is defined as a purpose or goal or why one performs an act. Intent originates in the head of an individual today just as it did before. In the past, however, intent could be measured in terms of cold steel by observing the mobilization of a country's resources, the movement of tanks to the front, or their deployment into battle formations. Measuring the intent of electrons, their purpose, goal, or what act they are performing, is another matter. Take, for instance, the difficulty in exposing the intent of electrons sent from a private computer "somewhere" in the world and rerouted through several intermediate countries. Where did the electrons originate? Who was the initiator of the electron stream? What is the goal or purpose of the electrons and what are they doing?

The "soldier-operator" (S-O) behind a computer monitor or radar screen is usually the front line defense in the battle to detect and understand electronic intent. The S-O works in and relies on virtual space for his contextual understanding. This work space is where the tension among space-based information capabilities, intent, and understanding/comprehension of what is transpiring escalates due to the uncertainty and resulting pressures on operators and commanders to act. A captain who "hesitates too long while trying to identify conclusively that radar-screen blip" could lose his ship and the lives of all those aboard.[372] This is ultimately why there are hair-trigger rules of engagement (ROE) for naval forces in the Gulf that require only "some convincing indication that a ship or plane is approaching with hostile intent" in order to ask headquarters for permission to shoot.[373]

In the past, when an opponent's intent appeared aggressive, planners had time to perform opposing force calculations where the unit focus was critical—battalion versus battalion, tanks versus tanks, and so on. While it is possible to perform a correlation of opposing electronic forces (systems), a correlation of opposing electrons is more difficult. The units of measure for such a comparison are simply unknown. So is a way to measure their intent and focus—is it at the unit or strategic level?

Electronic intent is easy to mask, as skilled computer programmers are now demonstrating. For example, screensavers with a soothing appearance and intent may in fact be invasive viruses designed to destroy the system. A year or

---

[372] Church, p. 17.
[373] Ibid.

so ago there was a "Sex and the City" screensaver with the wording "Warning! Adult Content." When curious people opened the screensaver, they introduced a worm into their computers that in most cases deleted hard drives.

Responding to someone's destructive, electronic intent is an imprecise science, as the responder must decide how and where to respond, how much is enough, and what the originator's intent is in the first place. It is very difficult to ensure that the culprit in question was actually the one who originated the action. What if he or she was just an unsuspecting intermediary for another's criminal act? Such a response is not nearly as clear as one's response to a tank that shoots at you, where you simply hide or shoot back.

Problem Two: Software's Cultural and Embedded Scenario Dimensions

During the Cold War, Soviet and American analysts studied each other's military establishments in great detail. The debate focused on examining the opposing nation's capabilities, intentions, and decision-making processes to expose hostile activity and defeat it in a timely manner. These processes represented a unique combination of the specific linguistic, environmental, historical, philosophical, and cultural elements in each country. Unfortunately, too often analysts failed to account for these complexities in a nation's strategic culture. Instead, they resorted to mirror-imaging capabilities and intentions through their own prism of reality.[374] This produced forecasts tainted with prejudices and expectations and led to an analysis lacking insight and context.

These factors are equally important today when studying the software packages that drive a country's military logic and rationale, and they must not be ignored. For example, software programmers are driven in specified directions by a culture's military science and theory, budget restraints, discoveries in hardware and software capabilities, local brainpower's ability to create mathematical code, the existing technological infrastructure (how many layers deep can an analysis or development proceed), and even the rationale of procurement and threat analysis. One programmer noted that programming "has

---

[374] For a Western discussion of Russian and US capabilities and intents during the Cold War period, see Ken Booth, <u>Strategy and Ethnocentrism</u>, New York: Holmes and Meier, 1979; and Fritz Ermarth, "Contrasts in American and Soviet Strategic Thought," <u>International Security</u>, Fall 1978, Vol. 3, pp. 138-155. Ermarth underlines the values and methods involved in the strategic culture of the arms race. For a book that offers both Russian and US views of strategic culture, see Carl G. Jacobsen, editor, <u>Strategic Power: USA/USSR</u>, Macmillan Press, London, 1990.

remained maddeningly undefinable, some mix of mathematics, sculpting, scrupulous accounting, and wily, ingenious plumbing."[375]

That is, as suggested earlier, all nations may not write computer code the same. Computer code may not reflect some international language of logic and rationale as most suspect. It is affected by many other factors, and each country may develop scenarios or programmed responses that are unique. This may make weapons and the systems to which they are tied respond in different ways than planned when confronted by various culturally driven scenarios. We play as we practice, and if there actually are variations of computer software that are culturally driven, we will have trouble responding properly.[376]

In addition, what if the software has been corrupted or damaged (unknown to the owner), or what if there are anomalies or scenarios that cause unintended, incoherent, or disjointed software responses with unintended consequences? This high-stakes game of digital roulette is further affected by the fact that some of the software for new weapons are written by anywhere from several to hundreds of companies or programmers. As a result, unintentional problems may develop from overlapping or contradictory code. As one scientist working closely with ABM software has noted:

> Already we are at the point where it is difficult to understand how software works. Codes are so large, and made up of so many components that have been developed by so many different people, that getting a fail-safe piece of software that is 100% understood is virtually impossible. The cost of code validation and verification can easily exceed the cost of writing the damn thing to begin with.[377]

Reprogramming the computer to react to new situations may be nearly impossible in the short term due to human ignorance of the algorithms required for the processes involved and (increasingly) due to the complexities of the software.

---

[375] Ullman, email discussion.

[376] Dr. James Schneider, School for Advanced Military Studies, adds: "Such a reliance places increased pressure on C4I and indicates that *software* is replacing *'staffware'* (or normal staff procedures). The intelligence fusion process is increasingly being taken over by the software (recall the Vincennes incident was virtually a software/fusion problem)." Software, unlike a machine, will continue to operate without indicating that it broke until it is too late, and one must always be looking for software-generated information garbage.

[377] Willis, discussion.

One answer to the problem of anomalies has been offered by Peircean Semeiotics, the science of self-controlled, deliberate reasoning while focused on problem solving. It is a body of thought that offers the opportunity to construct a system that is able to deal with and react to a new situation in a non-programmed manner. All artificial intelligence systems developed to date do not fit these criteria.[378] Complexity theory is another approach to solving the problem that could be investigated.

These features of software demonstrate the growing complexity of working in virtual space. More importantly, this puts a new spin on the old saying "if there is the perception of a problem, then we have a problem...even if the problem is simply the perception." What if the perception problem is in the software? Will cultural software research become a new branch of investigation as a result? And will the new "enemy-image" manifested as software-generated blips and pixels so dehumanize adversaries into images that the use of force will be more likely instead of less likely?

Problem Three: The Human Dimension
The context within which decisions are made is complicated today by an increasing reliance on a virtual image of reality (or simulacrum, an image or representation of reality). Often the analyst/decision-maker's frame of reference, expectations, and training leaves them unprepared for what is represented in virtual space and for its interpretation. From nation to nation an analyst's vision of virtual space varies, dependent not only on the software and analytical tools available but also on the cultural and religious philosophies shaping the analyst's/programmer's view of reality. Unaccustomed to studying a virtual "enemy-image," analysts struggle to interpret the virtual images they see or hear within their own context.

The interpretation of the intent of an electronic image or the detection of electronic waves depends on the picture of virtual reality for which the country-specific analyst was trained. This implies that the decision-making focus has shifted some from planner/analyst/decision-maker and is now heavily influenced by the operator. Analysis now is more in the direction of operator/analyst/decision-maker. Greater reliance on the operator's interpretation implies that it is the tactical operator or the analyst who will have to make many of the incredibly vital and critical decisions about target engagements, not strategic leaders.

Another problem of the human dimension is that our reliance on computers is atrophying our manual skills to both perform an analysis and to

---

[378] Discussion with Mr. Ed Nozawa of Lockheed on 11 February 1999.

understand the phenomenon itself. What if we have to abandon our software altogether and rely only on manual operator processes? This latter point appears to be a very sensitive one since

> Perhaps nowhere is our vulnerability to asymmetric technologies greater than in our relentless pursuit of information superiority. Our vulnerability lies in the realization that the more proficient we become at collecting, processing, displaying, and disseminating relevant, accurate information to aid decision makers, the more dependent we become on that capability and therefore the more lucrative a target.[379]

The danger is real since

> ...by their very nature as automatons, computer systems have no inherent ability to recognize their own limitations. When applied in inappropriate circumstances, they will produce answers which may be 'logical' but quite incorrect. The entire process, from concept through design, testing, and doctrine development, must include recognition of this inherent problem.[380]

Most commanders still have trouble taking that leap of faith that puts the world's fate in the hands of automatic code generation. We are losing our ability to preserve some manual skills. Yet software is forcing commanders and decision-makers more and more to rely on program code as the new maestro or conductor of warfare.[381]

Finally, future analysts must focus their attention on the heart of the information weapon, the algorithm. They must become adept at recognizing the computer graphics of potential enemies, understand their computer logic as well as the logic of their military art, and become familiar with the techniques and contextual factors within which the logic is developed. This aspect of the human dimension, its analytical factor, must not be forgotten. Computers cannot do this by themselves. It is up to humans to collect data, sort it, and digest and reproduce it into some comprehensible form. The "network warrior analyst" will be one of the most important future soldiers America can produce. He must be able to analyze and not just collect, process, and disseminate information. If the latter is all that the analyst can achieve then we may have to

---

[379] Jay M. Garner, "Asymmetric Niche Warfare," Phalanx, March 1997, p. 1.
[380] David S. Alberts, The Unintended Consequences of Information Age Technologies, National Defense University, Washington, D.C., p. 39.
[381] Ibid., p. 40.

witness another Kosovo-type campaign (which demonstrated that information war was just a myth).

Is There a Need for a Military Software Science?

The foregoing discussion has described the concept of electronic intent, the problems associated with so much reliance on software programming, and the role of the human dimension in the problem. It appears prudent in the face of such developments to examine the potential for a new branch of theory called *military software science*. This scientific activity would serve as a clearing house to analyze various types of military software logic. Military software science would require very specialized analysts from the software engineering, culture, and military history and art domains. They would form a military software science directorate within the Department of Defense to handle the problem. Its importance cannot be overstated. Software is now the integrator and coordinator for the allocation and synchronization of forces. It enhances command and control logic and supervision. While the overseer of the battlefield analysis process remains the commander who applies the principles of war and military stratagem, it must not be forgotten that the commander receives his information from the operator, whose perception and analysis could be virtually manipulated. Thus the operator could provide commanders with inaccurate data upon which to make their decisions.

Conclusions

The discussion has attempted to outline emerging threats in the hot spot known as the ether or infosphere. It focused on some of the factors that a digitized force will encounter. It is tentative thinking and invites much further exploration.

The argument has been presented that nations have seldom considered the cultural aspects that may drive another nation's computer software programming mechanism. Neither do they have any idea how to measure electronic intent, nor a way to trust computer output that, because of its processing speed, detects threats and offers options quicker than humans can comprehend. The development of a military software science directorate may help with some or all of these issues.

With regard to software, many countries have already had a cultural invasion of sorts. Programmers in various countries wrote many of the first programs, and perhaps introduced a cultural bias for the way future programs are written that has become invisible to follow-on generations. Militaries worldwide may enter their own cultural biases via software programming, especially in the realm of military art or the principles of war (which vary from nation to nation).

The issues of determining the intent of electrons and unanticipated software responses received special consideration in light of the Y2K problem. For example, what happens if radar screens of countries possessing nuclear weapons went blank during the Y2K changeover? Was this malfunctioning software or a computer attack? Will we someday develop Software Control theories like today's Arms Control theories? The first question becomes particularly alarming when one understands that, for example, Russian military doctrine anticipates an attack on its military information system via a virus or electromagnetic attack (during the initial period of war) and then a follow-on nuclear strike against Moscow.[382] The US and Russia as a result developed an agreement that puts experts in one another's nuclear command centers during Y2K to prevent any miscalculations if systems went haywire.[383]

To deal with such uncertain circumstances, it appears highly advisable to construct an "information hotline" between countries similar to our nuclear hotlines to preclude potential horrific misunderstandings in this sensitive area. Perhaps it would be best to co-locate these lines and interests and hold one hostage to the other. Such a hotline would require preliminary work to agree on terminology, concepts, and theory (and a long discussion on capabilities and intent) and would go a long way to reducing tension and encouraging discussion.

Thought should also be given to developing a forum for discussing the idea of culturally driven software, the need for a *military software science*, and the consequences of digital roulette and the perception-reaction problem. The central question

> is whether technology may be pushing the fallible humans who operate it beyond their ability to make wise judgments instantly on the basis of what, with even the most sophisticated systems, will often be ambiguous information. This question applies not only in the Persian Gulf, but wherever there are fingers on buttons that can launch deadly weapons.[384]

More time needs to be spent on these issues. The stability of data in the computer of a private citizen is one thing, that in the computers and minds of decision makers and missile operators/launchers quite another.

---

[382] Colum Lynch, "Y2K Bug Worries US, Russia," <u>Boston Globe</u>, 12 December 1998, as downloaded from Johnson's List on 12 December 1998.
[383] Ibid.
[384] Church, p. 17.

CHAPTER TWELVE: THE AGE OF THE NEW PERSUADERS[385]

Peacekeeping operations, terrorism, and low intensity conflicts (LIC) are challenges that confront armies and governments throughout the world. A much overlooked manifestation associated with these phenomena is the overt and covert manipulation of events and actions, made easier by the Information Age. Individuals or groups can take advantage of a variety of factors, such as an organization's operating techniques and procedures, to augment their own operations. Often, the rational or sources behind these covet actions are soon forgotten.

So who was most responsible for US involvement in Somalia: President Clinton, the Joint Chiefs of Staff, or Ted Turner's news agency? None of the above! Former President George Bush was in charge at the start of the involvement, but nongovernmental agencies (NGOs) were initially responsible for drawing his and CNN's attention to the situation there.

The innocent victims of manipulation activities can include responsible decision-makers around the world who are persuaded by media coverage that influences public opinion and thus triggers demands for legislative action or assistance. Nations themselves become practitioners of manipulation techniques as well. Everyone is involved in this old art to some degree.

What is Manipulation?

Manipulation is not defined by the Department of Defense (DOD) Dictionary of Terms or by US Army Field Manual 33-1, Psychological Operations. The American Heritage dictionary defines manipulation as "shrewd or devious management especially for one's own advantage."

For this article's purposes, manipulation is defined as "the desired goal or result of a process that uses specific devices—such as semantic, technical, psychological, or behavioral—to deceive, misinform, influence, persuade, or control an object, either concrete (a person, state, or action) or abstract (thinking or perceptions), usually to gain an advantage."[386] Just who are the

---

[385] The original version of this article under the same title appeared in the May-June 1997 edition of Military Review, pp. 72-80.

[386] This is the author's definition since he found no accepted DOD definition while preparing this article.

"new persuaders?"[387] They may be computer hackers, animation or forgery specialists aligned with criminals and terrorists, specially programmed computer displays, journalists taken with interpretive reporting, or a host of other people or things. [388] They can also be intelligence services armed with these tools. Lower costs and more broadly available technology have made entry into this business much easier. Rapid technological change and renewed international instability give persuaders many new and potentially harmful opportunities to manipulate objects. Minor tactical or devastating strategic consequences may result.

Manipulation can be intentional or unintentional, transparent or hidden. For example, the technician's ability to produce morphed images and "movie magic" means that "seeing is believing" no longer applies. Fooled in the past by altered photos, people now can be easily duped by well-staged images even on the battlefield, especially if holograms become a tool of psychological operations (PSYOP) units. Thus, today is the opportune time to reconsider how manipulation should be understood, how such operations can be uncovered and managed, and why attention and resources must be devoted to them by decision-makers and society. The discriminate observer must be able to distinguish an intentional manipulation from simply having one's emotions or logic persuaded or influenced in a certain direction. The issue's seriousness was brought home during the June 1996 Russian election.

The Communist candidate for the Russian Presidency, Gennadiy Zuganov, charged that the mass media had manipulated constituents into voting for President Boris Yeltsin. His primary claim concerned the number of hours devoted to pro-Yeltsin and anticommunist programming on state and private networks. After the election, some journalists admitted they were manipulated. Zuganov consequently branded the mass media as a fourth estate or information weapon. He recommended that "information" acquire a place as an autonomous branch of power in addition to the legislative, executive, and judicial branches. He called for legislation to establish "norms prohibiting the mass media's use as

---

[387] The title is a modern-day adaptation of Vance Packard's famous 1957 novel The Hidden Persuaders, which discusses advertising's ability to direct or influence people to make certain choices.

[388] A recent poll showed the US public's mistrust of the media is growing. According to an Associated Press report, "A bare majority...says the news media usually 'get the facts right,' and substantial numbers say journalists are arrogant and cynical." For a poll results rundown, see "Poll Finds Journalists Distrusted," The Kansas City Star, 4 December, 1996, p. A-12.

a weapon for conducting psychological information warfare inside the country."[389] He recommended similar norms for international law.

Manipulation, from this perspective, could be branded a "tool of warfare." However, before undertaking a closer examination of manipulation and why it is evolving into a serious threat, a look at a practical application is in order.

Manipulation in Bosnia

Canadian General Lewis MacKensie, writing about his experiences as head of the United Nations Protection Force (UNPROFOR) contingent in Bosnia-Herzegovina in 1992, observed that "perception is often more persuasive than reality."[390] MacKensie was confronted with a multitude of incidents where one side attempted or succeeded in manipulating world opinion against another side, often at the expense of the UNPROFOR. MacKensie's credibility as a peacekeeper was frequently challenged by the *perception* of impartiality. Both sides used any opportunity to manipulate a peacekeeper's conduct to their advantage. In many cases, MacKensie's force had no weapons, and when they did, they could not fire unless fired upon or threatened. Knowing these rules of engagement (ROE), the antagonists worked to use them to their advantage, sometimes by threatening to use force and sometimes by taking hostages.[391]

The combatants manipulated news coverage, convoy assistance, mortar and other armed attacks, cease-fires, ROE, and the statements, actions and presence of the UNPROFOR. Disinformation, deception, perception management, or PSYOP were used to manipulate international mediators and to convince the opposing side to take some action or to make some decision. Examples included the following:

News Coverage

General MacKensie noted that on one occasion the UN High Commissioner for Refugees was missing several trucks, which eventually arrived a few hours late after being detained at roadblocks. Bosnian Defense Minister Doko's staff seized on the report that the trucks were missing and, not knowing they had arrived, informed the <u>New York Times</u> that the trucks had transported Serbian soldiers, giving them freedom of movement. Because the Serbs were in UN protected trucks, the principle of impartiality was violated

---

[389] Gennadiy Zyuganov, "On the Threshold of a 'Government of Seven Boyars,'" <u>Sovetskaya Rossiya</u> [Soviet Russia], 26 October 1996, pp. 1-2.
[390] Lewis MacKenzie, <u>Peacekeeper</u>, Harper Collins Publishers Ltd, 1994, p. 275.
[391] Ibid., p. 500.

because one side was helped. When he was confronted by MacKenzie and informed that the trucks had arrived, Doko apologized and said he had been given bad information. Regardless, the media and world opinion had already been manipulated.[392]

A fast learner, MacKensie also used the media to his advantage. Told that his men would come under heavy artillery fire if they did not move, MacKensie responded that he would order them into bunkers and cellars at their present locations and that if artillery shells began to fall, he would call every TV station in the world and tell them one side was attacking the UN.[393]

Convoy Assistance versus Ethnic Cleansing
In one instance, a UN observer was confronted by more than one hundred non-Serbs who were leaving a UN-protected area because they feared for their lives if they remained. Unable to talk the group into staying, the UN observer escorted them through a minefield. The next day the Croatian press accused the UN of "assisting the Serbs with ethnic cleansing" by marching refugees through a minefield and out of an area.[394]

Mortar Attacks
On 27 May 1992, people lined up for bread in the Sarajevo market place, as they had done for years. A mortar attack ensued, and seventeen people were killed. The Bosnian presidency said that the Serbs did it, but a number of facts contradicted that claim. It was possible that stories and reports had been manipulated to point the finger at one side. As MacKensie noted,

> Our people tell us there were a number of things that didn't fit. The street had been blocked off just before the incident. Once the crowd was let in and lined up, the media appeared but kept their distance. The attack took place and the media were immediately on the scene. The majority of the people killed are alleged to be "tame Serbs." Who knows? The only thing for sure is that innocent people were killed.[395]

To this day, the strong suspicion remains that the Bosnians were indirectly responsible for the attack.

---

[392] Ibid., p. 339.
[393] Ibid., p. 331.
[394] Ibid., p. 236.
[395] Ibid., p. 293.

Cease Fires

Anytime there was a chance that a cease-fire would freeze the status quo on the ground, the conflicting sides would launch last-minute offensives to gain what territory they could before the cease-fire began.[396] Then, they would manipulate the cease-fire by repositioning and resupplying their forces during the lull in the action.[397]

Clearly, manipulation was used in each of these vignettes, which represent only a few among hundreds of examples. Exactly what is manipulation, and how can we discern between it and the other persuasion concepts, such as perception management, PSYOP, deception, or disinformation?

Manipulation has traditionally been looked at as a means by which to accomplish an action. For example, the DOD definition of deception utilizes manipulation in this manner:

> Those measures designed to mislead the enemy *by manipulation*, distortion, or falsification of evidence to induce him to react in a manner prejudicial to his interests.[398]

The action verb here is to mislead, and the goal is to induce a reaction. Joint Publication 1-02 defines perception management and PSYOP in a similar manner:

> *perception management*–actions to convey and/or deny selected information and indicators to foreign audiences to influence their emotions, motives, and objective reasoning; and to intelligence systems and leaders at all levels to influence official estimates, ultimately resulting in foreign behaviors and official actions favorable to the originator's objectives. In various ways, perception management

---

[396] Ibid., p. 309.

[397] The combatants further adjusted to their new environment and used it to their advantage. For example, it was reported the combatants exploited the "confrontation line" that was one drawn on UNPROFOR maps designating the boundary between the sides. A road crossed the line several times. When a UN vehicle traveled on it—and thus moved in and out of the combatants' territories—a mortar crew from one side would sneak onto the other side's territory and fire on the UN vehicle making it look as if the "home" side did the shooting. In another example, there were reports that one side used a third country and a lot of money to plant stories in the US press to gain sympathy for its cause. See LTC John Sray's article "Selling the Bosnian Myth to America: Buyer Beware" at http://fmso.leavenworth.army.mil.

[398] Field Manual 33-1, p. 8 of the Glossary at the end of the manual.

combines truth projection, operations security, cover and deception, and psychological operations.[399]

The action verbs in this definition are to "convey/deny information" and to "influence estimates, emotions, motives, and reasoning." The goal is to change foreign behavior and official actions favorable to the originator's objectives. It includes PSYOP and deception in its efforts to persuade change.

Psychological operations are defined as planned operations to convey selected information and indicators to foreign audiences to influence their emotions, motives, objective reasoning, and ultimately the behavior of foreign governments, organizations, groups, and individuals. The purpose of psychological operations is to induce or reinforce foreign attitudes and behavior favorable to the originator's objectives.[400]

Again, the action verbs are to "convey information" in order to "influence emotions, motives, objective reasoning, and behavior." The purpose is also the same, to induce or reinforce behavior favorable to the originator's objectives. Manipulation does more than mislead, convey, or influence, and it does more than try to obtain a result favorable to the initiators objectives. It tries to exploit the conveyance or the influencing of actions for the benefit of the manipulator and against the object of the manipulation.

Manipulation is the end result of a process that exploits people, thinking, or capabilities by affecting the prism through which an individual's values, stereotypes, or interests are processed. A person or state does not have to be the primary agent initially manipulated. Most often, the person or state responds to something—information, an incident, or some other outside stimulus—which subsequently affects his decision-making processes or perceptions. Manipulation even involves attempts to influence or persuade the attitudes and opinions of a country's own populace or the people and government of an alliance to which the country belongs. For example, attempts may be made to get an ally's population to see an opponent as a threat by depicting the opponent as a ruthless enemy.

Americans tend to overlook the term manipulation when assessing their own system because they associate the term with foreign propaganda methods. Yet it is prevalent everywhere in our society, especially in advertising, where companies try to persuade or manipulate the public into buying products. Manipulation even extends to White House personnel efforts to shape the

---

[399] Joint Publication 1-02, p. 304.
[400] Ibid., p. 287.

216

President's image and garner votes or support. <u>Time</u> magazine's article on the "Morris Method"—a reference to Presidential political consultant Dick Morris—portrayed the image-making process as a game to that created a family-friendly policy to redefine the way Americans perceived President Clinton. The method included constituent previews of a script and images to provide feedback which the military's PSYOP personnel would call the pretest phase of the plan.[401] Methods similar to those used by Morris have been used by presidents for many years.

Today, increasingly sophisticated states and people try to exploit advantages resulting from technological developments, tactical situations, or openings offered by negotiations. This illustrates that the dictionary definition of manipulation—"shrewd or devious management, especially for one's own advantage"—still holds true. The threat of manipulation is intensified by today's unstable environment, partially caused by changes in ruling elites and in missions for international organizations, historical claims, or religious beliefs. Taking advantage of this instability, combatants have manipulated events and actions in Bosnia's UN operation and in Somalia and Chechnya with considerable success. Terrorists also have used the instability to their advantage.

In Bosnia, LIC combatants manipulated cease-fires by redeploying and resupplying forces. This is not deception, disinformation, perception management, or PSYOP, but the result of using time to one's advantage and exploiting an opportunity.

In another example, combatants took advantage of inexperienced or news-hungry TV and radio broadcasters by helping them present stories or versions of a complicated event that did not reflect reality. The August 1995, market square bombing in Sarajevo is a good example. Less than an hour after the event, a Bosnian official, interviewed on CNN, reported that the UN had conclusive evidence that the Serbs were responsible for the bombing. This report strongly influenced a decision to conduct a NATO bombing mission against the Serbs. As stated earlier, further investigation revealed that actions surrounding the bombing left great doubt as to who did it. The media, and the world, were deeply influenced by the tragedy's quick coverage.

The problem with today's near-instantaneous press coverage is that analysis is often offered before all facts are considered. Heavy competition among news agencies encourages the tendency to rush news reports and, intentionally or not, manipulates our understanding of events. One <u>Washington</u>

---

[401] Eric Pooley, "Who is Dick Morris?" <u>Time</u>, 2 September 1996, p. 29.

<u>Post</u> reporter recently stated that news which is more than twelve hours old is pointless and may as well be three days old for press purposes. According to this logic, immediate coverage is vital. This thinking is dangerous and grossly overestimates the time required to conduct an event's factual investigation. This implies that not only the media but also organizations can manipulate events by rushing to conclusions. This was most recently proved by the intense negative coverage Richard Jewell received concerning the Atlanta Olympics bombing. Using police statements, the press unwittingly applied tremendous societal pressure on Jewell. In fact, the FBI may have manipulated the press by offering its own version of events.

Unexpected and dangerous consequences can result from rapidly transferring information when consequences not thought out in advance. Jewell's experience is just one example. Consider what could have happened during the Gulf War if press images were relayed immediately—in real-time—during the conduct of the coalition ground attack, as many journalists desired. This would have allowed Saddam Hussein, who possessed chemical and biological weapons, an unprecedented view of events—and all on CNN. As Hussein watched his force quickly fall to the coalition and heard reporters tell the world that Iraq's command and control structures were destroyed and the road to Baghdad was open, he may have come to his own "real-time" conclusion: If all is lost, then everyone else can lose with me. He could have ordered the launch of chemical or biological missiles. In a manner of speaking, Hussein could have been unwittingly manipulated into taking such action.

Manipulation Devices
Specific "manipulation devices" have effects that are enhanced by the Information Age. These include informational, psychological, technical, semantic, rhetorical, real-time, and behavioral devices. M. E. Gorbachev, a professor writing for the Russian journal <u>Security</u>, provided one of the most interesting discussions of many of these devices. Although he was discussing manipulation from a business relations viewpoint, his descriptions apply to international relations and military as well. His descriptions of informational and psychological devices follow. They were chosen due to the Soviets' extensive research in the propaganda and agitation fields during the Cold War when many of these devices were used. The first three manipulation devices will be described below.

Informational Devices
These devices are associated with the manipulator's desire to intentionally change the content of communications reported to the receiver. Methods to accomplish this include:

- Presenting an intentional lie or partial distortion of information to disinform or giving neutral information where facts are arranged in such a way as to lead audiences to a particular conclusion.
- Giving a one-sided or subjective explanation of a subject under discussion.
- Concealing important information or delaying in the reporting of it.
- Reducing information by glossing over information that may be harmful to the manipulator while emphasizing desired information in greater detail.
- Chopping information by presenting it in fragmented form to benefit the manipulator.
- Presenting rumors as truths, especially if they appear indisputable.
- Reducing the criticality of information by overloading the receiver with information.
- Including self-criticism on unimportant issues to create the appearance of objectivity.
- Conveying information that can be ascribed to a neutral source that the receiver trusts.
- "Leaking" reputedly confidential information that is not confidential.
- Pretending to communicate information on behalf of "trustworthy" sources.
- Using slander to poison the receiver's opinion of others.

Psychological Devices

These devices turn personality weaknesses to one's advantage or provoke an individual to lose control. Under the influence of these conditions, the receiver may make mistakes that benefit the manipulator. These methods include:

- Making a statement with multiple meanings, which shows the receiver that much is known about him, but for some special motive is not being revealed.
- Citing authorities whose opinions of the subject cannot be substantiated.
- Making unsupportable pledges and promises in advance.
- Creating an atmosphere of trust, although the manipulator barely knows the receiver.
- Pretending there is unity of thinking and closeness in spiritual values and interests.
- Discrediting other competing influences on the receiver that interfere with the manipulator's goal.

- Offering sympathy and support to the receiver under circumstances that eventually can be turned to the manipulator's advantage. For example, one can use a receiver's vanity and conceit to advantage with flattery and respect and by drawing one's ally into the conversation against another.[402]

Technical Devices

In addition to the psychological and information manipulation devices described by Gorbachev, modern states must first and foremost focus on technical manipulation. Technical devices have been used at the highest levels and focus on computers—the lifeline of the Information Age. One of the most bizarre, yet successful, manipulations using a technical device may have involved the United States, according to Alvin Snyder, former director of worldwide television for the US Information Agency during the Reagan years. Snyder produced a film about the downing of Korean Airlines (KAL) Flight 007. The film, shown at the UN, was designed to display to the world the insensitive and illegal way the Soviets shot down a civilian airliner. Snyder now says that important data was intentionally withheld from him, data that made it clear he was not given information on the pilots' conversations with ground elements, the ground controllers' responses, or the fighter pilots' actions.

According to new information Snyder has, the pilot fired warning shots and tipped his wings in the international signal to force the plane to land, all of which failed to get the crew's attention. As a result, Snyder's film version of the incident, based on selected sound bites, was incorrect. As Snyder noted:

> Using text in Russian and an English translation, along with a chronology and map of the route, the tape supported the contention that the Soviets wanted to only shoot down what they knew to be a passenger plane. They fired no warning shots nor gave any signal for the plane to land. The video became a key factor in what Secretary of State George Shultz promised in a memo to President Reagan would be a massive public relations effort "to exploit the incident." The intent was to link the incident to nuclear disarmament issues. Raising concerns about Soviet integrity could do serious damage to the

---

[402] The discussion of information under information and psychological devices was taken from M. I. Gorbachev, "Manipulyativnye priemy delovogo obshcheniya" [Business Translation Techniques], Bezapasnost' [Security], Moscow, No. 7-12 (23), July-December 1994, pp. 101-104. The author would like to thank Harry Orenstein of Supreme Headquarters Allied Powers, Europe for translating selected pages of this article.

Kremlin's peace campaign to dissuade NATO allies in Europe from placing upgraded American nuclear weapons on their soil.[403]

The film eventually led to the Security Council's condemnation of the Soviet action. Snyder's conclusion was that

> The video tape was powerful, effective, and wrong...Skilled technicians of today's multiplying forms of information make it easier to reach, and bamboozle, the public instantly...Technology may well spawn disinformation more insidious than any we have yet known. What replaces 1980s-style disinformation in the future may make it seem wholesome by comparison, and the press must be ever more vigilant.[404]

Technical devices thus produced a dramatic manipulation on an international and strategic level. The inability to identify a manipulation at the strategic level could be catastrophic for any nation in both the short- and long-terms because totally unforeseen consequences could result. A computer hacker can manipulate financial records, credit card listings, and other computer-stored data to suit his own interests. In fact, a computer operator in St. Petersburg, Russia, hacked his way into a Citicorp Bank of America account and transferred $10 million before being caught.

Allowing new and faster methods for groups to mobilize public opinion and coordinate actions, cellular phones, satellite TV, the Internet, and hand-held fax machines are some of the new tools or weapons that have energized the manipulation threat. The ammunition or bullets are provided by disinformation devices or items such as computer viruses, electronic warfare assets, or electromagnetic pulses which can destroy or disable a system. Disabling the satellite connections that allow many of these tools to operate is hardly an option for dealing with the manipulation threat because these connections are tied to the communication capabilities of major states. Other means to deal with the use of these assets must be developed. It is especially important to remember that the manipulation of events and actions through information-age tools is not limited to the battlefield. Serious strategic risks will require states to re-evaluate their defensive systems.

US reliance on information devices such as computers and communication networks to run critical power, finance, and transportation systems represents an especially lucrative and rich technical target group.

---

[403] Alvin Snyder, "Flight 007: The Rest of the Story," The Washington Post, 1 September 1996.
[404] Ibid.

Manipulation of these assets could divert energy or data and cause problems that could last for years. As one analyst recently noted in the <u>Federal Computer Week</u>, this reliance

> Has created a tunnel of vulnerability previously unrealized in the history of conflict and could have a catastrophic effect on the ability of DOD to fulfill its mission. The report of the Defense Science Board Task Force on Information Warfare-Defense (IW-D), obtained by <u>Federal Computer Week</u>, called the threat of an IW attack "significant," adding that the nation's "vulnerabilities are numerous, and the countermeasures are extremely limited..."[405]

There is another, more serious danger in the technical computer-manipulation arena, one which many Americans might expect to find in the pages of the <u>National Enquirer</u>. It does not involve semantic, informational, or psychological devices but focuses instead on a combination of technical and psychological devices that allegedly affect body processes. For the most part, this danger has been attributed to the Russian press and Russian scientists. Today, these scientists are studying how the display of information on computer monitors can affect the computer operator's bodily processes. They are looking for ways to manipulate the operator to make him press certain buttons or pass along or destroy certain information as if he were hypnotized. The Russians are seriously investigating the potential of this phenomenon.

There are reports that the Russians have developed "Virus 666," which displays certain color and number combinations on a computer screen to affect bodily processes. According to a Russian report delivered by a scientist from the renowned Russian Baumann Technical Institute at an information warfare conference in Washington, D.C., Virus 666 has been responsible for shutting down the bodily functions of more than fifty people, resulting in their deaths.[406]

Can such things happen? Americans are doubtful because there is no proof computer screens can be used to control or kill people. Most believe such reports are not credible, even though Russian scientists, supported by highly

---

[405] Bob Brewin and Heather Harreld, "US Sitting Duck, DOD Panel Predicts," <u>Federal Computer Week</u>, 11 November 1996, from internet site httpL//www.fcw.com/pubs/fcw/1111/duck.htm, as downloaded 3 December 1996.

[406] Victor I. Solntsev, "Information War and Some Aspects of a Computer Operator's Defense," paper given to the author at a conference on information war in Washington, D.C., 4-6 September 1996, p. 7. The incident in question reportedly occurred in August 1994.

influential people close to Russian leadership, are responsible for the information. Is Virus 666 a manipulation effort to make the US spend money on countermeasure research and development? Perhaps. Yet in hindsight, man once could not comprehend electricity either, and we should at least consider the possibility of this phenomenon. As the Russians have noted on several occasions, he who makes the first inroads into this area will control the destiny of mankind in the near future.

Is Manipulation a Real Threat?

Interestingly, the DOD <u>Dictionary of Military Terms</u> does not define either the term "threat" or, as mentioned above, the term "manipulation." The <u>American Heritage</u> dictionary defines a threat as "an indication of impending danger or harm." Thus, a threat does not have to be a person or country—the old concept of enemy. It can be a skill, a competency, an intention, or any other type of dangerous "manifestation." For example, the term "nuclear threat" has for years referred to a capability, not a person or state.

US Army Training and Doctrine Command Regulation 381-1, <u>Threat Management</u>, defines threat as "the ability of an enemy to limit, neutralize, or destroy the effectiveness of a current or projected mission, organization, or item of equipment." This definition focuses on the word "enemy," which limits it to people, and pays no particular attention to the tools an enemy might use.

A manipulation can be an "indicator of impending danger," especially if a computer system is the manipulation object, and it can be an enemy's ability to "limit, neutralize, or destroy the effectiveness of a current or projected mission." Therefore, manipulation appears to be a credible threat using this logic.

Yet this is only the beginning. It is not enough to say that our perceptions are being managed, or that a PSYOP, deception, or disinformation operation has been uncovered or that a manipulation operation is a threat. We must ascertain what has been manipulated (the end result), who or what has been affected, and how to rid the system or thinking of the manipulation effort. Then, the target audience must be informed of what has transpired. To say that a propaganda operation has, for example, "influenced" actions, emotions, and events is only the first step. Determining the manipulator's goals and assessing the damage must be done. Evaluating manipulation damage may be a new mission for PSYOP personnel in the military or for the US Information Agency at the national level. Both have personnel who should be trained to deal with this threat type.

As a result, military staffs and government decision-making agencies must devote more attention and expertise to identifying, exposing, and neutralizing manipulation techniques and efforts. This may mean realigning military staff responsibilities among PSYOP, S3 (operations), and command, control, communications and intelligence personnel to form manipulation "watch groups." Second, it means having the tools to uncover a deception and assess the resulting manipulation and determine at what levels or in what areas it has occurred.

Conclusions

In the 1930s, Orson Welles read the story "War of the Worlds" on public radio. While neither a deception nor disinformation operation, it produced sheer panic in many parts of the country. The broadcast merely exploited the average citizen's logic and prism through which he processed information and the means through which he received reliable information—the radio. It was an unintentional manipulation of the populace's rational thought. "Yellow journalism" and "jingoism" are also old manipulation devices. One need only recall William Randolph Hearst's comment to a newsman about the quiet in Cuba to understand the power of journalists. Hearst noted that "You do the reporting and I'll give you the war."

Often, the simple reporting of facts or their appearance can have an effect. For the Soviet Union, the US announcement about its plans to proceed with a "Star Wars" project produced panic among its military—how could they keep up with the evil Americans? In a similar manner, panic would spread among Americans if someone took over the stock market's computer system and told us about it! Both events potentially could produce long-term consequences. The Russians are still living with the effects of military overspending during the Cold War on systems they did not need. The stock market example would initially produce a run on funds and probably result in reduced investor confidence in the system. The stock market example invites a troubling question as well: If such a problem is detected, is it better to censor TV reporting to avert a panic while the authorities try to solve the problem? Clearly, manipulation, especially in its technical form, offers many challenges.

The idea of a manipulation operation does not initially stir the blood to action. It is a bland, unexciting threat that does not produce loud bangs or devastating physical destruction. Rather, its destruction is directed at the disruption of computer processes and logical thought and the disruption, distortion, or alteration of the context and information database on which important decisions are made. This results in seemingly benign choices. However, many of these choices can produce sheer panic or potentially devastating consequences, as the examples above demonstrate. Will

224

manipulation be with us as we approach the next century? Most certainly, and it would be foolish to believe otherwise. It will be used by many governments worldwide. In the fight over national interests, every advantage and all available assets will be exploited to produce favorable outcomes.

There are several lessons learned from this encounter with manipulation phenomena:

- Everyone must be more sensitive to the manipulation threat. As we read an article, computer message, or leaflet, it is extremely important to understand who and what the source is and what motivations are behind the report. Sometimes the publisher inserts biases for monetary or ideological reasons. Readers must be more attuned to the possibility of bias and view articles as information, not facts.
- Readers and decision-makers must consider the context within which reporting is conducted. Is it instantaneous? If so, one must carefully weigh the information until all the facts come in. Is the reporting well-reasoned? Has the reporter become emotionally attached to the environment in which he is working? Even more important for context is that today the political consciousness of citizens around the world has advanced to what one author has called the "proliferation of information." Entire classes of people who were once silent are now involved in the decision-making process. If they are manipulated, these people can mobilize groups and assets faster than ever before to support a cause or person.

  After considering an article's or television broadcast's source and context, the reader/viewer should decide if there has been any attempt to manipulate his thinking. Were any of the devices previously listed used? If manipulation is suspected or detected, then the reporter's intent should be questioned.
- We must learn how to neutralize damage and conduct battlefield assessments following a manipulation. The term "battlefield" refers primarily to a military operation although it can also apply to a civilian operation.[407] Simple articles in a newspaper or journal, a

---

[407] To uncover and foil a computer crime, one Russian recommended the following: form an integrated, interconnected system of measures of a legal and administrative nature aimed at combating this type of crime; organize interaction between public and private structures carrying out practical measures in ensuring security and protection of information processed in electronic form; inform the population about potential consequences of computer crime; bring the mass media into coverage and analysis of crimes in the information sphere; protect the interests and restore the rights of persons,

computer manipulation of the stock market, or the manipulation of a computer-operated reconnaissance-strike complex all require extensive neutralization and damage control. This will require that government, business, and military staffs allocate more assets and attention to this area.

The Information Age is propelling us forward faster than we ever imagined possible and is creating instantaneous global communications. Today's Pentium chips will soon become tomorrow's computer dinosaurs. Offices in Moscow viewed the Gulf War on CNN, just as we did in America, or others did in London and Toyko. Opportunities abound for practitioners of an old art to become the "new persuaders" of the Information Age. Unfortunately, our ability to neutralize the harmful effects or spinoffs of new technologies and to comprehend the opportunities offered to combatants by the instability in our international system paralyzes our sensitivity to the phenomena of manipulation operations. We must become more aware of what manipulation can do to our understanding of events and what we can do to neutralize its affects. One should read *this* article through that prism. To what extent was objectivity demonstrated? Have you been manipulated, and, if so, how and what can or should you do about it? But be careful—this type of thinking can cause paranoia.

public organizations, institutes, and enterprises that have become victims of computer crime; and expand international cooperation and teamwork in combating computer crime. To read more, see Dmitriy Maslennikov's article, "A Real Danger to Citizens Lives: MVD and FSB Specialists have Drafted a Federal Program Uncovering and Stopping Computer Crime," Nezavisimoye Voyennoye Obozreniye, [Independent Military Review] Supplement to Nezavisimaya Gazeta,[Independent Newspaper], No. 13, 11 July 1996, p. 7.

CHAPTER THIRTEEN: HUMAN NETWORK ATTACKS[408]

US information warfare (IW) theory consists of some very basic premises: attaining information superiority or dominance, maintaining a quick tempo and decision cycles, integrating efforts whenever possible, and working constantly to exploit the information environment. This theory is based on six capabilities: operations security, psychological operations, deception, destruction, electronic warfare, and computer network attack.

One of the overriding concerns of the US military is the security of these IW capabilities, especially computer networks. The Pentagon has poured millions of dollars into constructing an infrastructure-protection package aimed at limiting hacker access to manipulate or corrupt our data storage resources in peacetime or wartime. One specific data processor, however, has received far less attention in US thinking. It is the security of the data processor known as the mind, which unfortunately has no innate firewall to protect it from either deceptive or electromagnetic processes. As a result, the mind of the soldier on the battlefield is potentially the most exploitable and unprotected IW capability our military possesses. Soldiers' vulnerability to human network attacks (HNA) should be an area of close attention for scientists in the early years of the new millennium.[409]

China and Russia, in addition to studying hardware technology, data processing equipment, computer networks and "system of systems" developments, have focused considerable attention on several nontraditional targets of the information weapon, to include the mind.[410] This attention differs from the US approach for both practical and cultural reasons. Neither China nor Russia has the financial capability or the infrastructure to compete with Western IW technological advancements. However, both countries have a

---

[408] This article was published under the same title in the September-October 1999 issue of <u>Military Review</u>, pp. 23-33 and reflects definitions in vogue at that time. This is a slightly shortened version of the original.

[409] HNA is the author's term to describe the impact of human, computer, or nonlethal generated attacks, such as deception or electromagnetic effects, on the human nervous or cognitive systems. It is neither a Chinese nor a Russian term, merely a descriptor.

[410] For two traditional discussions of Chinese and Russian IW thinking by this author, see "Behind the Great Firewall of China: A Look at RMA and IW Thinking from 1996-1998" and "Dialectical versus Empirical Thinking: Ten Key Elements of the Russian Understanding of Information Operations," both located on the Foreign Military Studies Office web page, found at <http://fmso.leavenworth.army.mil/fsmo.htm>

wealth of outstanding mathematicians, philosophers, and scientists that can offset this shortcoming through the development of nontraditional approaches, as well as historical and cultural proclivities that draw their focus to this area.

The US armed forces, a producer of HNA variants, as demonstrated by psychological operations or nonlethal weapon options, could profit by studying the approaches developed in China and Russia. Examining other approaches to HNA activities would assist in uncovering HNA techniques and vulnerabilities. This article examines China's psychological warfare and knowledge concepts (including the impact of the Information Age on China's strategic culture) and "new concept" weapons (variants of nonlethal weapons); and Russia's development of information-psychological operations, "intellectual IW" stratagems, and human behavior control mechanisms. The latter issue makes Russian thinking on HNA unique. It is clear that to both countries, "gray matter" does matter.

Chinese Nontraditional Practices

In military actions, attacking minds, that is the primary mission; attacking fortifications, that is a secondary mission. Psychological war is the main thing. Combat is secondary.[411]
—Third Century Chinese Military Theoretician

China's entry into the Information Age has proceeded with caution, anticipation, and good luck. Caution was used due to the sudden ability of its citizens to communicate with people around the globe, a new phenomenon in Chinese culture, where outside access and information is tightly controlled. Anticipation refers to China's opportunity to quickly catch up with other world powers through the information medium. China has many outstanding mathematicians to speed this process, especially in the development of software. Good luck refers to acquiring Hong Kong at a time when the information revolution was reaching its peak. For purposes of launching a Chinese information-based economy, access to Hong Kong's telecommunications and financial markets is akin to winning the lottery. The market will insert new life into the six or so semiconductor fabrication lines already operating in China. In addition, China's ideological and economic changes have proceeded more slowly than Russia's, ensuring some stability through the 1990s. Russia's population has paid the price for moving too quickly.

---

[411] Sergei Modestov, "Kutay gotovitsya k informatsionnym voynam" [China is Preparing for Information War], <u>Nezavisimoe voennoe obozrenie</u> [Independent Military Review], No. 13, 1998, p. 2.

A widespread Chinese view is that information technology (IT) has given rise to a new, worldwide military revolution as well. IT is the

> Core and foundation of this military revolution, because information and knowledge have changed the previous practice of measuring military strength by simply counting the number of armored divisions, air force wings and aircraft carrier battle groups. Nowadays, one must also consider invisible forces, such as computing capabilities, communications capacity and system reliability.[412]

A key component of this revolution is information warfare.

In 1995, Dr. Shen Weiguang, known in China as the father of its IW theory, wrote an IW introductory research piece for the Chinese military newspaper Jiefangjun Bao [PLA Daily Newspaper]. Shen defined information warfare as command and control warfare or *decision control warfare*, where information is the main weapon designed to attack the enemy's cognitive and information systems and influence, contain or change the decisions of enemy policy makers and their consequent hostile actions. The main target of IW is the enemy's cognitive and trust systems, and the goal is to exert control over his actions. The Chinese sometimes refer to this idea as "guidance control." Here the term "cognitive system" refers mainly to information and computer decision-making systems. This thinking is similar, Shen notes, to "electronic beheading" at the beginning of an IW operation.[413]

Four years later, in an article describing the use of NATO IW during the conflict in Kosovo, Wang Baocun described how NATO worked first to behead the command systems of the Yugoslav armed forces. Take away the mind and the body will follow. Wang also noted, however, that the Yugoslav armed forces—the inferior—successfully thwarted NATO attacks— the superior—through the skillful use of three defensive concepts. First, they concealed personnel and armaments to preserve strength (hiding planes in caves or by ring roads; concealed tanks in forests, beside large buildings, or on mountainsides; dispersed the army into each village to mingle with the Albanians; and moved command organs underground). Second, the Yugoslav armed forces successfully used their technical means to avoid detection by not

---

[412] Hai Lung and Chang Feng, "Chinese Military Studies Information Warfare," Kuang Chiao Ching [Wide Angled Lens], 16 January 1996, pp. 22-23 as translated in FBIS-CHI-96-035, 21 February 1996, pp. 33-34.

[413] Shen Weiguang, "Focus of Contemporary World Military Revolution-Introduction to Research in Information Warfare," Jiefangjun Bao [PLA Daily Newspaper], 7 November 1995, p. 6 as translated in FBIS-CHI-95-239, 13 December 1995, pp. 23-25.

switching on air defense radars, or switching them on infrequently; obtaining the coordinates and operational orbits of reconnaissance satellites; switching off engines, putting equipment close to other heat sources or putting fake heat sources in mock-up tanks; and taking advantage of weak points in electronic surveillance equipment (for example, some systems do not work if a target is stationary). Finally, the Internet was used to communicate the opinions of ordinary citizens to the outside world and to hack or overload NATO email sites.[414] Asymmetric options offset information superiority.

The Chinese also dissected the success of the superior coalition forces against the inferior Iraqi forces in the Gulf War. They cited Iraq's economic dependence, inflexible strategies, and passive defensive tactics as adding to its inferiority. This led, according to one People's Liberation Army (PLA) officer, to the erroneous conclusion that it is impossible for a weak force to defeat a strong force in a high-technology war. It *is* possible for a weak force to win against a high-tech force in war, but this requires bringing the overall function of its operational system into full play, to persevere in defeating the superior with the inferior in crucial battles and, through the integration of the above two aspects, turn the inferior into the superior and finally defeat the enemy.[415]

Information war conducted between China and Taiwan is increasing tension in the area. On 18 August 1999, the London Times reported that Taiwanese computer experts were repairing damage from a Chinese hacker attack on the National Assembly, where Chinese flags were planted and a message in Chinese and English noted that "Only one China exists and only one is needed." Taiwanese hackers have targeted China's Securities Regulation Commission and the Science and Technology Bureau, among other targets. At one provincial tax bureau, the note that "China should stop playing with fire; we will declare independence should you dare to attack us" was attached to a site as part of a raid. Such declarations indicate that the Information Age can allow tensions to quickly escalate by direct exchanges of strategic importance that were impossible to make on such a wide scale in the past.[416]

To the Chinese, technology per se is relevant but not sufficient in the long run, especially if viewed from the current inadequate Chinese position

---

[414] Wang Baocun, "Information Warfare in the Kosovo Conflict," Beijing Jiefangjun Bao [PLA Daily Newspaper], 25 May 1999, as downloaded from the FBIS website on 28 June 1999.

[415] Shen Kuiguan, "Dialectics of Defeating the Superior with the Inferior," Chinese Views of Future Warfare, revised edition, edited by Michael Pillsbury, National Defense University Press, Washington, DC, 1998, pp. 216-217.

[416] David Watts, London Times, 18 August 1999, as downloaded from the Internet.

regarding IT. One must also create new military theories to complement technological advances and overcome the technological superiority of other nations. Chinese history is rich in the theory of military art, and its analysts can draw from historical examples and stratagems.

Strategic Culture and the Information Age

The world's military theoreticians are intimately familiar with the wisdom and insights contained in the works and stratagems of China's military philosophers. Now, these same stratagems are being reexamined by Chinese theorists for their relevancy to the Information Age.

The ancient Chinese strategic concept of "not fighting and subduing the enemy" has received particular attention within the context of information-age technologies in China and the West. This concept has found especially fertile ground in political and strategic warfare circles. Even the Chinese game of Wei-chi ("Go" according to many American translations), requiring strategic thinking and foresight (similar to chess in that respect), involves an initial strategy of "not fighting and subduing the enemy."[417] This concept most likely affects modern Chinese political strategists in Beijing as well, prompting moves to control islands in the Spratleys and the takeover of shipping companies in the post-US controlled Panama Canal region in an effort to control flow in and out of the canal. Using information to influence (speed up or impede) financial transactions involved in the Canal negotiations (financial information war), to intercept counterpart negotiating strategies (the electronic warfare aspect), or to deceive a negotiating partner are but a few examples. The latter example is particularly important, since manipulation of human perceptions is an ancient Chinese art and strategic tradition. One report on computer network attacks, for example, noted that a situation could be "shaped" to China's advantage by psychological means, then deception, and, finally, dynamic means.

Recent military mobilization moves by China against Taiwan might just be a psychological and deceptive method to uncover an alliance strategy in the region through IW assets that monitor and analyze Taiwanese and its allies' information operations (as well as Western responses to these moves). The game of cat and mouse continues, only now the animals are studied as much for their virtual characteristics as for their real ones.

---

[417] George Capen, "Wei-chi: The Game of War," <u>Proceedings</u>, August 1999, p. 60. This game focuses on territorial expansion, attacking, and defending. Territorial expansion occurs in peacetime, according to the rules of the game.

Upon closer analysis, the "not fighting" theory certainly is not a singular representation of Chinese strategy in the Information Age but one among many that warrants closer analysis. Another strategy, "absolute flexibility," received much less attention until recently when the book Unrestricted Warfare caused a furor in the West. It offers just the opposite view from "not fighting," and the strategic analogy is closer to the concept of "absolute flexibility" or the notion of quan bian. This strategy requires one to "respond flexibly . . . and create conditions for victory."[418] The nonmilitary means the authors advance include such IW related concepts as the use of hackers, the mass media, and financial information terrorism. The key is the unique alignment and integration of psychological, diplomatic, resource, and other warfare techniques, all of which have information aspects. One of the authors, Colonel Qiao Liang, noted that "unrestricted warfare is in the final analysis a way for a weak and small country to cope with 'evil,'" as in another old stratagem, "defeating the superior with the inferior." This might involve breaking rules and exploiting loopholes, according to Qiao, and favors nonmilitary means such as soft strikes, magnetic weapons (computer logic bombs), media weapons, and electromagnetic energy weapons that do not cause hard destruction.[419] Thus, the "new concept" weapons listed below should be viewed in the light of their potential use as an HNA agent.

Unrestricted Warfare indicates that "not fighting" is not necessarily the ideal to follow in the Information Age. "Not fighting" gained notoriety in the West primarily because it was the principal slogan used by IW proponents to promote their theories. "Not fighting" was the basis for the clean IW rules that the West hoped to play by in the Information Age—no casualties, just a victory from a stand-off position. Perhaps this is why the publication of Unrestricted War caused such an uproar. It indicated that conflict might actually be preferred in some cases in the Information Age, depending on priorities set by Chinese leaders. As Qiao noted, "the stronger side is never the first to break the rules and use irregular methods."

---

[418] Alastair I. Johnston, Cultural Realism, Princeton Academic Press, 1995, p. 102. Johnston's outstanding book should be reinterpreted through the lens of the Information Age in order to get at the heart of the Chinese use of information technologies as strategic tools or methods today.

[419] Sha Lin, "Two Senior Colonels and 'No-Limit' Warfare," Beijing Zhongguo Qingnian Bao [China Youth News], 28 June 1999, p. 5. The author has taken the liberty to use the term unrestricted in place of no-limit, as it has been translated in other places. The article was translated and downloaded from the FBIS web page on 28 July 1999.

IW's Relation to Psychological Operations

The PLA has not published a great deal on the subject of psychological operations. What it has published does not seem to be strikingly different from Western theory except that there is more emphasis on peacetime psychological operations. In fact, there is even some agreement among Chinese and Russian psychologists about the growing importance of both countering and conducting peacetime information-psychological defensive and offensive operations. These operations set the stage for wartime IW and by Chinese estimates can sap the morale of the soldier by a factor of several times greater than in previous wars due to the power and manipulative ability of IT. Failure to confront this information-psychological invasion is more serious than military backwardness in other areas, according to some Chinese analysts.[420] In the Gulf War, only after reducing combat morale among some 40 to 60 percent of the Iraqi forces did the multinational forces decide to attack, in the Chinese view.

Technological developments have made it possible to subject all people, from ordinary citizens to heads of state, to a complex information offensive. Simulated and reproduced voices, fabricated provocative speeches delivered by virtual heads of state, and projected images of actual life situations can affect troops psychologically.[421] In the area of psychological warfare, author Liu Ping stressed that China recognizes special information media, such as language, texts, images, and sound, as future enemy weapons capable of exerting a "multilevel operational effect" instead of simply a political or economic one. The target remains the enemy's decision-making processes, both human (the mind's soft data processor) and material (hardware data processing). The main task is to overwhelm opposing forces through the use of terror tactics, thereby upsetting their psychological stability. Psychological war usually starts in peacetime and, if war erupts, will run throughout its course.[422]

Liu noted that psychological warfare is now planned at the highest levels of the armed forces or state leadership. The equipment of psychological warfare supports this idea, since "facts" can now be fabricated in a much more realistic form (real-time on radio or TV) using high-tech voice and image recording and editing equipment. Perhaps even more important, the means of psychological warfare are now more diversified, and its striking force has increased.

---

[420] Miao Jinyuan, "Information Psychological Offensive," Jiefangjun Bao [PLA Daily Newspaper], 9 July 1996, p. 6 as reported in FBIS-CHI-96-168, 9 July 1996.

[421] Ibid.

[422] Liu Ping, "Some Remarks on Future Psychological Warfare," Jiefangjun Bao [PLA Daily Newspaper], 18 August 1998, p. 6 as translated and downloaded from the FBIS web page, 31 August 1998.

Today, simulation, stealth, and various types of camouflage technologies allow for the "mixing of the spurious with the genuine" and can cause errors in the enemy's decision-making. More important is acoustic technology because it creates deafening noises, such as explosions, whizzing sounds, rumblings, and heartrending screams, to upset psychological stability. Liu notes that other countries' psychological warfare offensives will attempt to penetrate the mind of PLA soldiers or key decision-makers to throw them into a psychological maze or cause psychological disorders or panic.[423] This psychological warfare organization bears closer scrutiny as it develops. As a result, the following was recommended to counter enemy IW techniques:

> It is necessary to set up an organization for psychological warfare; form a theoretical system for modern psychological warfare with the characteristics of our army; promulgate a training program for psychological warfare and regulations for psychological warfare operations and standardize the training and combat of the whole army; set up specialized psychological warfare units; and strive to raise our army's capabilities in psychological warfare.[424]

Knowledge Warfare

One Chinese analyst has noted that the human must be able to comprehend what happens when two systems collide, such as two command and control systems or an electronic warfare (EW) system and a counter EW system. The human must be able not only to control or manipulate such interactions and their consequences but to comprehend what has happened and why.[425] If the human can master this interaction, then he employs "knowledge warfare," which the Chinese believe rivals information warfare in importance. While the latter is data, the former is how to use the data to one's advantage. Even though knowledge is invisible, it can be transformed into combat power and affect combat effectiveness. This concept will not be fully realized until after the first full-scale confrontation between highly technical combatants. Then, for the side that has not taken knowledge warfare into consideration, it will be too late. Simulations cannot provide true understanding of such confrontations.

Analyst Wu Jianguo, speaking at a Chinese conference devoted to studying knowledge warfare, stated that "knowledge confrontations are the focus of military confrontations and the hallmark of an army's strength is its *intellectual* combat capability." Soldiers must depend on their ability to apply

---

[423] Ibid.
[424] Ibid.
[425] Ibid.

knowledge and innovate. The information engagement will not be between the soldier and the battlefield as some expect but rather it will test the soldier's mastery over the network and his ability to prevent the enemy from paralyzing it.[426] The knowledge confrontation system will have the most decisive significance in the era of smart warfare where, according to Wu, it will be more important than the firepower, mechanical, electronic, and even information confrontations. It is the subsystem that requires top priority in development and should become the core mission of military education, training, and war preparation in China. Wu recommends the establishment of a coordinating department for the entire military and national security systems to synergize all forms of knowledge-based confrontations.[427] As one Chinese analyst noted about knowledge:

> New information technologies are permeating and functioning in all spheres of society in an all-pervasive way, making information and knowledge important resources and wealth. If we say knowledge equals wealth in economic life, then in the military field it equals victory. With the advent of an era of intellectual militaries, changes in the military field will lead to dazzling military changes as if thousands upon thousands of pear trees blossomed overnight in the wake of a spring wind.[428]

There is also a desire in the Chinese military to manipulate information, a tendency much stronger in the Russian nontraditional approach. Chinese analyst Wang Zhi, for example, noted that warfare is changing from "organizing around the weapon system" to "organizing around information." Processes are under development to prevent an enemy from using information correctly or to paralyze him, leading to mistakes in recognizing or responding to a situation or in decision-making.[429]

New Concept Weapons

Chinese writings have not emphasized psychotronic weapons or suggestive influences, as have the Russians. Rather, they have focused on the

---

[426] Zhang Guoyu, "Symposium on the Challenge of the Knowledge Revolution for the Military," Beijing Jiefangiun Bao [PLA Daily Newspaper], 5 January 1999, p. 6 as translated and downloaded from the FBIS web page.
[427] Ibid.
[428] Wang Yongyin, "Intellectualization: Inevitable Trend of Future Military Development," Jiefangjun Bao [PLA Daily Newspaper], 20 April 1999, p. 6 as translated and downloaded from the FBIS web page on 10 May 1999.
[429] Wang Zhi, "Lessons Learned from the Historical RMA," talk presented in Beijing in November 1998.

impact of what they term "new-concept weapons," such as infrasound weapons, lasers, microwave and particle-beam weapons, and incoherent light sources.[430] Speaking to foreign participants, analyst Wang Zhi added ultraviolet radiation, anti-environment (earthquakes, for example), and biological weapons to this list. These innovations will allow decision-makers to select and adjust the intensity of war according to their needs.[431] One needs simply to "turn up the volume" if a technique is not working.

Infrasound weapons use sound waves with frequencies lower than 20 Hz to cause cardiac, respiratory, digestive, and central nervous system malfunctions, disorientation, and emotional disorders. The journal People's Military Surgeon noted that such a weapon has already been developed and tested, and that infrasound waves generated by the device are adjustable to cause controllable amounts of disorientation, nausea, vomiting, and incontinence.[432] The journal also describes the use of microwave weapons to cause electronic interference, lasers to disable equipment, and incoherent light sources and super-high frequency weapons, with the latter capable of interfering with the functioning of the human nervous system and capable of causing unbearable noise and whistling sounds.[433] The People's Military Surgeon article ended on the ominous note:

> Weapons generating interference and causing blindness have become practical to use. Foreign armed forces already have corresponding prevention and protection measures, standard, and diagnostic techniques, and have conducted further research . . . [and] microwave electronic interference equipment is already widely utilized. Therefore, medical protection against microwaves is already being developed.[434]

The Chinese military apparently believes these devices will be used in future war since its doctors are investigating treatment for injuries caused by special types of high-tech or new-concept weapons.[435]

---

[430] "New Concept Weapons and its Medical-Related Problems," Beijing Renmin Junyi [PLA Military Medicine], No. 9, September 1997, pp. 507-508.
[431] Wang Zhi.
[432] The monthly journal Beijing Renmin Junyi of the PLA General Logistics Department Health Department carries many technical articles on military medicine.
[433] "New Concept..."
[434] Ibid.
[435] Rui Yaocheng, Wei Shuiyi, and Chen Shengxin, "Progress in Military Pharmacological Research, Application," Zhongguo Yaoxue Zazhi [China

Russian Nontraditional Practices

> *The image is fragmented and introduced in pieces into 'normal' frames by an unnoticeable element and the subconscious mind instantly `reads' the pieces as the encoded image.*[436]
>
> —*Russian Medical Journal, September 1998*

Russia entered the 1990s in an entirely different context than the Chinese. The country has been fragmented, with the former republics receiving their independence from the center. The concepts of Perestroika and Glasnost' have upset the ideological prism through which Russians viewed the world. Some believe this has led to a spiritual vacuum, while others think this has led to a disregard for state interests, to money-laundering schemes and the growth of criminal structures, among other phenomena. Russia's economic troubles have been well documented. At the same time, the country has embraced the information revolution. Now it is much easier to contact ordinary citizens through the Internet than in China. Russia is also faster at adapting to information innovations and applying them to industry. The problem remains finding the money to do so.

However, like China, Russia has felt that it is the object of information-psychological aggression from abroad and has attempted to establish some legal and doctrinal criteria for thwarting such attacks. The country has a draft information security doctrine, a Duma subcommittee devoted to information security issues, and a security service that increasingly is patrolling and regulating cyberspace. Russian authorities consider citizens extremely vulnerable to outside influences and information weapons. Some blame the West for using these means to accelerate the Warsaw Pact's disintegration.

Russian Major S.V. Markov, writing in the journal Bezapasnost' [Security], defined an information weapon as "a specially selected piece of information capable of causing changes in the information processes of information systems (physical, biological, social) according to the intent of the entity using the weapon."[437]

Pharmaceutical Journal], Vol. 32, pp. 662-667 as translated and downloaded from the FBIS web page, 23 September 1998.

[436] Translation of FBIS that was downloaded from their web page.

[437] S.V. Markov, "O nekotoryk podkhodakh k opredeleniyu sushchnosti informatsionnogo oruzhiya [Several approaches to the determination of the essence of the information weapon]," Bezopasnost' [Security], No. 1-2, 1996, p. 53.

Thus, an information weapon could be a virus, incorrect commands, or disinformation, among other things. The information weapon can be used to destroy, distort, or steal data files; to mine or obtain the desired information from the files after penetrating defense systems/firewalls; to limit or prevent access to systems and files by authorized users; to introduce disorganization or disorder into the operation of technical equipment; and to completely disable telecommunication networks, computer systems, and all the advanced technology that supports society and the operation of the state.[438] Such information weapons can be used at the strategic, operational, and tactical levels.

Russian IW modelers try to foresee the application and utility of information weapons. They study an information model of the psyche of a person and then attempt to simulate the interaction between people, social groups, and other factors. The formation of methods to ensure moral-psychological stability is important to Russian modelers. They want to counter the influence of information weapons that aim to suppress the will to resist, "zombify" the psyche through manipulation and reconfigured thinking, reprogram human behavior, and demoralize and psychologically degrade people.[439]

IW and Information-Psychological Operations

With the elevation of the information-psychological factor to such prominence in discussions of information weapons, the psychological factor has become a prime consideration in many current IW definitions. The various national security agencies in Russia look at the concept from their own contextual situation. The definition of the Foreign Intelligence Service, for example, differs from that of the Federal Agency for Government Communications and Information. This article uses a military definition. An officer from Russia's General Staff Academy defined information war as a technical/psychological activity:

> Information warfare is a way of *resolving a conflict* between opposing sides. The goal is for one side to gain and hold an information advantage over the other. This is achieved by exerting a specific information/psychological and information/technical influence on a *nation's decision-making system, on the nation's populous and on its information resource structures*, as well as defeating the enemy's control system and his information resource structures with the help of

---

[438] Ibid., p. 56.
[439] Ibid., p. 59.

additional means, such as nuclear assets, weapons and electronic assets.[440]

Information-psychological security, defined as "the condition and use of information to guarantee the functional reliability of the psyche and consciousness of a person in peacetime or wartime," must remain a goal of commanders in the field.[441] A system of information-psychological security is important because:

> In the past half century the potential for working on the consciousness, psyche or morale of a person, society or the composition of an armed force has grown dramatically. One of the main reasons is the considerable success achieved by many countries in their systematic research in the areas of psychology, psychotronics, parapsychology, other new psychophysical phenomenon, bio-energy, biology and psychoenergy in the fields of security and defense.[442]

While Western analysts place less credence in these latter issues, it is nevertheless important to recognize the attention and assets Russia directs to them. Some Russian military analysts have warned that the country is and will be the object of information-psychological strikes, aggression, expansion, and pressure. A recommendation was made by one officer to construct an information-psychological counteraction (IPC) program.[443]

In fact, the information-psychological factor is so important to the Russian military that it considers the information-psychological operation as an independent form of military activity. A military activity is defined by the Russian military as "an activity conducted in the form of engagements, battles, operations, strikes and systematic combat actions." The term usually refers to

---

[440] Discussion with a Russian officer in Moscow, May 1995. An *information resource* as used here refers to: information and transmitters of information, the method or technology of obtaining, conveying, gathering, accumulating, processing, storing and using that information; the infrastructure, including, information centers, the means for automating information processes, switchboard communications and data transfer networks; the programming-mathematical means for managing information; the administrative and organizational bodies that manage information processes, scientific personnel, creators of databases and knowledge, as well as personnel who service the means of informatization.

[441] Markov, p. 47.

[442] Ibid., p. 45.

[443] Ye. G. Korotchenko, "Information-Psychological Warfare in Modern Conditions," Military Thought, English edition, No. 1, 1996, p. 25.

operations on a strategic scale. Thus, the military is looking for ways to construct or win information-psychological engagements, battles, and operations. These operations may include the normal leaflets and loudspeakers but could extend to atypical responses. Traditional IW uses, such as planned engagements of the enemy's information systems on the battlefield, might join nontraditional uses, such as striking at the enemy's perception of reality or attempting to control behavior or break the mental stability of combatants through the use of high-tech (holograms, satellite destruction) or nonlethal (acoustic or electromagnetic) means. Conversely, the goal of defensive information-psychological operations would be to protect the military collective and operations from such activities and counter any negative enemy action aimed at the psyche of the soldier.

One of the leading proponents of this idea is General Major E.G. Korotchenko, deputy chief of the chair for military art at the General Staff Academy. Korotchenko views information methods and techniques as nontraditional forms of power wielding. The main goal of IW against Russia in the information-psychological sense, Korotchenko believes is "to capture the consciousness of the population of the Russian Federation, to undermine the moral and fighting potential of the armed forces and set the stage for political, economic and military penetration."[444] Agents of this activity are considered to be the foreign mass media and the "activities" of tourists, foreign intelligence agents, and certain businessmen, advisers, and journalists. This characterization implies the peacetime use of IW and Korotchenko includes foreign agents' use of either special psychotropic or possibly even psychotronic means.[445]

Russian theorists have gone so far as to attempt to mathematically calculate the morale-psychological stability of the modern soldier and figure this component into their assessment of success or failure in engagements and battles. Some scientists are working on a mathematical model to calculate under

---

[444] Ibid., p. 22.

[445] Ibid., 23. Psychotronics is defined as "an inter-disciplinary area of scientific knowledge, which, mediated by consciousness and by perceptual processes, investigates distant (noncontiguous) interactions among living organisms and the environment. It studies the energy and information phenomena of such interactions." See V.D. Ts'gankov and V.N. Lopatin, Psikhotronnoe Oruzhie i Bezopasnost' Rossii [Psychotronic Weapons and the Security of Russia], Moscow 1999, pp. 16-17.A psycho-physical (psychotronic) weapon is defined as "a technically generated means designed to exert an information and/or energy influence on the functions of the human psyche and on the physiological functioning of human organs and systems. It belongs to the category of non-lethal weapons." See M.I. Abdurakhmanov, V.A. Barishpolets, V.L. Manilov, V.S. Pirumov, Geopolitika I Natsional'naya Bezopasnost' [Geopolitics and National Security], Moscow 1998, p. 144.

what conditions the spirit of the soldier becomes a mass multiplier (an idea based on Leo Tolstoy's description of the spirit of the fighting man in War and Peace).[446] Other scientists are studying the moral-psychological impact of certain information actions, such as cutting access to a soldier's global positioning system (GPS).

Reflexive Control: an Information Weapon Subset

The Soviet Union had a propaganda machine second to none. One of its most intriguing methods for managing information and getting people (or an opponent) to perform a certain action was described by the theory of reflexive control (RC). In a military context, it can be viewed as a means for providing one military commander with the ability to indirectly maintain control over his opposing commander's decision process.[447] Reflexive control involves creating a pattern or providing partial information that causes an enemy to react in a predetermined fashion without realizing that he is being manipulated. Its aim above all else is to influence command and control systems and decision-makers. Colonel S. Leonenko stressed the importance of using RC against systems in the IW age:

> Under present conditions a need arises to act not only on people, but also on technical reconnaissance assets and especially weapon guidance systems, which are impassive in assessing what is occurring and do not perceive what a person reacts to.[448]

Thus, a system may be easier to deceive than a person. Colonel Leonenko further noted that under today's conditions the importance of the commander's personality in deciding what RC action to use is somewhat diminished, since collective decision-making has become the standard way of doing business. In Leonenko's opinion, in addition to the increased potential for being fooled, computers hamper RC by making it easier to process data and calculate options. That is, computers' speed and accuracy make it easier for an

---

[446] V.I. Tsymbal, "Kolichestvenno-kachestvennyi analiz vliyaniya informatsion-nykh sredstv na khod i iskhod vooruzhennoi bor'by [Qualitative-Quantitative Analysis of the Influence of Information Means on the Course and Outcome of Armed Conflict]," report published in Analiz Sistem Na Poroge XXI Veka: Teoriya i Praktika [Systems Analysis on the Verge of the 21st Century: Theory and Practice], conference proceedings, Moscow, 1997, p. 281.

[447] Clifford Reid, "Reflexive Control in Soviet Military Planning," in Soviet Strategic Deception, edited by Brian Daily and Patrick Parker, Lexington Books, p. 294.

[448] S. Leonenko, "O Refleksivnoe upravlenie protivnikom [On Reflexive Control of the Enemy]," Armeyskiy sbornik [Army Journal], No. 8, 1995, p. 28.

opponent to "see through" an RC attempt by an opposing force if the information is processed correctly.[449]

From the X-Files

The Russian armed forces are studying a host of unusual subjects, almost all of which center on how information or electronic waves affect the mind. For example, a recent book offered an extensive set of algorithms designed to implant "suggestive influences" or what the author called "psycho viruses" into a person's mind. This officially sanctioned book was commissioned by the Security Committee of the State Duma. The leader of a Security Committee subset, the Information Security Committee of the State Duma, coauthored a book titled Psychotronic Weapons as well.

This latter subject has been one of intense military interest over the past several years. An article that appeared in the armed forces journal Orientier [Reference Point] a few years ago was titled "Can a Ruler make 'Zombies' Out of the World?" with a subtitle reading "It is completely possible that humanity is standing on the verge of psychotronic war." The article described many of the "psy" weapons available for use, such as VHF generators, lasers, x-ray equipment, ultrasound and radio waves. A psychotronic generator, for example, was described as a device that produces powerful electromagnetic emanations.[450]

The Ministry of Defense reportedly has a special unit known as 10003. According to the newspaper Novaya Gazeta-Ponedelnik (clearly not a mainstream newspaper and therefore suspect), this unit studies mysticism and the occult, primarily to understand the essence of mind control (for use in recruiting and other situations).[451] In other words, the Russians are exhaustively exploring what makes the mind tick and how to manage it.

It is important to note that many, if not all, of the "X-file" subjects listed here are highly suspect in the West. Even the newspapers in which such articles appear must be viewed with caution. Whether these ideas work or not is

---

[449] Ibid., p. 29. On the other hand, computer processing may actually improve the chances for RC's being accepted since a computer may not have the intuitive capability of a human.

[450] I. Chernishev, "Poluchat li poveliteli 'zombi' vlast' nad mirom?" [Can a Ruler Make 'Zombies' Out of the World?] Orientier [Reference Point], February 1997, pp. 58-62.

[451] Roman Shleynov, "Armed Evil Forces: The Dubious Experiments of the Ministry of Defense," Novaya Gazeta-Ponedelnik [New Newspaper-Monday], 26 October-1 November 1998, No. 42, 1 and 5 as translated in FBIS, 11 November 1998.

not the point. The issue is they form one of the elements of the Russian understanding of IW.

In their search to offset Western supremacy in the IW arena, Russian and Chinese theorists are exploring nontraditional, asymmetric approaches. One is to utilize the capabilities of psychological operations and deception to fool one's cognitive processes, especially the case in China, on the strategic level. Another is to control the mind and to affect the nervous system. This effort involves HNA methods designed to upset the data-processing capability of the human nervous system. In China these efforts are referred to as "new concept" weapons and in Russia as psychotronic war. Similar efforts with nonlethal weapons have produced some results in the West.

The Chinese approach to date, based on open-source materials, approximates efforts in the West (perhaps by design) in the psychological operations and deception fields. Chinese thinking in the HNA arena will be supplemented and integrated with the rich Chinese traditions in military art that impart a distinctive flavor to their strategic culture that is different from most Western theories. Russia's approach is more direct in exploring capabilities to corrupt or manipulate mathematical algorithms that control software packages and human behavior.

The ability to study the mind for all its strengths and weaknesses has always been a Chinese and Eastern culture strength. Russia also has had a strong capability in operational thinking in the military field and became most adept at using propaganda to the fullest extent during the days of communism. Data-processing capabilities of the mind is a new but logical extension of these tendencies. The West should absorb what is said about these matters in Russia and China, just as these countries have done with our debates over hardware. There is much to be learned from both countries.

CHAPTER FOURTEEN: RUSSIA'S REFLEXIVE CONTROL THEORY AND THE MILITARY[452]

Introduction

One of the prime goals for a commander in warfare is to interfere with the decision-making process of an enemy commander. This goal is often accomplished by the use of disinformation, camouflage, or some other stratagem. For Russia, one of the primary methods is through the use of the theory of reflexive control (RC). This principle can be used against either human-mental or computer-based decision-making processors. The theory is similar to the idea of perception management, except that it attempts to control more than manage a subject.

Reflexive control is defined as a means of conveying to a partner or an opponent specially prepared information to incline him to voluntarily make the predetermined decision desired by the initiator of the action. Even though the theory was developed long ago in Russia, it is still undergoing further refinement. Recent proof of this is the development in February of 2001 of a new Russian journal known as Reflexive Processes and Control. The journal is not simply the product of a group of scientists but, as the editorial council suggests, the product of some of Russia's leading national security institutes, and boasts a few foreign members as well. The editorial council (which is different than the editorial board) includes a member of the Federal Agency for Government Communications and Information (FAPSI), a diplomat, a Canadian and two Americans, and the deputy head of the Information Security Committee of the Russian Security Council, among others.

There are many examples, from a Russian perspective, of the use of reflexive control theory during conflicts. One of the most recent and memorable was the bombing of the market square in Sarejevo in 1995. Within minutes of the bombing, CNN and other news outlets were reporting that a Serbian mortar attack had killed many innocent people in the square. Later, crater analysis of the shells that impacted in the square, along with other supporting evidence, indicated that the incident did not happen as originally reported. This evidence also threw into doubt the identities of the perpetrators of the attack. One individual close to the investigation, Russian Colonel Andrei Demurenko, Chief of Staff of Sector Sarejevo at the time, stated, "I am not saying the Serbs

---

[452] This article under the same title was originally published in the Journal of Slavic Military Studies, Vol. 17, April-June 2004, No. 2, pp. 237-256 and has been republished with the permission of the journal's editors.

didn't commit this atrocity. I am saying that it didn't happen the way it was originally reported." A US and Canadian officer soon backed this position. Demurenko believed that the incident was an excellent example of reflexive control, in that the incident was made to look like it had happened in a certain way to confuse decision-makers.

This chapter will discuss the military aspect of Russia's concept of reflexive control in some detail, and its role as an information warfare weapon. It will also briefly examine how US writers interpret RC theory.

Nature of Reflexive Control

The concept of reflexive control (RC) has existed much longer than the concepts of information warfare and information operations; in fact, it appeared in Soviet military literature 30 years ago. At that time, V. A. Lefebvre, who was working within the context and logic of a reflexive game, defined reflexive control as "a process by which one enemy transmits the reasons or bases for making decisions to another."[453] The development of reflexive control theory encompasses four distinct periods:

- research (from the early 1960s to the late 1970s)
- practical-orientation (from the late 1970s to the early 1990s)
- psychological-pedagogical (from the early to the mid 1990s)
- psycho-social (from the late 1990s).

The concept of reflexive control is still somewhat alien to US audiences. However, the Russians employ it not only on the strategic and tactical levels in war but also on the strategic level in association with internal and external politics. Equally significant, the concept has not always benefited the Soviet Union and Russia. For example, some Russians consider that the Strategic Defense Initiative (SDI) is a classic example of US use of reflexive control. In this case, the US "compelled the enemy to act according to a plan favorable to the US." By doing so, it forced the Soviet Union to try to keep pace with America' achievements in the SDI arena (or at least what we said were our achievements) and ultimately exhausted the Soviet Union economically as it spent money to develop corresponding equipment. As a result, some Russians are now asking themselves whether the concept of information warfare is yet another US attempt to control them "reflexively" and to force them to invest vast sums of money in a realm that is simply beyond their technological reach in the near future.

---

[453] Vladimir E. Lepsky, "Refleksivnoe upravlenie v polisubektnikh i mnogoagentnikh sistemakh" ["Reflexive Control in Multi-object and Multi-agent Systems"], an article given to the author, p. 1.

The Soviet and Russian armed forces have long studied the use of reflexive control theory, particularly at the tactical and operational levels, both for maskirovka [deception] and disinformation purposes and, potentially, to control the enemy's decision-making processes.[454] For example, the Russian Army had a military maskirovka school as early as 1904 that was later disbanded in 1929. This school, the Higher School of Maskirovka, provided the bases for maskirovka concepts and created manuals for future generations.[455]

Since the early 1960s, there have been many Russian intellectual "giants" who have emerged in the field of reflexive theory. In the civilian sector, these include G. P. Schedrovitsky, V. E. Lepsky, V. A. Lefebvre (who now lives in the West), D. A. Pospelov, V. N. Burkov, and many others. The foremost theorists in the military sector include V. V. Druzhinin, M. D. Ionov, D. S. Kontorov, S. Leonenko, and several others. One of the civilian theorists, Lepsky, who also is the editor of the new RC journal, hopes that the current US-Russian cooperation in the realm of reflexive control will move Russo-American relations from the paradigm of IW/IO (confrontation, struggle) to a paradigm of partnership (the control of confrontation). His is a noble cause and one that must be taken seriously.

There is a growing realization on both sides that Lepsky's two paradigms will evolve in parallel. US and Russian theorists are engaged in joint work regarding conflict prevention theory and are working together in Bosnia and Kosovo. At the same time, both countries are carrying out reflexive control work independently in the military sector.

RC is also considered an information warfare means. For example, Major General N.I. Turko, an instructor at the Russian Federation's General Staff Academy, has established a direct connection between IW/IO and

---

[454] Disinformation is a Russian technique that manipulates perceptions and information and misinforms people or groups of people. Some disinformation procedures are quite obvious, some are unconvincing, and others work through delayed perceptions, rumors, repetition, or arguments. Specific persons or particular social groups can serve as disinformation targets. The purpose of a disinformation campaign is to influence the consciousness and minds of men. In Russia today, where an unstable public-political and socio-economic situation exists, the entire population could serve as the target of influence for an enemy disinformation campaign. This is a major Russian fear.

[455] Major General Evgenii Korotchenko and Colonel Nikolai Plotnikov, "Informatsiia -- tozhe oruzhie: O chem nel'zia zabyvat' v rabote s lichnym sostavom" ["Information is also a weapon: about which we cannot forget in working with personnel"] Krasnaia zvezda [Red Star], 17 February 1994, p. 2.

reflexive control. He noted:

> The most dangerous manifestation in the tendency to rely on military power relates more to the possible impact of the use of reflexive control by the opposing side through developments in the theory and practice of information war rather than to the direct use of the means of armed combat.[456]

In Turko's judgement, RC is an information weapon that is more important in achieving military objectives than traditional firepower. In this regard, Turko's understanding is most likely influenced by his belief that American use of information weapons during the Cold War did more to defeat the Soviet Union and cause its demise than any other weapon. An excellent example was the Strategic Defense Initiative. Finally, Turko has mentioned reflexive control as a method for achieving geopolitical superiority and as a means for arms control negotiations. The latter area should be one of heightened awareness for countries entering such negotiations with the Russians.

Reflexive control theory does indeed have geopolitical significance, according to Turko. For example, he and a colleague described a new containment theory under development that portrayed new means for coping with confrontation between new large-scale geopolitical groupings.[457] This theory involves information warfare means; specifically, the threat of inflicting unacceptable levels of damage against a state or group of states by attacking their information resources.

One of the most complex ways to influence a state's information resources is by use of reflexive control measures against the state's decision-making processes. This aim is best accomplished by formulating certain information or disinformation designed to affect a specific information resource best. In this context an information resource is defined as:

- information and transmitters of information, to include the

---

[456] A. A. Prokhozhev and N. I. Turko, "Osnovi informatsionnoi voini" ["The Basics of Information Warfare"], report at a conference on "Systems Analysis on the Threshold of the 21st Century: Theory and Practice," Moscow, February 1996, p. 251.

[457] See N. I. Turko and S. A. Modestov, "Refleksivnoe upravlenie razvitiem strategicheskikh sil gosudarstva kak mekhanizm sovremennoi geopolitiki" ["Reflexive Control in the Development of Strategic Forces of States as a Mechanism of Geopolitics"], report at the conference on "Systems Analysis on the Threshold of the 21st Century: Theory and Practice," Moscow, February 1996, p. 366.

method or technology of obtaining, conveying, gathering, accumulating, processing, storing, and exploiting that information;

- infrastructure, including information centers, means for automating information processes, switchboard communications, and data transfer networks;
- programming and mathematical means for managing information; and
- administrative and organizational bodies that manage information processes, scientific personnel, creators of databases and knowledge, as well as personnel who service the means of <u>informatizatsiya</u> [informatization].[458]

Russia's political elite also employs RC in analytical methodologies used to assess contemporary situations. For example, during a recent conference in Moscow, a representative from President Yeltsin's administration noted that, when making decisions, the Kremlin pays attention to reflexive processes. Thus, Turko's revelation about the central role of Reflexive Control in Russian concepts of information warfare, and RC's potential use against information resources to destabilize the geopolitical balance, are two important points to consider when analyzing intent.

By definition, "reflexive control" occurs when the controlling organ conveys (to the objective system) motives and reasons that cause it to reach the desired decision,[459] the nature of which is maintained in strict secrecy. The decision itself must be made independently. A "reflex" itself involves the specific process of imitating the enemy's reasoning or imitating the enemy's possible behavior and causes him to make a decision unfavorable to himself.

In fact, the enemy comes up with a decision based on the idea of the situation which he has formed, to include the disposition of our troops and installations and the command element's intentions known to him. Such an idea is shaped above all by intelligence and other factors, which rest on a stable set of concepts, knowledge, ideas and, finally, experience. This set usually is called the "filter," which helps a commander separate necessary from useless information, true data from false and so on.[460]

---

[458] Prokhozhev and Turko, pp. 257-258.

[459] S. Leonenko, "Refleksivnoe upravlenie protivnikom" ["Reflexive Control of the Enemy"], <u>Armeiskii sbornik</u> [<u>Army Journal</u>], No. 8, 1995, p. 28.

[460] Ibid.

The *chief task of reflexive control* is to locate the weak link of the filter and exploit it.

According to the concept of reflexive control, during a serious conflict, the two opposing actors (countries) analyze their own and perceived enemy ideas and then attempt to influence one another by means of reflexive control. A "reflex" refers to the creation of certain model behavioral in the system it seeks to control (the objective system). It takes into account the fact that the objective system has a model of the situation and assumes that it will also attempt to influence the controlling organ or system. Reflexive control exploits moral, psychological, and other factors, as well as the personal characteristics of commanders. In the latter case, biographical data, habits, and psychological deficiencies could be used in deception operations.[461] In a war in which reflexive control is being employed, the side with the highest degree of reflex (the side best able to imitate the other side's thoughts or predict its behavior) will have the best chances of winning. The degree of reflex depends on many factors, the most important of which are analytical capability, general erudition and experience, and the scope of knowledge about the enemy. Military author Colonel S. Leonenko added that, in the past, stratagems were the principal tool of reflexive control, but today camouflage and deception [maskirovka] have replaced stratagems, a conclusion disputed by many. For example, the Chinese have demonstrated that electrons can be used as stratagems and operate as effectively as camouflage and deception in the traditional sense.

Although no formal or official reflexive control terminology existed in the past, opposing sides actually employed it intuitively as they attempted to identify and interfere with each other's thoughts and plans and alter impressions of one, thereby prompting an erroneous decision.[462] Leonenko's theories about varying degrees of reflexive control can be explained as follows. If two sides in a serious conflict – "A" and "B" – have opposing goals, one will seek to destroy the other's goals. Accordingly, if side A acts independently of the behavior of side B, then his degree of reflex relative to side B is equal to zero (0). On the other hand, if side A makes assumptions about side B's behavior (that is, he models side B) based on the thesis that side B is not taking side A's behavior into account, then side A's degree of reflex is one (1). If side B also has a first degree reflex, and side A takes this fact into account, then side A's reflex is two (2), and so on.

If successfully achieved, reflexive control over the enemy makes it

---

[461] Ibid., pp. 29-30.
[462] Ibid., p. 30.

possible to influence his combat plans, his view of the situation, and how he fights. In other words, one side can impose its will on the enemy and cause him to make a decision inappropriate to a given situation. Reflexive control methods are varied and include camouflage (at all levels), disinformation, encouragement, blackmail by force, and the compromising of various officials and officers. Thus, the central focus of reflexive control is on the less tangible element of "military art" rather than more objective "military science." Achieving successful reflexive control requires in-depth study of the enemy's inner nature, his ideas and concepts, which Leonenko referred to as the "filter," through which passes all data about the external world. Successful RC represents the culmination point of an information operation.

So defined, a filter is a collective image (termed "set") of the enemy's favorite combat techniques and methods for organizing combat actions, plus a psychological portrait of the enemy. Thus, reflex requires study of someone else's filter and the exploitation of it for one's own ends. In the Information Age, this filter is represented by human and machine (computer) data processors. The most important question then becomes, "How does one side achieve this higher degree of reflex and, hence, more effective reflexive control over the enemy?" It does so primarily by employing a broader range of means for achieving surprise. In turn, it achieves surprise by means of stealth, disinformation, and avoidance of stereotypes [shablon].[463]

The Military Experts Speak: Ionov, Leonenko, Komov, Chausov

Major General (ret.) M. D. Ionov, one of the military specialists mentioned earlier, wrote several articles on the subject of reflexive control in Voennia mysl' [Military Thought]. He was one of the first military theorists to appreciate the value of reflexive control, although, at first, no one was inclined to listen to him. The term reflexive control was simply not listed in any Soviet military encyclopedia when he began writing in the 1970s and, thus, could not exist! Therefore, in many of his initial articles, Ionov simply spoke about "control" of the enemy rather than reflexive control. At the same time, Ionov also realized the close link between advertising and reflexive control ("sell the holes, not the drill" and "temptation by benefit" were two of the techniques he recognized) and the combined use of various reflexive methods for waging different types of conflicts (low-intensity, etc.).[464]

---

[463] Discussion with a Russian military officer in Moscow, September 1998.
[464] M. D. Ionov, "Psikhologicheskie aspekty upravleniia protivnikom v antagonisticheskikh konfliktakh (refleksivnoe upravlenie)" ["Psychological Aspects of Controlling the Enemy during Antagonistic Conflicts (Reflexive Control)"], Prikladnaia ergonomika [Applied Ergonomics], No. 1 (January 1994), Special Issue, pp. 44-45.

Given his advanced thinking about reflexive control, it is instructive to analyze one of his articles from 1995. In it Ionov noted that the objective of reflexive control is to force an enemy into making objective decisions that lead to his defeat by influencing or controlling his decision-making process. Ionov considers this a form of high art founded of necessity on an intimate knowledge of human thinking and psychology, military history, the roots of the particular conflict, and the capabilities of competing combat assets. In this instance, control over the enemy is realized by undertaking a series of measures, related by time, aim, and place, which force enemy decision-makers to abandon their original plan, make disadvantageous decisions, or react incorrectly to their ultimate disadvantage (for example, when facing a counter-offensive). The successful use of reflexive control becomes all the more likely if the enemy's original plan is known. This makes it easier for the controlling side to force the enemy into making wrong decisions by employing reflexive control techniques such as intimidation, enticement, disinformation, deception, concealment, and other measures designed to shorten his decision-making time by surprising his decision-making algorithms.[465]

Ionov also stated that the content and methods employed must accord with the interrelationship between the enemy's thought processes and basic psychology. They also had to be realistic, and newly-created methods had to be considered within the context of new technologies. Furthermore, he recognized that any coalition of enemy forces represents a far more complex system, the stability of which changes depending upon the nature of the situation in each individual state and the condition of the coalition. Finally, because sharp differences exist in thinking, aims, politics, and ethical approaches of each state, each side must conduct an internal appraisal to determine the possible results of any action conducted in accordance with complex criteria reflecting the nature of the confrontation.[466]

Ionov identified four basic methods for assisting in the transfer of information to the enemy to promote control over him. These methods, which serve as a checklist for commanders at all levels, include:

- **Power pressure**, which includes: the use of superior force, force demonstrations, psychological attacks, ultimatums, threats of sanctions, threats of risk (developed by focusing attention on irrational behavior or conduct, or delegating powers to an irresponsible person), combat reconnaissance, provocative

---

[465] M. D. Ionov, "On Reflexive Control of the Enemy in Combat," <u>Military Thought</u> (English edition), No. 1 (January 1995), pp. 46-47.
[466] Ibid., pp. 49-50.

maneuvers, weapons tests, denying enemy access to or isolating certain areas, increasing the alert status of forces, forming coalitions, officially declaring war, support for internal forces, destabilizing the situation in the enemy rear, limited strikes to put some forces out of action, exploiting and playing up victory, demonstrating ruthless actions, and showing mercy toward an enemy ally that has stopped fighting.[467]

- **Measures to present false information about the situation**, which includes: concealment (displaying weakness in a strong place), creation of mock installations (to show force in a weak place), abandoning one position to reinforce another, leaving dangerous objects at a given position (the Trojan Horse), concealing true relationships between units or creating false ones, maintaining the secrecy of new weapons, weapons bluffing, changing a mode of operation, or deliberately losing critical documents. The enemy can be forced to find a new target by conflict escalation or de-escalation, deliberate demonstration of a particular chain of actions, striking an enemy base when the enemy is not there, acts of subversion and provocation, leaving a route open for an enemy to withdraw from encirclement, and forcing the enemy to take retaliatory actions involving an expenditure of forces, assets, and time.[468]
- **Influencing the enemy's decision-making algorithm**, which includes: the systematic conduct of games according to what is perceived as routine plans, publishing a deliberately distorted doctrine, striking control system elements and key figures, transmitting false background data, operating in a standby mode, and taking actions to neutralize the enemy's operational thinking.[469]
- **Altering the decision-making time**, which can be done by unexpectedly starting combat actions, transferring information about the background of an analogous conflict so that the enemy, when working out what seems feasible and predictable, makes a hasty decision that changes the mode and character of its operation.[470]

According to Ionov, one can assess human targets of reflexive control either by personality or group depending on the specific individual's or group's psychology, way of thinking, and professional level of training. Both universal

---

[467] Ibid., p. 47.
[468] Ibid., pp. 47-48.
[469] Ibid., p. 48.
[470] Ibid.

and role-based characteristics apply to individuals and groups. Universal characteristics include rejection or fear of danger, unwillingness to do someone else's work, or an arbitrary and uncompromising orientation toward confrontation. Reflexive control focuses on the role played by a particular person or group of persons (history, leadership, subordination, etc.).[471]

In another article entitled "Control of the Enemy," which appeared in the Navy journal, Morskoi sbornik [Naval Journal] in July 1995, Ionov argued that information is needed on the status of enemy forces, the nature of their actions, and their capabilities in order to control him and, simultaneously, to halt or to retard his counter-control efforts.[472] Ionov advanced several distinct principles necessary for control of the enemy. First, he underscored the reflexive nature of the desired response, stating that commanders must visualize the possible enemy response to the conditions one desires to impose. Second, the response will be problematic, since the enemy may discover the activity and undertake his own counter-control measures. Third, the level of technical development of combat weapons, and especially reconnaissance, is of growing importance. This makes the exposure of an action aimed at misinforming the enemy more likely. The final principle is the use of harsh forms of pressure on the enemy, specifically those that consider social elements and intellectual, psychological, ethical, and ideological factors. Deliberate cruelty toward the civilian population or prisoners of war in a combat region, a declaration of unrestricted submarine warfare (to sink any vessels to include those of neutral countries), and so on serve as excellent examples of the latter.[473] In short, in Ionov's view, reflexive control is a specific, yet traditional, Soviet and–now Russian–form of an informational or psychological (PSYOP) attack.

Colonel S. Leonenko integrated information technologies and reflexive control theory in his writings. He noted that the use of computers could hinder the use of reflexive control by making it easier to process data and calculate options. This is so since an opponent can more easily "see through" a reflexive control measure by an opposing force by simply using a computer. The computer's speed and accuracy in processing information can detect the reflexive control measure. On the other hand, in some cases, this may actually improve the chances for successful reflexive control, since a computer lacks the intuitive reasoning of a human being.[474]

---

[471] Ibid.

[472] M. Ionov, "Control of the Enemy," Morskoy sbornik [Naval Journal] No. 7 (July 1995), pp. 29-31, as reported in FBIS-UMA-95-172-S, 6 September 1995, pp. 24-27.

[473] Ibid., p. 25.

[474] Leonenko, p. 29. Who can say, however, what powers computers might assume in the future?

Computer technology increases the effectiveness of reflexive control by offering new methods adaptable to the modern era that can serve the same ends. Writing in 1995 from a military perspective, Colonel S. Leonenko defined reflexive control as follows:

> RC [reflexive control] consists of transmitting motives and grounds from the controlling entity to the controlled system that stimulate the desired decision. The goal of RC is to prompt the enemy to make a decision unfavorable to him. Naturally, one must have an idea about how he thinks.[475]

Leonenko then assessed the new opportunities that the use of computer technology afforded to reflexive control, stating:

> In present conditions, there is a need to act not only against people but also against technical reconnaissance assets and especially weapons guidance systems, which are impassive in assessing what is occurring and do not perceive to what a person reacts.[476]

If an IW or IO operation system cannot perceive what a person reacts to and is unable to assess what is occurring, does this mean that it provides only insignificant data? Or does it mean that there are two layers to reflexively control? The first layer consists of the "eyes, nose, and ears" of sensors, satellites, and radars. The second layer is the "brain software" of humans, which gathers, processes, and produces knowledge from the information or makes decisions based on it. But what happens if the "eyes, ears, and nose" are manipulated? How does that affect the input into decisions and knowledge? The recent use of such military activity by Yugoslav forces in the Balkans fooled NATO sensors over Kosovo and resulted in NATO shooting at targets that were fakes.

Yet, in the end, we do leave some decisions to computers. This indicates to Leonenko that we live in a much more frightening existence than we care to believe if, in fact, decisions are in the hands of machines that are "incapable of assessing what is occurring and do not perceive what a person reacts to."

---

[475] Leonenko, p. 28. This is akin to how British and American perception management theorists view the purpose of deception.
[476] Ibid.

Further, Leonenko noted that "how the enemy thinks" is shaped by combat intelligence and a collective image (set) made up of concepts, knowledge, ideas, and experience. This set, which he calls a filter, helps a commander separate necessary from useless information. Then, the chief task of reflexive control is to locate the weak link in the filter and find an opportunity to exploit it.

Leonenko's definition of reflexive control fits well with Russian Major Sergei Markov's understanding of an information weapon. Like Markov, Leonenko defines an information weapon as a "specially selected piece of information capable of causing changes in the information processes of information systems (physical, biological, social, etc., in this case, decision-making information) in accordance with the intent of the entity using the weapon." Accordingly, it causes change in the information processes of an opponent by persuading them to make decisions according to the design of the controller, and it affords the information weapon a methodology for controlling an opponent. So defined, reflexive control can be applied in the modeling and decision-making contexts of various types of conflicts (international, military, etc.). It can also be used in social processes and systems.

At the present time, there is a reflexive control movement underway in Russia that is influencing approaches to various branches of knowledge. This embraces philosophy, sociology, psychology, pedagogy, problems of artificial intelligence and computer science in general, computer "control" influence, military affairs, intelligence, counterintelligence, and a number of other areas.[477] For example, The Applied Ergonomics Association devoted a special edition of its journal (No. 1, 1994) to reflexive control processes.

Another Russian military theorist who wrote on the information impact on RC was Colonel S. A. Komov, who was perhaps the most prolific Russian military writer on information warfare topics in the 1990s. Writing in the journal Voennaia mysl' [Military Thought], Komov supported Ionov's emphasis on reflexive control. He renamed reflexive control over the enemy as "intellectual" methods of information warfare. He then listed the basic elements of an intellectual approach to information warfare, which he described as:

- **Distraction,** by creating a real or imaginary threat to one of the enemy's most vital locations [flanks, rear, etc.] during the preparatory stages of combat operations, thereby forcing him to

---

[477] Lepsky, p. 2.

reconsider the wisdom of his decisions to operate along this or that axis;

- **Overload,** by frequently sending the enemy a large amount of conflicting information;
- **Paralysis,** by creating the perception of a specific threat to a vital interest or weak spot;
- **Exhaustion,** by compelling the enemy to carry out useless operations, thereby entering combat with reduced resources;
- **Deception,** by forcing the enemy to reallocate forces to a threatened region during the preparatory stages of combat operations;
- **Division**, by convincing the enemy that he must operate in opposition to coalition interests;
- **Pacification**, by leading the enemy to believe that pre-planned operational training is occurring rather than offensive preparations, thus reducing his vigilance;
- **Deterrence**, by creating the perception of insurmountable superiority;
- **Provocation**, by forcing him into taking action advantageous to your side;
- **Overload**, by dispatching an excessively large number of messages to the enemy during the preparatory period;
- **Suggestion**, by offering information that affects the enemy legally, morally, ideologically, or in other areas; and
- **Pressure**, by offering information that discredits the government in the eyes of its population.[478]

Finally, an article by Russian Captain First Rank F. Chausov continued the discussion of reflexive control. He defined RC as "the process of intentionally conveying to an opposing side of a certain aggregate information (attributes) which will cause that side to make a decision appropriate to that information."[479] More important, Chausov discussed the risk involved with using RC:

To justify the methods of using force while taking risk into account, the numerical measure R_0 is introduced as the

---

[478] S. A. Komov, "About Methods and Forms of Conducting Information Warfare," MilitaryThought (English edition), No. 4 (July-August 1997), pp. 18-22.

[479] F. Chausov, "Osnovi refleksivnogo upravleniya protivnikom" ["The Basics of Reflexively Controlling an Enemy"], Morskoi sbornik [Navy Journal], No. 9, 1999, p. 12. The author would like to thank Mr. Robert Love of the Foreign Military Studies Office for his help in translating this and other segments of Chausov's article.

difference between the assessments of guaranteed effectiveness, or E_g, and the projected (situational) effectiveness, E_s. The estimate of the guaranteed effectiveness represents the lower limit of the effectiveness indicator, given any type of enemy action and fixed actions by our own forces. Situational effectiveness refers to the effectiveness of a force's action which is achieved through a certain type of action based on a commander's decision. Ordering or establishing preference among the values of the risk looks like this: $R_{0,1} > R_{0,1+1}$.[480]

Chausov listed the principles of RC as: (1) a goal-oriented process requiring a complete picture of all RC measures needed; (2) an "actualization" of plans, that is providing a sufficiently complete picture of the intellectual potential of commanders and staff officers (based on their reality), especially when conditions are determined by global information space; (3) the conformity of goals, missions, place, time and methods for RC's conduct; (4) the modeling or forecasting of the condition of a side at the time actions are being implemented; and (5) the anticipation of events.

US Interpretation of Russia's RC Theory

While V. A. Lefebvre remains the premier authority on RC issues in the US, and perhaps in the world, other US analysts have tried to decipher the principles of RC. Several years ago, American Clifford Reid demonstrated a thorough understanding of reflexive control theory in a chapter he wrote for the book Soviet Strategic Deception. By using only Soviet sources, Reid distilled Russian reflexive control mechanisms into the following categories of reflexive interactions:

(1) transfer of an image of the situation: providing an opponent with an erroneous or incomplete image of the situation.
(2) creation of a goal for the opponent: putting an opponent in a position in which he must select a goal in our favor (for example, provoking an enemy with a threat to which he must rationally respond).
(3) form a goal by transferring an image of the situation: feigning weakness or creating a false picture.
(4) transfer of an image of one's own perception of the situation: providing an opponent with false information or portions of the truth based on one's own perception of the situation.

---

[480] Ibid., p. 14.

(5) transfer of an image of one's own goal: a feint by a basketball player is a classic example where you change the enemies perception of where he thinks you are or are going.

(6) transfer of an image of one's own doctrine: giving a false view of one's procedures and algorithms for decision-making.

(7) transfer of one's own image of a situation to make the opponent deduce his own goal: presenting a false image of one's own perception of the situation, with the accepted additional level of risk.

(8) control of a bilateral engagement by a third party.

(9) control over an opponent who is using RC: exploiting opportunities identified as imitation of the initiators own process of RC.

(10) control over an opponent whose doctrine is game theory.[481]

Most analysts consider the US term most closely associated with RC to be perception management, the difference being in the quantifiable differences in the terms manage and control. Much has been written in the US on perception management. Lockheed Martin Aeronautics analyst E.T. Nozawa took a different perspective on RC, however, comparing and contrasting the theory with that of the scientific philosophy of Charles Sander Peirce (1839-1914). This term is not as well known to the US public as perception management, although it is gaining a lively following of late. Peircean Semiotic, a subset of scientific philosophy, refers to the totality of scientific Peircean knowledge. Semiotic [pronounced See-My-Oh-Tick] is the science of signs. For Peirce this meant a higher logic that included speculative grammar, critique (lower logic), and speculative rhetoric.

Nozawa has noted that Russian specialists discuss two different types of reflexive schools of thought. One is the school of Reflexive Processes, and the other is a subset of those processes, Reflexive Control, the idea under consideration here. Most Americans have difficulty making this distinction. Nozawa notes that a comparison of the Russian scientific paradigm of Reflexive Processes as described by Vladimir Lepsky and Vladimir LeFebvre with Peirce's concepts shows that they are very similar in their subject content and goals.[482] It may be said that Peircean Semeiotic is more advanced in its theoretical conceptual development, whereas Reflexive Processes is more

---

[481] Clifford Reid, "Reflexive Control in Soviet Military Planning," Soviet Strategic Deception, edited by Brian Dailey and Patrick Parker, (Stanford, CA: The Hoover Institution Press, 1987), pp. 293-312. Essentially, the first seven principles are those of deception.

[482] E. T. Nozawa, private communication with the author, October, 2001.

advanced in having developed practical applications.

There is nothing equivalent in the Peircean domain (or any other Western school of thought) to the Reflexive Control equations developed by Lefebvre and Lepsky with the supporting developments in characterizing Free Will. Lefebvre, according to Nozawa, combined the integrated concepts of Feelings, Free Will, and Thinking with the concepts of situational awareness and reality. The integrated processes became known as Reflexive Processes, filling the void in mentalistic sciences created by Behaviorism. A study of the proceedings of the October 2000 Reflexive Control Symposium held in Moscow would probably reveal additional areas of development. It may be said that Reflexive Processes is a form of Peirce's highly developed Scientific Philosophy and that it could easily be replaced by Peirce's Scientific Philosophy. The following table shows Reflexive Processes and the corresponding elements of Peircean Scientific Philosophy:

Reflexive Processes	*Scientific Philosophy*
Situational Awareness	Phaneroscopy (Situational Awareness)
Reflexive Control	Normative Science
Feelings	Esthetics
Free Will	Ethics
Thinking	Semeiotic
Reality	Metaphysics (Reality)

Although the terminology is different, the words describing Peirce's categories have the same general meaning as those of Reflexive Processes. Peirce, however, was more precise in his definitions, and the underlying construct of his theoretical knowledge is better developed, according to Nozawa. The Peircean categories should be interpreted as scientific categories and not metaphysical or theological.

Recent Examples of RC

The Russian military has actively attempted to exploit the concept of reflexive control during the recent past. For example, during the temporary occupation of the Russian White House by members of Parliament in October 1993, the Russian military reputedly employed reflexive control to remove the parliamentarians and their supporters from the building, albeit against the explicit orders of Russian President Boris Yeltsin. How they did so is quite interesting. For days, President Yeltsin had not been able to make the White House's occupiers budge. Additionally, the occupiers even refused to come out to address their supporters who had surrounded the building, probably because the Russian security police (MVD) or regular police were also in the crowd and might try to overpower them.[483]

Therefore, the security services developed a reflexive control plan. According to the plan, on the day of an immense demonstration in support of the White House's occupiers, the police permitted one of its communication posts to be overrun by the protestors. At the same time, the military authorities broadcast deceptive messages over an inactive frequency, while making it appear that the messages were actually a conversation between two high ranking Ministry of Internal Affairs (MVD) officers, who were discussing the imminent storming of the White House. The two officers discussed details of the "operation," which they implied was an attack designed to clear the occupants out of the building. One of the officers said repeatedly, "No matter what, get the Chechen. Kill him if you have to." In fact, the reference was to Ruslan Khasbulatov, the speaker of the Parliament, who was a Chechen and one of two key figures in the occupation (the other being former Vice President Alexander Rutskoi). Within a few minutes of receiving this information, both Khasbulatov and Rutskoi emerged on the White House's balcony and asked the crowd to go instead to the Ostankino TV station and capture it. The reflexive control operation had indeed worked. As a result, Yeltsin now had a raison d'être to act against both Khasbulatov and Rutskoi based on the latter's call for civil disobedience.[484] In effect, the two MVD officers had effected both leaders' actions and put ideas into their heads that provided grounds for the demise of this plan. They did so by literally "getting into" the leaders' minds.

Another excellent example of Soviet use of reflexive control theory occurred during the Cold War when the Soviet Union attempted to alter US perceptions of the nuclear balance. The aim of this reflexive control operation was to convince the West that its missile capabilities were far more formidable than they actually were. To do so, Soviet military authorities paraded fake ICBMs to deceive the West. The Soviets developed the fake missiles so as to make the warheads appear huge and to imply that the missile carried "multiple warheads." In this case, the Soviets understood their opponent's "reflexes." Soviet authorities realized that foreign attachés regularly attended these shows, since this was one of the few opportunities to obtain military information legally. Moreover, since the Soviet Union did not even participate in arms control fairs, the parade held special significance for intelligence officers. After observing the parade, the Soviets knew that the attachés would then report their

---

[483] The Ministry of Internal Affairs (MVD) has no counterpart in the United States. In addition to the Russian regular police force, it also consists of elements tasked with containing ethnic conflict or riots throughout the country, missions somewhat similar to those of the US National Guard.

[484] As related by an MVD lieutenant to the author in Moscow in 1994.

findings in great detail to Western intelligence organs. In addition, the Soviets knew that members of the Western military-industrial complex also studied the parades closely.

However, the deception did not end here. The Soviets also prepared other disinformation measures so that when Western intelligence services began to investigate the fake ICBMs, they would find collateral proof of their existence and would be led further astray. Ultimately, the aim was to prompt foreign scientists, who desired to copy the advanced technology, down a dead-end street, thereby wasting precious time and money.[485]

Final Thoughts on RC
Russian civilian and military theorists will undoubtedly continue to study the problem of reflexive control and the associated tools of manipulation and deception. For example, the Russian Academy of Science's Institute of Psychology has a Psychology of Reflexive Processes Laboratory that studies elements and applications of the "reflex" in considerable detail. It is studying not only ways to use the concept, but ways to keep the concept under control through international discussions and awareness. The Institute is playing a very positive role in that regard that should not be overlooked. In the Information Age, however, military analysts will continue to use the concept to manipulate an adversary on the field of battle. The most complex and dangerous application of reflexive control will remain its employment to affect a state's decision-making process by use of carefully tailored information or disinformation.

A detailed information security doctrine is one of the most important deterrents or defenses against an enemy's use of reflexive control or similar processes against Russia, according to many Russian scientists. Russia's September 2000 Information Security Doctrine is a step in this direction. According to Turko and Prokhozhev, information security means the degree to which a state is protected against both deliberate and unintentional actions that can lead to the disruption in the functioning of state and military command-and-control. The most significant of those threatening actions is disinformation that seeks to exert a goal-oriented effect on public opinion or on decision-makers for the purposes of reflexive control.[486] The dialectical interaction of reflexive

---

[485] Aleksei Baranov, "Parade of Fakes," <u>Moskovskii komsomolets</u> [Moscow Komsomol], 8 May 1999, p. 6 as translated and entered on the FBIS website, 11 May 1999.
[486] Prokhozhev and Turko, p. 259.

control against a state, and information security countermeasures within a state, will inevitably have a significant geo-political impact on that state as well. Thus RC theory will remain a most important area of study for the immediate and long-term future for Russian and other international groups alike.

Part Five

Conclusions
and
Appendixes

PART FIVE: CONCLUSIONS AND APPENDIXES

Part Five contains conclusions and appendixes. There are ten conclusions designed to encourage further thinking on issues raised. The three appendixes include the following: IO related articles by the author; the author's article on asymmetric thinking that provides a thought pattern much like that used for IO; and an article the author wrote in conjunction with Ms. Karen Matthews on the dual roles of the computer: cybercop or cybercriminal?

CHAPTER FIFTEEN: CONCLUSIONS

Terminology, Unintended Consequences, and Other Issues

It is the author's hope that this work has induced some creative thinking on the part of the reader concerning current US IO theory and practice in order to make recommendations to align it with the current environment. It is not the goal of the author to engage in further polemics on IO or the term Information Age. It appears certain that militaries around the world will continue to use the IO paradigm and societies the Information Age paradigm. But hopefully this work's examination of our environment has pointed out other ways to view our evolving world.

The **first conclusion** of this work is that current US military information operations terminology and doctrine are inadequate to confront the cyberbattlefields and cyber-related theories that have emerged over the past ten years. US IO doctrine writers would benefit by studying cyber-related concepts more closely and by adding more cyber-related concepts to their doctrinal base. This would also remedy the divide in terminology between civilian and military theorists. Such studies and additions would provide a more comprehensive analysis of contemporary scenarios and may better prepare the military for conflict management issues.

At the start of the 1990s or earlier, the world enjoyed a surge in the ability to obtain and share information. Caught up in the excitement of the moment, analysts began to talk about the advantages of the Information Age. But as noted in Chapter One, many Internet definitions of "Information Age" describe it as the use of computers. Computers and networks form the basic infrastructure of current society. They are the work horses that provide access to the information which we use and crave. More appropriately, then, we live in a Cyber Age and not in an Information Age.

Further, there has always been an "information threat" whether it be perception management, deception, or pure manipulation of data. There hasn't always been a "cyber threat" which is yet another indicator of why IO is the wrong term. A term like "cyber operation" would be a more appropriate term as would the term "Cyber Roadmap." Satellites, sensors, computers, networks, and other devices may pass information, but these are cyber devices, not information devices. The Cyber Age is what is new. We should be discussing the GCP (Global Cyber Process) instead of the GIE (Global Information Environment). A GPS "produces" information, but it is based on the GCP. The vision of the Federal Communications Commission is to focus on digital broadband migration. These are the devices that move information and are responsible for the changes in society, not information itself.

The US IO definition conundrum appears to continue unabated. The new draft Joint Publication 3-13, Joint Doctrine for Information Operations is available online. Several new terms were clearly considered (before being crossed out in the draft) and some new definitions appear to have endured the drafting process. As reported in Chapter One, there is a new definition of IO. As soon as the draft goes final the new IO definition will be placed in JP 1-02. There is also a new definition of information superiority which is completely different from the old definition. The old definition stated that information superiority was represented by "the capabilities to collect, process, and disseminate an uninterrupted flow of information while exploiting or denying an adversary's ability to do the same." The new definition states that information superiority is "that degree of dominance in the information dimension which permits the conduct of operations without effective opposition."[487] By omitting any reference to processing or analysis, it appears that even this new definition is inadequate. You can conduct operations without opposition and in the meantime collect nothing but bogus information upon which to act. That won't give you information superiority. Whether this is the intended meaning of the JP's information superiority definition is unknown to the author. Insurgents appear to have a small degree of information superiority in Iraq since the US does not designate a counterpropaganda apparatus to offset "that degree of dominance in the information dimension which permits the conduct of [insurgent] operations without opposition." Their recent video newscast is only the most recent example of their ability in this area.

US IO has become prisoner to IO prisms, paradigms, soundbites, and institutional thinking. In the large sense, it is quite ethnocentric. Nothing could better illustrate this point than the recent article in Joint Force Quarterly about the information roadmap. The information roadmap is an information plan signed by Secretary of Defense Donald Rumsfeld in October 2003. The roadmap allowed Pentagon planners to treat IO as a core capability for future forces and as one of six operational goals for the Department of Defense's transformation process. The point was made in the JFQ article that the "key assumption underlying the roadmap is that exploiting information has become critical for military success."[488]

---

[487] Draft Joint Publication 3-13, Information Operations, downloaded from the Internet on 22 February 2005, p. GL-12-13.
[488] Christopher J. Lamb, "Information Operations as a Core Competency," Joint Forces Quarterly, Issue 36, p. 89.

If this is the key assumption of the roadmap, and IO theory in general, then we have been wasting lots of time and money. Information has always been the key ingredient of our operating environment, as essential as the air we breathe. Highlighting the importance of information in this manner underscores a problem with US military culture—it is composed of a lot of elements, and one of these is unintended soundbites. Often, however, we fail to look beyond the tip of the last letter in the bite and question its utility or authenticity. We accept terms at face value when we should be questioning or reevaluating them often. We simply can't become prisoners to the theory of unquestioning acceptance. Appendix Two of this work, an article on the US soundbite "asymmetric warfare," demonstrates this fact more explicitly and shows that other nations do not understand the term asymmetric warfare as the US does. In fact, there are almost as many definitions of asymmetric warfare as there are teachers and writers describing it.

Due to our terminology and paradigm faults, our military analysts may have missed several of the cyber-associated issues of this decade such as cybermobilization, cyberrecruiting, and cybermanipulation. Instead our analysts are focused on the more traditional terms of operational security, PSYOP, deception, and electronic warfare as core capabilities and the baggage inherent in them. Only computer network operations (CNO), the fifth core capability, is relevant and able to describe the complexity of the current operating environment. Unfortunately, the US military examines CNO primarily from an attack and defend paradigm. Of more relevance would be new terms such as CYOP (the mix of psychological operations and cyber capabilities), CYFORMATION (the union of computers and information), CYTRONIC (the integration of computers and electronics), and other related terms. The "cy" prefix indicates the Cyber Age (the ability of computer chips to allow us to access and share information) and distinguishes it from just the use of information. Such a designation would help us extricate ourselves from the information paradigm. The complexity and richness of cybernetics disappears in the term IO which is far too simplistic to represent all that is happening.

The ability of insurgents to cybermobilize their compatriots is key to understanding some of their success. Mobilization is the foundation for an insurgency as laid out in US insurgency doctrine, yet we very seldom, if ever, discuss this idea. Focus is on the offensive aspect of an insurgency. Are we overlooking these areas and concepts due to our reliance on the wrong paradigm? One would think so. Our troops in Iraq, facing an environment much more complex than this simple explanation, are certainly affected by it.

It is not, of course, that the other four IO capabilities do not involve digital processes. On the contrary, the author recognizes, and is amazed by, the

267

technical developments that are proceeding in all of these core capabilities. It is just that our IO paradigm doesn't allow us to think in cyber terms with the clarity and focus needed. Instead, our IO vocabulary is focused around offensive and defensive words like disrupt, corrupt, or usurp. Just the simple use of the word "information" causes us to miss many issues. For example, perhaps there is such a thing as an information crime or an information cop, but in the civilian world computers are classified as being either cybercriminals or cybercops. Immediately it is clear that these are computer-related incidents just as they should be understood.

Finally, relatively new developments such as blogs and "smart mobs" must be studied for they have the potential to be used by insurgents (perhaps they already are). While most people are familiar with blogging, they are not as familiar with smart mobs even though they have been discussed as long ago as 2002:

> A "smart mob" is the newest form of social organization. A smart mob is a self-organizing group of people who operate like a swarm of bees or a flock of pigeons...but texting on cell phones is now allowing humans to behave in the same way—forming into a group that is controlled by no single person, yet which moves as if it has a mind of its own. Since mobile text-messages can be instantly forwarded like e-mail pass-arounds, the mobs frequently involve masses of people who have never even met. "They enable people to act together in new ways and in situations where collective action was not possible before," writes the technology thinker Howard Rheingold in his book <u>Smart Mobs</u>, published this fall [2002].[489]

A **second conclusion** is that other nations are taking a different perspective on the components of IO and are describing them differently. For example, the Chinese and Russians discussed information operations at the start of the 1990s. The Russian definition was the most interesting, incisive, and innovative. It included only two subgroups as components, information-technical and information-psychological, as IO categories. The Chinese tended to focus first on electronic warfare as the equivalent of IO in the early 1990s, and then accepted the core-capabilities concept of the US around the year 1995. Thereafter they sought to develop a Chinese theory of IO that reflected Chinese cultural characteristics. The latter included an extended discussion of the use of stratagems and how they might apply to cyber technologies. The same was true

---

[489] Clive Thompson, "The Year in Ideas: Smart Mobs," <u>The New York Times</u>, 15 December 2002.

of the mechanization and motorization of warfare before WWII when different nations discussed the same technological innovations in very different terms.[490]

It is well past the time to have begun a discussion of these issues (terminology, applications, etc.) of IO with other nations. China's Shen recommended discussing IO rules of engagement, while the Russians asked why there was never any discussion of information peace (and why the US initially discussed information war)? As we go our separate ways, are we (the large powers) encouraging more radical or abstract behavior on the part of all nations concerned? Can we get this IO "thing" under control or will it evolve into something else, as the Russian idea of including special pharmaceuticals as part of their IO means indicates? In the past there was a reluctance to discuss these issues because computer operations were new and nations were afraid to divulge what they were working on (yet another indication of the importance of "cyber operations"). What may be legal in one country's use of IO on the battlefield may be illegal in another. The time to begin talking was five to ten years ago, making it more important now than ever.

A **third conclusion** is that too much time and thought has gone into developing the ability to use information technologies in conflict and not enough time and thought has gone into developing the ability to apply these technologies to prevent or preempt conflict, or to understand their unintended consequences. That is not all bad news. Without the fighting machine the US military has developed, no campaigns based on these principles would be possible. Based on the US combat experiences in Iraq in February 1991 and March-April 2003, and in Kosovo in April-May 1999, there is no armed force that currently can confront the US armed forces in a high-tech battle. Most nations realize that. In that sense US IO theory and equipment is working very well even if not all of the IO-related definitions appear totally adequate or in sync.

But we do need to work harder at using IO to prevent or preempt conflict. Noted New York Times columnist Thomas Friedman believes there are ten "great levelers" that are driving the globalization of human thought. If this is true then military forces should be able to access and use these same "levelers" to mobilize and integrate efforts toward cyber peace as much as they can utilize these forces to mobilize and integrate efforts to conduct warfare. Perhaps too little time has gone into the military's creative thinking on the "use of forces" such as in-forming, open-sourcing, insourcing, and work flow

---

[490] Harold R Winton and David R. Mets, editors, The Challenge of Change: Military Institutions New Realities, 1918-1941, University of Nebraska Press, 11 August 2000.

software[491] for peacekeeping utilization and too much time has been spent on the "use of force." We will need to step back from this paradigm when the conflict in Iraq ends and find other more creative military outlets for these emerging technologies. Cyber peace may be a process for some in the military to start developing now. Likewise the terms "cyber pre- and post-conflict actions" need to be contemplated, developed, and adopted.

There are key institutes in the US where cyber peace studies could be undertaken. The US Institute for Peace is one such place, but there are others such as the Peacekeeping Institute at the Army War College. It is important to keep in mind that virtual or cyber processes can be used by militaries for purposes other than warfare. It is clear, however, that the area of "virtual peacemaking" continues to be underutilized in the management of world affairs.

A **fourth conclusion** is that cyber technologies have had many unintended consequences–the most important being the manner in which they have empowered terrorists, insurgents, and criminal elements with tools that only nation-states possessed in the past. Technologies have enabled cyberplanning, cyberrecruiting, cybermobilization, and cyberfinancing among a host of other capabilities.

A short review of al Qaeda's and other extremists' websites over just the past few months demonstrates several of these points. The headlines from extremist websites indicate not only the web's propaganda value, but also several technological operating strategies:

- In early January, the al Basrah Net, a website known for posting Iraqi resistance news, listed their insurgent operations from 16 September 2004 to 1 January 2005. This was an open demonstration of their successes and a sign of the ease with which they operate.
- A new website, www.abumusab.cjb.net, contains material purportedly from Abu-Mus'ab al Suri who is suspected of being behind the Madrid train bombing. This indicates that leaders of terrorist actions other than Osama bin Laden and Abu-Mus'ab al Zarqawi use the web to express their thoughts and issue proclamations.

---

[491] Daniel H. Pink, interview with Thomas Friedman, "Why the World is Flat," <u>Wired</u>, May 2005, p. 152.

- The website www.almijlah.net/vb warned Iraqis shortly before the election not to vote. Here the attempt was to incite virtual fear in potential voters.
- The Qala website, in early February 2005, posted a photo of captured US soldier John Adams, which turned out to be a photo of a Dragon Model USA toy.[492] This was a failed deception operation, but it shows how easily the Internet can be used for such activities.
- The Islamtoday website proclaimed the successes of "resistance" fighters, offered religious guidance, emphasized men's role in the world today, and harshly criticized US actions in Iraq. The website thus served as an agitation and guidance reference.
- In December 2004, www.ansar-alsunnah00.8k.com was used to post videotapes of the insurgents' attack on the US army base in Mosel. Such postings do two things. First they provide a degree of proof that extremists did actually attack the base. Second, they demonstrate that the US is unable to stop some attacks.
- Also in December 2004, www.yaislah.org was used to post a videotape from Osama bin Laden. Such tapes demonstrate that not only is bin Laden alive, but he is still able to communicate and provide leadership even when in hiding.
- In early January 2004, the website moradokislam.org posted many photos that showed violent US actions and Iraqi suffering. Here the attempt was to gain sympathy for the insurgent cause and to incite hatred against the US. Like images on many of the sites listed above, these photos could have been doctored or were entirely faked. Detailed, high-tech analysis is required before any conclusions can be drawn. Such analysis isn't always performed by the average Iraqi who draws his or her own conclusions.
- Al Qaeda recently stated that it had released a web magazine. The publication outlined the Sunni Muslim group's aims, and it called on Iraqi security forces to "repent" and stop serving the "cross."[493]

In a related event, the US State Department declared in mid-December 2004, that the Hezbollah-associated website al Manar was a terrorist organization. This prompted al Manar to denounce the US decision as "a flagrant attack against free media," an act of "intellectual terrorism," and "an

---

[492] Yassin Musharbash, "How Islamic Extremists are Turning the Web into Terror.com," Spiegel Online, 7 February 2005.

[493] Ghaida Ghantous, "Al Qaeda Branch Launches Web Magazine," Herald Sun, 4 March 2005, downloaded from www.heraldsun.news.com.au

attack against Arab and Muslim rights." The website also showed footage of Hezbollah officials attacking the US with their fiery speeches.[494]

Such postings and events are now commonplace. They demonstrate that there is no sole point of reference to understand a conflict. In 1991, during Operation Desert Storm, CNN fulfilled that task. Now there are a multitude of websites that offer a summary of events from almost any point of view. All one has to do is search the web to find what one is looking for in the way of images, directives, viewpoints, or testimonials.

A **fifth conclusion** is that counterpropaganda is neither a core nor a supporting capability of current US IO doctrine. This issue is listed separately from other IO concerns because it is so important. With no counterpropaganda capability to contend with, insurgents have found the cyber or propaganda battlefield much easier to manipulate.

After the initial coalition campaign ended in Iraq in April 2003, US forces were as likely to conduct police operations as combat (patrolling, reconnaissance, raids, etc.) operations in the stalemate environment that ensued. It has done so now for over two years, and at the same time the insurgents' cyber activities have grown more effective. The US appears to need a counterpropaganda capability to maintain the IO high ground that can be too easily conceded to the insurgents.

The term counterpropaganda does not appear in the new JP 3-13 slated for release in 2005. Is it the word "propaganda" that is offensive? If so then a new term is needed. Perhaps counterinfluence is a good candidate for inclusion as a supporting activity. Without such a capability we have given the insurgents an entire media field in which to play. Norvell De Atkine, a former US Army colonel and well-known PSYOP specialist for Middle East affairs, reported from Iraq that "there can be no higher priority than coming on line and on the air with a massive information blitz to get the full story in the game."[495] He also added that in the media war the US has "been a massive and inexplicable failure."[496]

Some would disagree with this assessment, especially those focusing on the strategic level. And they have an argument. The White House has a

---

[494] "FBIS Analysis: Lebanon—Al Manar Highlights Hezbollah, Iranian, Iraqi Anti-US and France Rhetoric," 22 December 2004 as translated and downloaded from the FBIS website on 22 December 2004.
[495] Norvell B. De Atkine, "It's an Information War," Proceedings, January 2004, p. 65.
[496] Ibid.

Muslim World Outreach Strategy. Radio Sawa, a music-news station which began operation in 2002, and Alhurra, a satellite-TV news network which started in 2004, were aimed at Arab audiences. The US Agency for International Development (USAID) also does some excellent strategic work. All of these organizations are looking at countering anti-US propaganda and fostering more tolerance on the part of Arab nations in the Middle East.[497] Further, the US military has formed a new Joint Psychological Support Element (JPSE) in Tampa, Florida. US News and World Report stated that it is designed to replace the Office of Strategic Influence that was created in 2001 and disbanded in 2002.[498]

At the same time, insurgents are moving forward with their own IO organization and plans. A recent speech delivered by Stephen Ulph at a Jamestown Foundation conference in 2005 on insurgency underlined these insurgent capabilities. A new March 2005, jihadi web magazine, Dhurwat al Sanam, was described as "a periodical issued by the information department of the organization of the Qaedat al Jihad in the Land of the Two Rivers."[499] Just knowing that an insurgent organization has an information department is usually a signal for nation-states to employ a counterpropaganda capability.

The information department was initially inward-focused, supporting jihadi morale. However, a recent development cited by Ulph is that insurgents have developed an information brigade with several subcomponents to include a propaganda attack mechanism. He noted that

> On March 4, a statement was posted on the Minbar Ahl al-Sunna wal-Jama'a, a jihadi forum, from the newly constituted Information Jihad Brigade [Katibat al Jihad al I'Iami], which introduced itself as "a support and aid to our mujahid brothers to break the Zionist control over the media." The statement outlined the Brigade's specific aim: a full-scale propaganda war to constitute the newest arm of jihad. Its purpose is "to influence the morale of our enemies" and "expose the reality of what is happening to them in Iraq, so that the soldiers lose their faith in themselves and their commanders."[500]

---

[497] Islam Online (UK), 20 April 2005.

[498] David E. Kaplan, "How Rocket Scientists Got into the Hearts-and-Minds Game," US News and World Report, 25 April 2005, p. 31.

[499] Stephen Ulph, speaking at the Jamestown Foundation Forum "Insurgency and Jihad: The Iraqi Theater and Beyond," Panel One, 11 April 2005, as accessed and downloaded from the Jamestown Foundation website (www.jamestownfoundation.com), on 4 May 2005.

[500] Ibid.

Structurally the brigade has three parts: a design division which performs picture layouts and inserts; a language division that produces commentaries in the languages of enemy participants; and a publication division which, in addition to publishing, tracks reactions and offers recommendations for improvement. There is a plan, the brigade notes, to attack foreign websites and forums.[501]

Ulph also related that Jihadi forums compete with international news agencies and broadcast their own updates on breaking news (in places like the magazine al Bashara which came out every Tuesday). Further, the Mujahideen have targeted news organizations, such as the Arabiyya Arabic channel, for refusing to show insurgent films.[502] The webs also have pure information and pro-active reader communication, to include "Jihadi cells" and "electronic Jihad" sections. The former handles requests (supplies, funding, how to join a cell, etc.) or specific information on military technology. The latter provides instructions or warnings on how to penetrate websites as well as suggestions for targets or timing of attacks, to include advice on methods.[503]

There is little doubt about the ability of insurgents to use cyber capabilities to influence entire segments of a populace in conflicts fought in the modern age. Today the faceless Internet writer is the mobilizer (and thus, according to Pentagon jargon, a combat multiplier) and recruiter for insurgents just as the newspaper or TV reporter was during the Cold War. Insurgents in Chechnya created entire departments of Internet propaganda to support their goals long before the insurgents did so in Iraq. With no counterinfluence or counterpropaganda aspect to US IO, there is hardly a way to confront the insurgents' web-based mobilization, manipulation, and recruiting practices unless that is a job of JPSE.

Measures of effectiveness (MOE) were developed for kill or destruction ratios during the Vietnam War. It will be interesting to see if a new measure of effectiveness can be implemented to determine the value of a cyber operation. Can such an MOE help curtail the persuasive effect of websites that now prolong conflict or induce chaos? Causing disruption in a system or website can, after all, induce delays in or cause an operation to be suspended.

---

[501] Ibid.
[502] Ibid.
[503] Stephen Ulph, "A Guide to Jihad on the Web," Terrorism Focus, Volume 2, Issue 7 (31 March 2005).

A **sixth conclusion** is that the subjective nature of war, its characteristics, is changing and evolving. Carl von Clausewitz noted in <u>On War</u> that "very few of the new manifestations in war can be ascribed to new inventions or new departures in ideas. They result mainly from the transformation of society and new social conditions."[504] The subjective nature of war is about how every society has its own characteristic form of war.[505] Iraqi society fits that description of an evolving form of war today. Here small unorganized units utilize the social fabric of organized society (networks, miniaturized devices, etc) to conduct war. The objective nature of war, on the other hand, is close to being a constant and involves two sides that are organized and pitted against one another in a battle of violence and hatred.

Author Hans Magnus Enzenberger noted as long ago as 1994 that the nature of war was changing from "purposive, ideologically driven enterprises undertaken by highly organized industrial powers" to "molecular civil war."[506] Insurgent tactics in Iraq appear to fit Enzenberger's description. A social transformation is underway that has enabled the insurgents' tactics, especially on the boundaries of societies where the most interesting permutations are taking place. Unfortunately too few people are in touch with this transformation and its significance for the armed forces, which is attempting to decipher what is unfolding before it. Coalition forces have only a limited frame of reference for understanding the world that plays out around them, where groups meet and plan virtually without legal constraints. Analysts may find less utility in studying Clausewitz in the near term and more use for comprehending the operating principles of the Smart Mob.

Perhaps some aspects of Clausewitz's theory need to be reexamined in this modern context. Is war now a continuation of religion by other means? Is Clausewitz's second trinity (the people, commander, and government) only applicable in a European and nation-state context? In the Middle East, there is a religious force that Clausewitz did not encounter. The religious leader sometimes represents or is the government, and religion becomes the motivating impulse behind society and the armed forces. There is a precedent for such reinterpretations. Lenin rewrote Clausewitz for the class and ideological struggle, and the West had to adapt to that in its conduct of the Cold

---

[504] Colin Gray, "Clausewitz, History, and the Future Strategic World," The Strategic and Combat Studies Institute, The Occasional, Number 47, Contemporary Essays, June 2003, accessed at http://www.army.mod.uk/img/doctrine/scsi47.pdf.
[505] Ibid.
[506] Hans Magnus Enzenberger, <u>Civil Wars: From LA to Bosnia</u>, New York: New Press, 1994.

War.[507] Thus the situational setting has serious implications for the trinity whose shape is now somewhat altered by context.

While not specifically highlighted earlier but scattered throughout this book is the **seventh conclusion**, the notion that some changes are required in specific aspects of who implements IO and how its integration should be viewed (as the key element of an IO plan in an IO cell or as integrated technological information that is obtained, processed and transposed into a fire mission of lethal destruction). For example, as mentioned above, on more than one occasion artillery officers have been put in charge of IO affairs at division or higher level. Why? There are usually two answers: first, because they have few actual missions to run in a stability operations environment; and second, because they understand "targeting."

It is hard to comprehend this logic. It is easy to understand the necessity of keeping troops busy. But targeting of a location with artillery rounds (the need to achieve destruction) does NOT qualify someone to understand how to integrate and employ the five core capabilities of IO, nor does it allow for these capabilities to be integrated within a cultural understanding of the situation at hand. Just because artillery officers understand "targeting" does not mean they understand postconflict IO in the human dimension. US personnel must understand the population they are trying to influence and that demands an in-depth understanding of languages, cultures, values, signs, and symbols from the target's perspective. With all of its cultural and ideological implications, local IO is simply too complex for untrained personnel. Can an average artilleryman sip tea in a local café and speak the dialect to understand how and why people listen to the news? Perhaps even more important, why does the US military have an IO Corps if they are not used as the lead IO element for which they train and educate their people? Do we need slots for generals in the IO field to enable the command to have clout and be taken seriously?

Foreign area officers (FAOs) and civilian area specialists should supplement IO specialists and help them plan IO operations. These officers are trained in language and cultural affairs, serve in embassies, and understand the regional specifics of the country in question. To leave them out of the IO process is a terrible oversight. If they are not to be included here, then why have a FAO branch at all? The FAO or IO specialist can explain to the commander

---

[507] For more on this issue, see Jacob W. Kipp, "Lenin and Clausewitz: The Militarization of Marxism, 1915-1921," <u>Soviet Military Doctrine from Lenin to Gorbachev, 1915-1991</u>, edited by Willard C. Frank, Jr., and Philip S. Gillette, Greenwood Press, 1992.

what information can or cannot potentially do for him in an area (again, much of IO is local!) and what enemy information is doing. The commander must make some intuitive calls based on the information imparted to him via this process.

It is the job of the FAO or IO specialist to avoid making the mistake of asking a blue (US) question of a red (Middle East) system and trying to get a blue answer. Such a scenario will only provide a stilted answer and not the information a commander may need. One needs to ask a red question of a red system, examine the red answer, and put the answer into a context by which a blue audience can understand and influence the red position. To postulate and comprehend these questions and answers requires a red security and cultural specialist, the FAO or IO specialist.

There is also disagreement among IO specialists regarding what supporting and related capabilities should be included in IO, and changes here must also be contemplated. For example, Colonel William Darley, a Public Affairs officer, wrote in Army magazine in early 2005 that "public affairs is not IO." Darley defines IO as a "doctrinal paradigm that seeks to cohesively link active information measures, both defensive and offensive, to enable the operational commander to manipulate information activities to achieve objectives."[508] Further, he states that IO is "designed to both confuse and deceive, and to manipulate, persuade or psychologically coerce targeted audiences" leading Darley to the conclusion that "where neither access nor truth is appropriate, public affairs is not appropriate."[509] What Darley is attempting to do is to delineate the difference between his own job and the job that IO is to perform. His job is to objectively state a situation and tell the truth. According to Darley's definition, IO is more adept at slanting the interpretation of a situation. Darley's definition appears to ignore the fact that not all IO is deceptive. At present public affairs is a "related activity" of IO, which means it remains a part of IO doctrine.

Also of vast importance when discussing IO is the fact that it is the integrating locus of a host of forces. Integration is key to future military success in the Cyber Age. That is, after all, the job of the IO cell, to take all of the cultural, historical, military, security, and electronic issues at hand and make an integrated plan out of them. EW, PSYOP, Civil-Affairs, and other branches and agencies meet in the IO cell to formulate an integrated and coordinated plan. Simultaneously, information technologies driven by the computer chip are

---

[508] William M. Darley, "Why Public Affairs is not Information Operations," Army, January 2005, p. 9.
[509] Ibid., p. 10.

277

enabling network-centric operations and the integrated, timely delivery of steel on target. While information is vital, it is how this information is integrated and utilized that becomes the key to success in the IO cell. How this information is obtained, processed, and transposed into a nonlethal or lethal fire mission becomes key to mission completion.

Perhaps the primary lesson that the US has learned from the Iraqi conflict is that postconflict studies will need to involve more "soft IO" and less "hard IO" topics. More study will be focused on the human dimension that involves the use of PSYOP and Civil Affairs. Potentially there will be studies that include new topics such as "IO in Cities" or "Internet Insurgencies."

This is the difficult part of the problem. It is hard to understand and influence populations that are afraid to express an opinion and where ministries seldom provide decent statistics. Moreover, the cultures in some parts of the world may make crafting messages a fundamental challenge for US forces. One has to choose among various tools to conduct research and apply results in an IO sense in the human dimension. Will it be communications research, cultural anthropology, or social science research? Is all IO "local" (dependent on local circumstances and culture) in the human dimension as some contend?[510] If so then the problem is huge and the complexity of issues before decision-makers is underexaggerated. IO often is not applied correctly as a result of this underestimation.

An **eighth conclusion** is that since time and distance have shortened while the speed of operations has increased dramatically in the Cyber Age, it is now much more difficult to find an insurgent leader and cell. The Internet allows insurgents to spread out geographically but stay united ideologically. Thomas Friedman's new book, The World is Flat: A Brief History of the Twenty-First Century, indicates that the time is ripe for global communication to be not only possible but also inevitable on a host of regional and global issues. He noted in a recent interview "several technological and political forces have converged, and that has produced a global, Web-enabled playing field that allows for multiple forms of collaboration without regard to geography or distance—or soon, even to language."[511]

As time and distance shrink, the management of information becomes crucial. For example, if properly managed could a "smart mob" manipulate the

---

[510] Bob Kerr, "Information Operations: Symposium Seeks Answers from Industry, Academia," The Lamp, 28 April 2005, p. 16.
[511] Daniel H. Pink, interview with Thomas Friedman, "Why the World is Flat," Wired, May 2005, p. 152.

market by telling the mob to buy or sell certain products and drive the market in certain preordained directions? Is the goal to disrupt as much as destroy in the Cyber Age?

When mechanization arrived, we "updated" the army with mechanized vehicles that changed the relation between time, distance, and place or space. We have met the challenge of our current change and its new dynamic as best we can. While we have internalized change in our systems and our lives, we still can't comprehend where we are heading at the present time since the pace of change is so great. Interruptions to our virtual processes, as we rely more and more on them, are bearing signs of becoming potentially cataclysmic. For example, if an information flow is interrupted we can lose much of our coherence and understanding.

A **ninth conclusion**, and a very important conclusion at that, is the growing impact of persuasive technologies to manipulate our abstraction of reality and consequently the truth. With regard to the former, there is a tremendous amount of material available on the impact of cyber technologies as manipulators of emotions or as instruments of persuasion, influence, or transmitters of fear. Some of these impacts are apparent, such as the beheadings shown on the Internet, while others are less apparent and subtler, such as the gradual loss of privacy we are experiencing. The nexus between government and commercial endeavors (law enforcement recordkeeping and commercial market research) is disconcerting. It is leading to concerns of security abuse and identity theft,[512] as if criminals weren't providing us with enough concerns already.

The collapse of big media should also be a psychological concern to societies worldwide for it implies a greater reliance on virtual products. A recent <u>Wilson Quarterly</u> article stated that since 1990, newspaper circulation in this country has dropped some seven million. Most people who are reading newspapers are over the age of 60 while younger news enthusiasts get their reports from mediums other than print. For example, to the question "time spent per day by 8-to-18 year olds with all media," the answer was 6 hours, 21 minutes; for "time spent per day with print media," the answer was 43 minutes.[513] Many Internet users, as noted above, rely on blogs for their news. According to the Pew Internet and American Life Project, which investigate how Internet use affects society, blogs are created every 5.8 seconds.[514]

---

[512] William Safire, "Goodbye to Privacy," <u>The New York Times Book Review</u>, 10 April 2005, pp. 9-10.
[513] Terry Eastland, "Starting Over," <u>Wilson Quarterly</u>, Spring 2005, p. 45.
[514] Joseph R. Chenelly, "The Blogs of War," <u>Army Times</u>, 14 March 2005, p. 14.

While it is good to have people with different values and beliefs weigh in on issues, it is not good if these same arguments are devoid of context and fact. The resulting psychological manipulation is often not perceived let alone understood. Results produced via virtual speed can often be as or more persuasive than well-informed and reasoned arguments that take time. The result is that the nontraditional thinker has found a presence, sometimes significant at that, in Internet media discussions. The tension is greater when other cultures are involved since they bring other cultural predilections to bear on any discussion.

Finally, the emotional bond between computer and user should be noted. Users tend to get their news from sites they trust. These sites do not have the same constraints that many of the major news outlets have. In the Western world, news organizations must verify the news before they produce it. Websites don't have such constraints, even in the West. As a result Internet news may be devoid of necessary context to place the story in the correct frame of reference. People may trust these sites but they may not be getting the truth. The Iraqis, for example, get news from sources they trust but that news may not have been verified.

The ability of nonstate actors to directly impact the mind should be of immediate concern to US IO planners. Not only is it a major goal of an insurgency to secure the hearts and minds of the population, it is also an area on which other nations with IO capabilities are focusing more and more attention. The battle for the mind, as discussed in this book, covered topics of persuasion, perception management, manipulation, and on occasion the topic of special pharmaceuticals (the Russian imprint on IO) and reflexive control. Cultural awareness also is necessary if one hopes to manage perceptions and change attitudes and behaviors as PSYOP is intended to do.

US forces must come up with a way to counter or neutralize the insurgents' advantages on the Internet. US forces are learning how to become more culturally aware of the messages they need to present to the local populace. Our forces must understand the local populace and the methods needed to inform them of our positive intentions. Any insurgent use of digitized means must be countered or neutralized. US PSYOP is doing a good job, the question is whether its current operating theories, tools, and response time are adequate to handle the problems at hand.

With regard to this perspective, US Army Captain Bill Putnam discussed his encounter with cultural awareness and the misapplication of US IO in Iraq. He served there for a year as the head of Open Source Intelligence that produced a daily intelligence document reporting on street rumors in Baghdad. His insights on the cultural foundation of Iraqi society and their relation to IO are of acute interest and importance.

Putnam believes animosity still runs high among Iraqis because the US is ineffective at disseminating its message to the Iraqi people. Most importantly, this is because the US military is determined "to make the Iraqi information environment conform to its information operations and public affairs doctrine on how things should be done, rather than vice versa."[515] It is clearly one of the most important observations regarding how we are conducting the war for hearts and minds.

Putnam believes there are two problems. The first problem is that the US is using Arab media outlets as its middlemen, and they often have their own agendas. Thus, the coalition message isn't getting out. Second, he believes that the coalition has "failed to grasp how Iraqis receive their information and formulate their opinions."[516] As a result Iraqis trust us less and are more susceptible to anti-coalition propaganda. It is this latter point that appears to be the most important because it strikes at the heart of cultural awareness.

Putnam believes that the populace obtains information from satellite TV, family and friends, the streets, religious figures, and newspapers. Once this "circle of influence" disseminates information, family and friends discuss it. They in turn process the information. Attitudes are developed from these discussions. These discussions are then shared with others, and the information spreads on the street.

A question put to Putnam was why the US didn't have a local TV network put out an unprejudiced viewpoint on what was occurring. When presented this question, a local TV network representative told Putnam that the network could not appear too neutral because it would lose viewers to al Jazeera's "stranglehold on the Arab populace."[517] The insurgents understand the "circle of influence" according to Putnam and know how to shape the opinions of the Iraqi people. They place rumors in a trusted medium where Iraqis will accept them as true. Insurgents also dominate the information environment by spreading fear amongst the populace. People are afraid to say anything positive about the coalition, and thus the anti-coalition rumors become uncontested

---

[515] Bill Putnam, "Winning Iraqi Hearts and Minds," Army, January 2005, p. 7.
[516] Ibid.
[517] Ibid.

fact.[518] It is this focus on cultural awareness that is important if the US is ever to crack the code on how to "change attitudes and behavior."

Putnam recommended two things. First he recommended that the US should produce its own TV and newspaper outlets and that they conduct their TV broadcasts in the evening from 6 p.m. to 10 p.m. On such programs there could be discussions of street rumors among various members of society and there could be programs of benefit to the local populace such as how to file damage claims. Newspapers distributed during the day could focus on coalition messages and editorials, along with local Iraqi news, to supplement the nightly TV programs.[519]

Second, Putnam recommended that anti-insurgent and pro-coalition perspectives should be put out on the Arab streets. He recommended trying to use taxi cab drivers or market shoppers to do this. Additionally, if successful inroads can be made with newspapers and TV channels, they might give the "circle of influence" something to discuss. Perhaps such opinions would find their way to the street. Putnam's stress on countering the monopoly on anti-coalition propaganda that the insurgents spread melds perfectly with the discussion in Chapter One for a counterinfluence supporting activity to US IO theory.

As the discussion in Part Four revealed, other nations are not looking at this issue of the mind in the same manner as the US, that is simply "changing attitudes and behaviors" with information. Both the Russians and the Chinese are engaged in studies of information weapons. The Russians are very interested in finding ways to influence the brain whether it is by parapsychological methods or by the use of chemicals/drugs or nonlethal weapons. These latter two methods would not be considered as IO methods by the US, but they are by Russia. The Russian National Security Council sponsored one book in which author S. P. Rastorguyev attempted to develop an algorithm generated "psycho virus" (similar to a computer virus but focused on the brain) to influence attitudes and behavior.

The Chinese also have stepped up their study of cognitive space. One article in the Chinese journal Contemporary Navy, for example, demonstrated a Chinese penchant to look at events surrounding the manipulation of the mind in a manner similar to the Russians. The Chinese article described efforts at conducting mind control, using telepathy, and using secondary sound waves in the 3-17 hz range, the latter case designed to shut down a human's ability to

---

[518] Ibid.
[519] Ibid.

function. The use of blinding lasers, weapons of sound, holograms, and "camouflage by transfiguration" was also described.

Insurgents are perhaps more expert at mind warfare than nation-states. It is one of the few yet relatively lethal arrows in their quiver, and they are not limited by any legal ramifications as are nation-states. A recent raid on an al Qaeda hideout in Saudi Arabia revealed the usual set of insurgent weaponry: AK-47s, SAM-7 surface-to-air missiles, grenades, explosives, and so on. The raid also revealed the elements of the new insurgent "mind warfare": video cameras, laptop computers, CD burners, and a high-speed Internet connection. As author Henry Schuster portrayed it, these are users of "21st century technology in pursuit of 14th century, even 7th century goals."[520]

Computer games today are also beginning to look at the mind to a deeper degree than in the past. For example, Psychonauts is a new computer game in which you are a psychic who climbs around in other people's brains. You fight their nightmares and demons and unlock emotional baggage to understand the background to each character. This game would be especially interesting and appropriate if played with religious or terrorist baggage that you unlock and through which you understand an insurgent's view of the contemporary world.[521]

Military, Academic, and Law Enforcement Use of IO
The cyber paradigm offers different alternatives and options for planners to consider than does a sole focus on IO. There are, of course, military cyber applications ongoing daily. For example, there is an army recruiting website that is entirely cyber-based. Also, two of the most often read websites have nothing to do with IO—they are platoonleader.org and companycommander.com. Here ideas are exchanged via a cyber and not an IO platform. A recent article about the US military titled "Band of Bloggers" further highlighted this fact.[522] But these developments appear at the individual level in the military and are not accorded a place in current US IO theory.

The cyber-threat environment is probably more acute now than it was just a few years ago. Again, to use a Chinese example, the PLA has invested a great amount of time in finding a way to utilize EMP devices to neutralize the digital devices of the 7th Fleet if the latter decided to intervene in any potential conflict between Taiwan and China. Both Russia and China are investing in

---

[520] Henry Schuster, "Studios of Terror," CNN.com, 16 February 2005.
[521] Brian Lam, "Psychonauts," Wired, April 2005, p. 063.
[522] Chenelly.

C4ISR technology to ensure that they can protect their digital systems in space and potentially cause harm to an opponent's C4ISR capability.

Better understanding of cyber-related terminology and concepts makes it more likely that the US can conduct cyber-based counterinsurgency on the Internet. The US and other nations have done much to monitor al Qaeda's online techniques. In the US, academic and other organizations such as the Site Institute continue to monitor and analyze al Qaeda websites on a daily basis. The Homeland Security Department hired Dartmouth University to undertake a study of Islamic websites and foreign information operations— both of which they successfully completed. The website Internet Haganah (or "defense" in Hebrew) has developed a methodology to track and find the servers from which terrorists are sending their messages. The organization then explains the situation to the proprietors of the servers on which an insurgent or terrorist site exists and asks them to do something about it. This has resulted in the movement of many terrorist websites over the past few years from one site to another, putting them always on the run and disrupting their operations.[523] CNN reports that Jeremy Reynalds, who runs a faith-based homeless shelter, combs the Internet in his free time for illegal terrorist postings. He is given credit for discovering that the soldier identified as John Adams (a toy doll dressed as a US soldier with a rifle at his head) was a fake.[524] Such efforts must continue. Other creative strategies to deal with insurgents must be developed to supplement these efforts. However, monitoring is not countering, and herein lies the problem.

New methods of analysis are being discovered that might help the cybercop more than the cybercriminal (see Appendix Three for more information on these topics). The Department of Defense's Cyber Crime Center (DC3) is changing the way it conducts large computer forensic investigations in the wake of recent cases. It was reported that

> In particular, the DC3 has established a section of its lab and a team of examiners just to work on cases with large data sets, replacing ad hoc teams created to address case requests as they come in. DC3 is also using a combination of commercial forensic software and proprietary tools to comb seized data stored on large capacity storage-area networks and network-attached storage devices. The new DC3 approach replaced individual examiners working on separate

---

[523] John Lasker, "Watchdogs Sniff Out Terror Sites," Wired News, www.wired.com, 25 February 2005.
[524] Henry Schuster, "The Internet War," CNN.com, 16 February 2005.

workstations, which led to inconsistencies in the forensic examination process and duplication of effort between examiners…[525]

Final Thoughts

Hopefully US doctrine writers will consider some of the issues raised here and also those of other countries that are on the borderline of the US IO comfort zone. These issues need to be explored more thoroughly by US analysts. To date there has been an apparent reluctance to study closely the experiences and theory of other nations. Perhaps this is because the US has been so successful in conflicts to date with its own theory. Obviously this fact is being challenged in the post conflict Iraqi IO environment.

Other nations are moving ahead with new proposals for the further expansion of IO. For example, recently China requested that Internet regulation be a United Nations undertaking.[526] Whether the US will study such proposals is not a question—it will. Our analysts do look at all proposals. The question is whether these proposals fit the current understanding of IO in the US or its future shape from a US perspective. Working with and responding to international community/partners is important. If we properly communicate our thoughts and definitions to international countries, and study other countries definitions, then we can work better with the UN and with NATO countries as well.

Of perhaps greatest concern is that some influential figures are postulating that the US is falling behind in the technologies that support our IO capabilities. Friedman notes that this fact makes this a very dangerous time in our history and that we have to get moving now if we are to stay competitive. Thomas Bleha, writing in the May/June issue of Foreign Affairs, supported this contention, noting that the US has fallen far behind Japan and other Asian states in broadband and mobile-phone technology.[527] Are our shortcomings somehow related to our focus on information at the expense of cyber issues? The apparent challenges to the US are great as it enters the twenty-first century.

---

[525] Paul Roberts, "Iraq Battle Plan Leak Sparks Overhaul of Cybercrime-Fighting Techniques," Computer World (www.computerworld.com), 31 January 2005.

[526] "China Pushes for Multilateral Control of the Internet at the UN," Beijing Xinhua, 1724 GMT, 24 February 2005 as translated and downloaded from the FBIS website on 24 February.

[527] Thomas Bleha, "Down to the Wire," Foreign Affairs, May/June 2005, downloaded from the Internet.

APPENDIX ONE: IW ARTICLES BY THE AUTHOR

The author has been writing about IT and IW since 1996. A chronological listing of his publications on those topics is presented below.

1996
"Russian Views on Information-Based Warfare," <u>Airpower Journal</u>, Special Edition 1996, pp. 25-35.

"The Influence of Information Operations on the System of Preventing Military Crises in the US," in <u>An Analysis of Systems on the Verge of the 21st Century: Theory and Practice</u>, Moscow 1996, Vol. 4, pp. 265-277 (in Russian).

"Deterring Information Warfare: A New Strategic Challenge," <u>Parameters,</u> Winter 1996-1997, pp. 81-91.

1997
"Virtual Peacemaking: A Military View of Conflict Prevention through the Use of Information Technology," an article in <u>Challenges of Peace Support into the 21st Century</u>, The Swedish National Defence College, Stockholm, 26-27 September 1997, pp. 179-213. A second version of the article appeared as "Preventing Conflict through Information Technology," <u>Military Review</u>, December 1998/January-February 1999, pp. 44-57.

"The Threat of Information Operations: A Russian Perspective," chapter in <u>War in the Information Age</u>, Brassey's Washington/London, 1997, pp. 69-89.

"Russian Information-Psychological Actions: Implications for US PSYOP," <u>Special Warfare</u>, Winter 1997, Vol. 10, No. 1, pp. 12-19.

"The Age of the New Persuaders," <u>Military Review</u>, May-June 1997, pp. 72-80.

1998
"Dialectical versus Empirical Thinking: Ten Key Elements of the Russian Understanding of Information Operations," <u>The Journal of Slavic Military Studies</u>, Vol. 11, No. 1, March 1998, pp. 40-62.

"The Mind Has No Firewall," <u>Parameters</u>, Spring 1998, pp. 84-92.

"Russia's Information Warfare Structure: Understanding the Roles of the Security Council, FAPSI, the State Technical Commission and the Military," <u>European Security</u>, Spring 1998, Vol. 7, No. 1, pp. 156-172.

1999

"Information Technology: US/Russian Perspectives and Potential for Military-Political Cooperation," chapter in <u>Global Security Beyond the Millennium: American and Russian Perspectives</u>, Macmillan Press LTD, 1999, pp. 61-79.

"Human Network Attacks," <u>Military Review</u>, September-October 1999, pp. 23-33.

"Infosphere Threats," <u>Military Review</u>, September-October 1999, pp. 46-51.

2000

"Kosovo and the Current Myth of Information Superiority," <u>Parameters</u>, Spring 2000, pp. 13-29.

"The Russian View of Information War," in <u>The Russian Armed Forces at the Dawn of the Millennium</u>, Michael H. Crutcher (editor), Center for Strategic Leadership, Carlisle, PA, pp. 335-360.

"Manipulating the Mass Consciousness: Russian and Chechen 'Information War' Tactics in the Second Chechen-Russian Conflict," in <u>The Second Chechen War</u>, A. C. Aldis (editor), Conflict Studies Research Centre, Sandhurst, England, pp. 112-129.

"China's Technology Stratagems," <u>Jane's Intelligence Review</u>, June 2000, Vol. 12, No. 12, pp. 37-39.

2001

"The Internet in China: Civilian and Military Uses," <u>Information and Security: An International Journal</u>, Vol. 7, 2001, pp. 159-173.

"IT Requirements for 'Policekeeping'," <u>Military Review</u>, September-October 2001, pp. 29-35.

"Deciphering Asymmetry's Word Game," <u>Military Review</u>, July-August 2001, pp. 32-37.

2002

"Confrontation Central to Chinese IW Aims," <u>Jane's Intelligence Review</u>, June 2002, Vol. 14, No. 6, pp. 52-53.

"Russia's 'Netwar' Capabilities," <u>Jane's Intelligence Review</u>, June 2002, Vol. 14, No. 7, pp. 52-53.

2003
"Al Qaeda and the Internet: The Danger of 'Cyberplanning'," <u>Parameters</u>, Spring Issue, pp. 112-123.

"Like Adding Wings to a Tiger—Chinese Information War Theory and Practice," <u>Military Intelligence</u>, July-September 2003, Vol. 29, No. 3, pp. 22-27.

"Information Warfare in the Second (1999-) Chechen War: Motivator for Military Reform?" <u>Russian Military Reform: 1992-2002</u>, Anne C. Aldis and Roger N. McDermott, editors, Frank Cass Publishers, 2003, pp. 209-233.

"Is the IW Paradigm Outdated? A Discussion of US IW Theory" <u>Journal of Information Warfare</u>, Vol. 2, Issue 3, 2003, pp. 117-127.

2004
"Russia's Reflexive Control Theory and the Military," <u>Journal of Slavic Military Studies</u>, April-June 2004, Vol. 17, No. 2, pp. 237-256.

<u>Dragon Bytes: Chinese Information War Theory and Practice</u>, 2004.

"Comparing US, Russian, and Chinese Information Operations Concepts," posted to the 2004 Command and Control Research and Technology Symposium website, San Diego, California, at http://www.dodccrp.org/events/2004/CCRTS_San_Diego/CD/papers/064.pdf

2005
"Chinese and American Network Warfare," <u>Joint Force Quarterly</u>, Issue 38, 3rd Quarter, July 2005, pp. 76-83.

"China's Revolution in Military Affairs: More Cognitive than Technological?" draft paper awaiting publication.

APPENDIX TWO: DECIPHERING ASYMMETRY'S WORD GAME

This article appeared in the July-August 2001 edition of <u>Military Review</u>, pp. 32-37 under the same title. It highlights the debate over the term "asymmetric war" and problems associated with the exclusive use of US sound bites and paradigms, resulting in misunderstanding terms and improperly applying them to situations. This wastes time and energy, and it confuses practitioners, much like the current debate over the definition of IO.

Introduction

The terms "asymmetry, "asymmetric warfare," "asymmetric approaches," and "asymmetric options" are popular sound bites found in many military journals today. Asymmetric-related terms are commonly associated with a potential opponent's operations or actions against US interests or forces. The attacks are commonly described as chemical, biological, nuclear, terrorist, or information attacks, or attacks against weak points. Arguably, these attacks are not asymmetric. In fact, except for the terrorist example, these are symmetrical attacks. The United States has chemical, biological, nuclear, and information means; therefore, such attacks cannot be asymmetric.

The asymmetric aspect of a chemical, nuclear, information, or traditional attack actually relates to asymmetries in capabilities, reliance, vulnerabilities, and values. The capabilities of certain forces—some information systems can shut down command and control systems and prevent nuclear systems from launching—constitute one variable. A nation's reliance on a particular system is another. For example, both sides can have information weapons, but one side may rely more on them than the other. The vulnerability of a system or platform's performance parameters, operations principles, or situational context is another asymmetric opening, the one most often associated with weak spots. Finally, cultural values determine whether a nation will or will not use one of these methods.

The Russo-US relationship provides an example of such reasoning. Both countries have had biological and nuclear weapons for decades, yet no one has called this an asymmetric Russian threat. Neither side has used these weapons because of discussions that led to a common understanding and because of a value structure that placed national interests above other interests. However, if a country that conducts operations based on very different values obtains biological weapons, then we should worry. In some cultures, social and religious reasons may override national interest when choosing whether to use such weapons.

What Is Asymmetry?

Judging by the multiple applications of the term in military journals—"not fighting fair," "attacking a weak point," "information or cyberwar," "public relations war," "weapons of mass destruction"—very few people understand asymmetry's formal definition. This is understandable since joint doctrine does not define the term.[528] One civilian lexicon explains asymmetry using the mathematical term "incommensurability," the relationship between things that have no common measure.[529] Another civilian definition refers to defective, disproportionate correspondence between things or their parts.[530]

Other non-English-speaking cultures define the term in more distinct ways. A Russian dictionary definition of asymmetry is "the absence or destruction of symmetry."[531] This concept implies a more active role in changing symmetry's parameters than the US or British definition, even the creation of asymmetry. Compared to Western deductive thinking, the Russian dialectic thought process of thesis and antithesis encourages an analysis of a situation from a different, more confrontational perspective.

There is no distinct word for asymmetry in Chinese. To express this concept one would negate the word for "to be symmetrical." This word for symmetry, duicheng, is also comprised of two characters. The word dui in ancient texts means "to respond," "to face or face off," "to match"—both in the sense of complement but also in the sense of enemies matching in skill. The term cheng initially signified the concept of "a balance" and then evolved into a broader semantic sense of "to accord with."[532] Thus, in China, asymmetry would involve things not in accord with, out of balance, not responding and not matching or facing one another.

These definitions indicate that our understanding of asymmetry has strayed and become misused. None of the recognized definitions discusses weak points, unfair fighting, or nontraditional means that many authors assert.

---

[528] Joint Chiefs of Staff, Joint Publication 1-02, Department of Defense Dictionary of Military and Associated Terms (Washington, DC: US Government Printing Office, 10 June 1998).

[529] Philip Babcock Gove, ed., Webster's Third New International Dictionary of the English Language (Unabridged) (Springfield, MA: Merriam-Webster Inc., 1981), p. 136.

[530] J.A. Simpson and E.S.C. Weiner, The Oxford English Dictionary, Second Edition, Volume 1 (Oxford, UK: Clarendon Press, 1989), p. 738.

[531] S.I. Ozhegov, Dictionary of the Russian Language (Moscow, 1984), p. 29.

[532] Discussion between the author and Dr. Deborah Porter, University of Utah, Associate Professor of Chinese, 4 August 2000.

The term apparently assumes whatever meaning military authors wish to portray and is thrown around like the grammatically incorrect term "irregardless."

While it may be hard for US military leaders to recognize, the dictionary definition suggests that the United States is the world's most asymmetric military force. While degrees of symmetry exist between other forces in developed countries, no one can symmetrically match up with US equipment and firepower. This was most evident in the after-action comments following the conflict over Kosovo. Department of Defense (DOD) officials admonished other NATO countries that their equipment was not compatible with or as capable as US equipment.

If the United States is the most asymmetric force in the world, why are potential threats to US security almost always labeled asymmetric? For example, the US National Defense University (NDU), in its 1998 strategic assessment, listed four asymmetric responses that other nations could take to counter US superiority: acquiring weapons of mass destruction; acquiring high-technology weapons; acquiring cyberweapons; and fighting in environments that degrade US capabilities. The logic of considering these approaches asymmetric escapes reason, for the first three responses would improve symmetry according to the dictionary definitions. The United States has all of these capabilities now; if someone else acquires them, then we are in a symmetric relationship. Threats are mislabeled "asymmetric" because we do not understand what asymmetry means.

Some highly respected publications stress that if an opponent does not fight the way we expect, then we automatically label his fighting technique asymmetric. The NDU study stated "asymmetric threats or techniques are a version of 'not fighting fair,' which can include the use of surprise in all its operational and strategic dimensions and the use of weapons in ways unplanned by the U.S." If this definition were accurate, Serbs and Iraqis could claim that NATO and the multinational coalition did not fight fair—face to face—but from afar with long-range, precision weapons. With such a broad application, any action can be considered asymmetric and further confuse the issue. The terms "atypical" or "nontraditional" better fit a situation in which an opponent uses an unexpected technique or exploits some factor better or faster than his opponent. The imprecise US terminology is faulty.

An Australian officer, Major J.J. Frewen, offered a reason for this imprecision. He noted that globalization has expanded the definition of national security beyond physical security to include economic, environmental, informational, and cultural security.[533] Threats to these elements are often considered asymmetric by many US academic institutes and leaders when, more precisely, these are matters for which our armed forces are not well designed. They undermine national interests without shots being fired and demonstrate that military intervention is problematic when the definition of "decisive force" is unclear. Frewen notes that problems in Somalia were caused not by a lack of armored vehicles but by failure to understand the environment. The problem was about "apples" attending an "oranges" event; any hardware-only solution suggests asymmetric vulnerability.

Some analysts have defined asymmetry with vision. Lloyd J. Matthews offers a strategic vision for his description of asymmetry. He defines it as any militarily significant disparity between contending parties that clearly fits the "lack or want" of symmetry idea expressed in Webster's. He notes: "The process of calculating the resultant of the various vectors of power wielded by two asymmetrically related opponents—in order to measure the dimensions of the threat that each poses to the other—can be quite problematic. But it is a process that must be undertaken if we are to give due weight to all the relevant elements of power."[534] Threats in the sense of capabilities, reliance on systems, and vulnerabilities are important in this regard.

Steve Metz and Douglas Johnson of the US Army War College offer another visionary definition of asymmetry: "acting, organizing, and thinking differently than opponents in order to maximize one's own advantages, exploit an opponent's weaknesses, attain the initiative, or gain greater freedom of action. It can be political-strategic, military-strategic, operational, or a combination of these. It can entail different methods, technologies, values, organizations, time perspectives, or some combination of these." The authors add that asymmetry can be short-term or long-term, deliberate or by default, discrete or pursued in conjunction with symmetric approaches and can have both psychological and physical dimensions. [535]

Retired Brigadier General David L. Grange writes that asymmetry is best understood as a strategy, tactic or method of warfare and conflict. It is not

---

[533] Discussion between the author and Royal Australian Infantry Major J.J. Frewen who was on a two-year exchange with the US Army as a G3 Strategic Plans Officer, Headquarters, US Army Pacific.

[534] Lloyd J. Matthews, Introduction in Challenging the United States Symmetrically and Asymmetrically: Can America be Defeated? Ed. Lloyd J. Matthews (Carlisle Barracks, PA: US Army War College [USAWC], Strategic Studies Institute [SSI], July 1998), p. 20.

[535] Steven Metz and Douglas V. Johnson II, "Asymmetry and U.S. Military Strategy," USAWC, SSI, January 2001, pp. 5- 6.

something new, he reminds us, noting that strategists define asymmetric warfare as conflict deviating from the norm or an indirect approach to affect the balance of forces.[536]

Perhaps the most asymmetric and least-discussed element is values. Operating principles—individual, social group, and national values—all play a role in the Information Age. There is always a lack of symmetry in values, even between two people. For example, discussions of abortion, homosexuality, and religion bring out individual differences. In the international arena, some decision-makers abide by international treaties; others do not. The values of President George H. Bush and Iraqi leader Saddam Hussein during the Gulf War clearly represented this asymmetry. Bush prevented a march on Baghdad because it was not in the UN mandate, while Hussein ignored international treaties and invaded Kuwait.

Vulnerabilities and Asymmetries

Many authors consider asymmetry to be the ability to exploit situations by attacking weak points or using nontraditional approaches in unexpected ways. These vulnerabilities can be uncovered by using a specific methodology to examine a situation. The methodology uses one of four means:

- Performance parameters
- Situational context
- Operating principles and rules of engagement
- Will.

Each mean uses nontraditional or intellectual methods to exploit a situation, degrading capabilities, and inducing unpredictability and chaos into military operations. It limits advantages, capitalizes on weaknesses, and tests patience and will. The methodology is a thinking man's strategy that encourages out-of-the-box concepts that could be labeled asymmetric because they capitalize on asymmetries in capabilities and reliance.

Such moves would be innovative or bold actions that could apply equally to either high- or low-tech opponents. It might mean using low-tech options to counter high-tech equipment—the rocket-propelled grenade (RPG) launcher versus a helicopter or using fuel-air explosives on an opponent. Or it could mean attempts to strike a people's political will and patience. The United States lost the battle of wills at home but not on the Vietnam battlefield.

---

[536] David L. Grange," Asymmetric Warfare: Old Method, New Concern," ROA National Security Report, March 2001, p. 1. Reprinted with permission from National Strategy Forum Review, Winter 2000.

Asymmetry can even express itself as a strategy of mass destruction or annihilation, prolonged attrition, or creating large groups of refugees.

Performance Parameters. Weapon parameters, whether signature (such as sound or image display) or performance characteristics, are susceptible to manipulation and are vulnerable. The Serbian military demonstrated its awareness of this principle during the recent conflict in Kosovo. The Serbs reportedly sent air defense crews to Iraq in February 1999 to study Iraqi procedures. The Iraqis have fought against these planes and tactics for 10 years. Who could better tell Serbian crews what a NATO or US air attack might look like? Every performance parameter was recorded on radar.

In another example, the Serbs reportedly used smoke to deflect NATO precision-guided weapons. When the pilot could no longer keep the cross hair on a smoked target, the weapons went off-course as the performance parameter was exploited. In Chechnya, the Chechens knew the elevation and depression limits of the Russian T-72 battle tank's main gun. They hid below the depression level in basements and in windows above the maximum elevation while fighting in Grozny during 1994 and 1995 and used RPGs to immobilize tanks.

When NATO's air forces engaged Serbia's armed forces, Serbian deceptions fooled NATO's high-tech equipment. The Serbian military found a flaw in NATO's electronic-reconnaissance system—targets could be seen but not clearly identified. Decoys and fake positions protected the real ones. When the Serbs wanted to block NATO's thermal-imaging systems, they used industrial heat sources to construct "thermal-cover" positions to protect tanks and artillery.

Another performance parameter is that of an actual force: tempo. Understanding an opponent's concept of operational tempo gets one inside an important performance parameter of his force and provides an asymmetric option.

Situational Context. Situational context includes an area's dominant historical, cultural, geographic, and political factors and how an opponent might manipulate them. For example, what is the regime protecting and what does it want? Other factors include a country's particular warrior culture, guerilla movements, or use of time and geography. In most conflicts, both combatants have some elements that can be exploited. Two unequal forces, such as a high-tech force confronting a low-tech force, fighting on similar terrain could use an asymmetric approach. If a low-tech force moves to the sanctuary a city offers, it can offset the high-tech force's superior firepower, maneuverability, and intelligence capability. In the city environment, the high-tech force often finds that its force structure does not fit the terrain. The high-tech force many find itself opposed by an entire population, as the Russians were in Grozny in 1996. A high-tech force, on the other hand, could prevent the low-tech force from entering the city.

Operating Principles and Rules of Engagement. Operating principles of presidents, parliaments, and armed forces vary from nation to nation. International treaties bind most nations to some common principles, but this adherence varies with time and opponents. Warsaw Pact members' allegiance to the Soviet Union waned and disappeared in the 1990s. The recent NATO operation over Kosovo offers a stark example. Breaking with traditions of time, opponent and principles, NATO acted out of area and may have placed human rights above sovereignty. If democratic nations bend their operating principles, what type of behavior and adherence to operating principles might we expect from totalitarian or rogue regimes?

Below the level of presidents and parliaments, combat involves operating principles. Combatants can estimate opposing leaders' tolerance for loss and damage, and threshold for capitulation. Unlike nation-states, guerillas are not bound by international treaties, codes of conduct, or operating principles. This difficulty is compounded by Western reliance on technology, a vulnerable operating principle in the age of off-the-shelf products. Sometimes underdeveloped countries can acquire high-tech equipment faster than developed countries because of research, development, and acquisition time lines: "In a world in which state-of-the-art is off-the-shelf, industry, and potentially our foes, can obtain better information systems and technology cheaper and faster than DOD because our current acquisition system buys computers in the same way we buy bullets."[537] Buying off the shelf becomes an asymmetric approach to developed nations' longer-term procurement cycles.

Operating principles also refer to the rules of engagement, strategy, tactics, and organizational principles that guide a side's actions and decision. NATO politicians decided that pilots could fly over 15,000 feet in Kosovo, a rule of engagement that affected precision.

Will. Colonel Charles Dunlap Jr. notes that the Western mind-set described by Samuel Huntington includes concepts (values) such as "individualism, liberalism, constitutionalism, human rights, equality, liberty, the rule of law,

---

[537] Ibid., p. 16.

democracy, free markets, [and] the separation of church and state."[538] However, entirely different principles and ideologies may drive logic in other cultures. Foreign societies may believe it is easier to attack the Western psyche or will to fight than to meet it on the battlefield in a contest between technologies, a truly asymmetric approach from the Western viewpoint. Many Russians believe that the United State did just that when it convinced Soviet Secretary General Mikhail Gorbachev to end the Cold War. His loss of will allowed the West to win the Cold War without firing a shot.

This discussion offers several conclusions. First the word "asymmetry" highlights the problem of using terms loosely or improperly. When this happens words are not properly understood, confusion reigns, and endless time is spent in futile explanation. The international arena further exacerbates the situation because different cultures interpret words with slight nuances. Not using one's own language correctly heightens misunderstanding. Second, a methodology that considers a situation asymmetrically offers a way to analyze and choose courses of action. Third, perspective is equally as important as methodology. The United States might be the most asymmetric force on Earth, but Americans do not see themselves that way. They view others as an asymmetric force or threat when, in fact, they are not. US citizens should be proud to be on the right side of the asymmetric ledger.

Asymmetries exist everywhere, of course. They can be found in market economies of varying degrees versus centrally planned economies and in political systems. There are also strategic, operational, and tactical asymmetries. Strategically, theorists discuss asymmetries in the force structure of intercontinental ballistic missiles or information warfare forces, while tactical-level analysts try to calculate the correlation of forces between sides. In these cases, asymmetries refer to quantities, total numbers, or different philosophies. Asymmetries also refer to approaches to attack vulnerabilities.

Asymmetry is a matter of two unlike systems interacting, each within its capabilities. Attacks can be swift (like an earthquake) or progressive (like termites or rust, silently undermining a formidable structure). Progressive attacks are usually associated with cultural strengths than can be maintained for long periods (sacrifice, resilience, deception, media sympathy). Unlike systems do not understand how to counter each other because of contradictory paradigms. Consider the term "rasingingin." When the term is understood as

---

[538] Charles Dunlap Jr., "Preliminary Observations: Asymmetrical Warfare and the Western Mindset," in Challenging the United States Symmetrically and Asymmetrically: Can America be Defeated?, Lloyd Matthews, ed. (USAWC, SSI, July 1998), p. 3.

"singing in the rain," then deciphering other terms is easier. For example, the word insertion paradigm helps interpret the term "beilld" as "sick in bed." Understanding the threat requires thinking in threat paradigms.

Agents using asymmetric analytic methodologies—performance parameters, situational context, operating principles, and will—start with an advantage. When striving to attack a vulnerability, having a template for action is the name of the game. Each methodology allows analysts to visualize better how to attack and defend enemy and friendly vulnerabilities. In the end, this is where the focus should be and not on the so-called asymmetric threats of weapons of mass destruction and chemical, biological, and information attacks.

APPENDIX THREE: THE COMPUTER: CYBERCRIMINAL OR CYBERCOP?[539]

Criminal Activities in the Cyber Age

Today nation-state militaries are reliant on advanced information technology for threat detection, weapon launch, guidance, and detonation. Within societies, cyber technologies offer law enforcement personnel new methods for catching criminals and terrorists. Simultaneously, these technologies offer criminals and terrorists the chance to attack nation-states and influence societies in ways never before anticipated. A criminal, terrorist, or state-sponsored computer information or network attack is difficult to predict or expose since these activities occur in the interdependent public, military, and private domains, and are often anonymous. Thus the military cannot stand between the threat and the public as it once did. Instead, the role of law enforcement agencies has increased dramatically to counter this criminal/terrorist threat. This fact is underscored by the creation of a Homeland Security Department in the US that has as one of its functions the protection of the US technological infrastructure.

People don't completely understand the consequences of the use of computers, can't watch certain aspects of a state or criminal's cybermobilization, and don't understand the fog and friction of the computer environment in which they operate. Plus they must deal with both military and societal threats simultaneously. Criminals and terrorists capitalize on this uncertainty. In many cases, states aren't even sure who the players are since criminals and terrorists hide behind the façade of a nation-state or Internet infrastructure to perform their activities–at times giving their activities the appearance of state sponsorship.

Controlling the consequences of the use of computers demands target intelligence far beyond that required by most weapons, a fact most criminals and terrorists recognize as an advantage. Law enforcement agencies can't respond indiscriminately. They must spend much time and effort on each issue. Criminals/terrorists usually don't care if their attacks have secondary consequences since the generation of chaos detracts attention from the source of

---

[539] Ms. Karen Matthews contributed over half of the material in this article. At the time, Ms. Matthews was an Army Reserve Major working for the Foreign Military Studies Office. She drew upon her vast experience and training in computers, law enforcement, and digital forensics in support of this article. Given the evolving nature of the topic, she has provided websites throughout the article for easy reference to current information. She has also provided a bibliography at the end of this article.

the attack. Law enforcement agencies handling these attacks must carefully consider any response since the response is capable of damaging not only the criminal/terrorist target, but also several unintended targets due to the integrated nature of society in the Cyber Age.

Additionally, it is difficult for citizens and law enforcement agencies to measure the "intent" of electrons. They may appear harmless when they enter your computer as a file, only to appear as a virus carrier or some type of logic bomb upon closer examination. Further, the use of electrons is scalable to an extent not feasible with most weapons in matters of both effect and size. Electronic attacks can be administered in small or large doses by individual hackers or entire detachments, and they can be increased or decreased on demand. Since the characteristics of an electron stream (invisible, anonymous, unknown intent, quantity, etc.) are vague, this makes any law enforcement response against a criminal electronic attack tricky at best.

These characteristics of the Information Age generate a host of questions for analysts and investigators to consider and act upon. For example, consider just the issue of anonymity. Is the reliability of a response negated due to anonymity, and if that is the case,[540] then how and against whom is the response to be directed? Should the attack be against the most likely aggressor even if one is not 100% certain? Is some type of proportionality response more desirable? Will one nation destroy another nation's information infrastructure only to later ascertain that the attacker is an individual, a "univirusbomber"? In light of such issues, what mechanisms are there for law enforcement agencies to control the use of these weapons? Further, is there a profile that fits the cyberterrorist or criminal? Who commits these cybercrimes? Since anyone with illegal intent and even a minimum of computer skills could find a way to involve a computer in almost any type of crime, there are a huge number of potential candidates. Think about it—a disgruntled employee who wants to inflict damage or to steal proprietary data for resale or personal gain is a candidate.

Three things are required for an incident to be considered a crime: motivation, access, and capability. The motivation may be as simple as "because it was there," or it may be to show power and expertise to other hackers, or it may be for a more sinister purpose such as corporate or government espionage. Access will vary depending on the computer system used. For instance, if an incident occurred on a stand-alone classified network, access would have to come from an insider. If it is from an internal network

---

[540] The attacker may eventually be exposed, but time plays a key role as a nation can only wait so long to respond.

300

that has a gateway to the Internet protected by a firewall, it could be an insider or an outsider who exploited vulnerabilities in computer security measures. Determining who had access may be tricky. These days anyone with a computer normally has a modem, cable, or Digital Subscriber Line (DSL) service making the pool of suspects nearly impossible to trace.

Capability is also hard to determine. Computer operations have become more intuitive and automated. Even hacker exploits have become a point and click process to some extent. However, if you are tracking an account holder that normally exhibits just enough knowledge to send and receive email, it is doubtful whether that person is the one who can capture the keystrokes of the company CEO's email. Coworkers, friends, and family can usually give you a good idea if a suspect has extensive computer knowledge. On occasion, hackers themselves will tell you how smart they are, especially the young and inexperienced ones. Most young hackers are just out to break and enter as many computers as possible, and usually they cannot do so without bragging to their peers. More sophisticated state-trained hackers, however, use this to their advantage. They may sit back and use the static of hackers as a smoke screen for their intelligence gathering. They may also recruit or use unknowing hackers to assist a break-in. Other places to find capability is any Internet Relay Chat (IRC) channel that is frequented by subjects.

This document will examine the computer from the perspective of its use by law enforcement and by criminals and terrorists. Representatives from other nations might view these operations in a slightly different manner.

The Computer as Cybercriminal

Just as the Internet has become a primary means of communication for commerce, banking, education, and entertainment, it has also become a medium for criminals to commit both old and new types of crime. Computer crime awareness began in the 1980s and 1990s. One early definition of computer crime was simply any violation of a computer crime statute. This definition was not very helpful, particularly at an international level. For example, it did not define what type of computer crime statute was under consideration. In the United States, there are federal, state, and local laws that could be applied to this definition. On the international level, there are some countries with national computer crime laws while others still have no specific laws addressing the issue. By including the word "computer" in the term "computer crime," some argue that it leaves off other digital means such as pagers, cell phones, personal digital assistants (PDAs), and so on. Thus the definition did not include a host of devices associated with the Cyber Age.

Cybercrime is a more accurate definition than computer crime. It evolved after the term "cyberspace" was made popular by the media. Although it did not fully define cybercrime, the Council of Europe discussed this issue and began developing a common language for dealing with such criminal activities. Throughout the documents from the Council of Europe, the terms "computer-related crime," "cyber-space offenses," and cybercrime are used interchangeably. Representatives noted

> The integration of telecommunication and information systems, enabling the storage and transmission, regardless of distance, of all kinds of communication, opens a whole range of new possibilities. These developments were boosted by the emergence of information super-highways and networks, including the Internet, through which virtually anybody will be able to have access to any electronic information service irrespective of where in the world he is located. By connecting to communication and information services users create a kind of common space, called 'cyber space'. [541]

The Council went on to define "cyber-space offenses" as those offenses committed against the integrity, availability, and confidentiality of computer systems and telecommunications networks. Examples include illegal money transactions, offering illegal services, violation of copyright, and issues that violate human dignity and the protection of minors.

The US government has no formal definition for cybercrime or computer crime. It does, however, have statutes that give examples (instead of definitions) of what is punishable under US federal code. The US statutes will be discussed in more detail later. What follows is a listing of types of cybercrimes as defined by US federal code.

(1) Data Manipulation for Reasons of Theft, Fraud, or Sabotage
Computer data by its nature is very volatile. The data on a computer system is stored electronically on some type of digital media. As the saying goes, it is all 1s and 0s. The manipulation of that data and the ability to know what has been changed depends on a variety of factors. Like other crimes, the criminal has to have motive, access, and capability to commit the crime of data manipulation. A disgruntled employee for a software company could install code into a commercial software package to make the program unmanageable at some point in the future and accomplish "date" manipulation. A bank worker could manipulate electronic transactions to siphon off funds to a surreptitious account. There could be outsiders who attack a networked system and then once

---

[541] William Gibson, <u>Neuromancer, 1984</u>

inside change data. For example, someone may want to get to medical records in order to fake an illness so that an insurance company drops a policy or to make sure a future employer doesn't hire someone. Enemy countries could try to change intelligence databases to remove suspicion about one of their own spies. Thus, there are a multitude of motivations for data manipulation. Access is the difficult element in this equation of motive, access, and capability. The insider may have to expand "user" access to an increased level to commit the crime. Such increases in access are traceable. Capability is simply the ability to know what piece of data to change. Those with a higher capability not only can gain access, but they can protect themselves by ensuring that logs are turned off and file dates are changed. This insures that such indicators do not point a finger at them.

(2) Destruction or Damage of Infrastructure Operations

If a hacker group is able to disrupt a 911 emergency phone service, it may cause human suffering, and it has the potential to cause loss of life. Other hacker groups have tried to disrupt power infrastructure systems on a smaller scale. This is a wake-up call for any nation not willing to adequately protect its critical infrastructure assets. During peacetime or time of war, a disruption of critical infrastructure resources can affect the government's ability to secure the country.

(3) Using the Computer as an Instrument to Break Into, Enter, Trespass, Steal, Damage, or Intercept Communications of Other Devices Through the Computer Network (Internally or From the Internet)

If a computer is used in the commission of a crime, it is then said to be an instrument used to commit any of the crimes above. If it is proven that a certain computer was an instrument involved in a crime, there needs to be no evidence of the crime on the computer.

A hacker usually has a purpose when breaking into other computer systems whether it is for mischievous or truly criminal reasons. But a crime is also committed when a user of a local area network exceeds his ordinary user access to system administrative rights and accesses prohibited parts of the system or network.

(4) Political and Economic Intrigue such as Money Laundering, Slandering a Political Candidate, or Using "Hactivism" Tactics

The advent of the computer has increased the ability of the criminal to launder money. The process of laundering money obtained from illegal activities is faster, safer, and simpler due to the use of networked systems and computers. The process can be made so convoluted that it is nearly impossible to trace the money flows or track the companies as they can be created and changed in an instant. The Internet and the ability to conduct online banking anywhere in the world further complicate the ability to regulate financial transactions. The laws of different countries also compound the issue.

The new use of computers reinvigorates old political motivations–discrediting competition, building mass hysteria, disseminating disinformation, and winning publicity for causes. This new computer form of protest/confrontation/activism has been termed "hactivism." Many countries, groups, and individuals use web page "graffiti" as a public medium to support their hactivist efforts.

(5) Using the Computer as an Anonymous Means to Conduct Illegal Activities, such as Producing, Distributing, or Downloading Child Pornography; Using the Computer to Find and Entice Victims such as Children for Pedophilia; Constructing Pyramid Schemes Via Email, etc.

Using a computer for communication through the Internet can give a person anonymity. An "anonymizer" is an Internet-connected service that takes email, strips it of the return header, and puts its return header on your email. Most of these services do not keep logs or records, and it is virtually impossible to find the originator of the email. The regular user may not know that there are many methods to identify and find him. The experienced user can make anonymity a reality, however. Other examples of how to remain anonymous are: Internet Protocol (IP) spoofing (using another IP address as a source), using cybercafés or other public Internet sites, obtaining someone else's Internet account, breaking into and using someone else's computer system, traveling through multiple systems that have been hacked to complicate the ability to trace them back to the original source, and deleting logs or other records of access. These methods make it difficult for law enforcement to find the perpetrator of any of these illegal activities.

(6) Copyright Infringements and Violations of Intellectual Property (Copying or the Illegal Distribution of Commercial Software, Music, and Digital Videos); Intellectual Property Violations that Include Plagiarism

Copyright infringements run rampant. Commercial software products have not only been copied for home use from work, but many sites can be found that contain copyrighted software for free download by anyone over the Internet. These sites are called "warez sites". Usually a hacker finds a vulnerable, and publicly accessible, anonymous File Transfer Protocol (FTP) server. The hacker gets into the system, creates a directory, and places all the illegal software in it. Then he notifies his friends to publicize the system and gives them the directory and any username or passwords so that people can get into the system. Copyrighted music was and still is available for download. The biggest site, Napster, was forced to shut down its use of copyrighted music but can still make available noncopyrighted music. Digital videos are the latest victim. During a computer security assessment at a US government agency, an FTP site that was hacked was found to contain digital videos that had not been publicly released on DVD yet.

(7) Virus Creation and Distribution

This type of crime fits many of the above categories. A virus can have many purposes, such as the destruction of data for sabotage reasons, the collection of data for intelligence purposes, network slowdowns for information warfare purposes, and so on. A virus is built to spread itself to other computers via several means, to include "Sneakernet", the manual transport of a diskette, or a worm that propagates itself in some fashion across the network. Most viruses are attachments to emails that are executed by the user. However, today's viruses are becoming even more lethal. They can be part of a website script, or they can be automatically executed by the function of the mail program. Destruction of data may occur or information may be intercepted and sent via email to other locations (data such as the password file). Some worms or viruses attack other systems until the network is clogged to a stand still. Others infect a system but then wait until a certain date to carry out their destructive task, such as wiping out all of the contents of the user's hard drive. These latter viruses are called "logic bombs," but the payload may be considered a virus.

Other Criminal Uses of the Computer

Computers help criminals by providing them tools available either commercially or on the Internet. These include deceptive messages, fake return addresses, encryption, and even steganography tools to hide communications. Deception can include disguising a site as a place to send money for a charitable cause, when, in fact, the money goes into a private account. Encryption is the method of encoding a file with a key to produce a scrambled document. The receiver of the encrypted message must have a key to decode the message. Steganography is the art of hiding or embedding a document or other file within another "carrier" file. Most standard steganography programs have the ability to encrypt the document first and then embed it in a carrier file such as a web graphic file or audio file. This presents two levels of difficulty in finding these illicit communications: first detection and extraction of the embedded file, and then the decryption of the encrypted document. Of course, law enforcement can benefit from the use of these tools as well.

Another communication device used by criminals is IRC. This is an Internet tool that indicates who is online at any time and enables you to contact them. This device is composed of a series of servers which provide "channels" for members to join. Chat channels are usually topic-specific. Members may establish their own chat channels which can be made private (by invitation only). Most IRC services do not log any activity on these channels. They provide the means to transfer files anonymously. Pedophiles, hackers, and other criminals use this method to further hide their communications.

The Computer as Cybercop

As a tool for law enforcement, computers can assist investigators in several ways. The following is a list.

(1) Computer and/or Hardware is Merely a Storage Device for Evidence of a Crime

Computers store crucial data that is both informational and evidentiary. Investigators can obtain evidence or information in the form of a trail of bits across the network (if the crime was perpetrated across the network) or from files stored on an information system (if the perpetrator used an information system in any part of the crime). Investigators now know to check all digital devices for clues, such as pagers, cell phones, PDAs, and computers. They also check Internet service accounts and billing records for these services. Computer files are stored according to the type of operating system. When a criminal believes he is erasing a file, he may in fact only be erasing a directory pointer to that data and not the actual data. Many investigators have benefited from the criminal's false belief that "if I erase a file, it's gone." For example, in one crime, the rape of a 15-year old, the perpetrator met and courted the victim through the Internet. The trail of evidence was extensive. It was possible to obtain the identity of the perpetrator from his "screen name" or alias from the Internet service provider. The victim's computer stored copies of emails between the victim and the subject. Further investigation from the subject's computer revealed those communications, such as the fact that the subject received a message from the victim revealing her age. Also found were other messages to potential victims of a similar age, to include travel arrangements and reservations that corroborated the victim's story.

(2) Computer and/or Hardware Is Instrumentality, Contraband, or Fruit of the Crime

Since the computer can be the instrument used to intrude or trespass into other computer systems, it becomes the "burglary tool." It may also be purely contraband. The computer is considered the "fruit of the crime" if, for example, a hacker uses fraudulent credit cards to purchase a computer system. This is not uncommon for hackers involved in "carding," which is stealing credit card numbers either through hacking e-commerce site customer databases or from other more traditional means.

(3) Computer and/or Hardware Can Be the Target or Victim of the Crime

The computer may be the target of the crime. A hacker may want to control or "own" a specific computer system. That computer becomes the hacker's target. "Owning" or having root level privileges may be the sole target of the crime. When this is the case, the computer may serve as a container of evidence.

(4) Computer and/or Hardware Can Be a Witness to the Crime

A local area network at a company or business has many resources that individual computers share when logged into the network. The network also may have perimeter security devices or computers that protect those internal assets, grant user privileges to those internal resources, and conduct bookkeeping on three things: the users, the assets, and the outside entries into the local area network. These logs, records, and other similar data may serve as a "witness" of a crime committed against one of its internal computers. One example is a border router log. A border router sits at the gateway between the Internet and a local area network, and it routes traffic or packets of data. This router has the capability to filter out unwanted traffic to some degree and to produce logs. These configurations are called access control lists. They are tailored to meet the needs of the local area network's operational requirements. These sets of rules may log certain events while the logs may contain information about a computer break-in. Another "eye-witness" report may come from a firewall. A firewall is a computer application or a combination of a hardware appliance and software that protects a network from outside connections. The rule set of a firewall is configurable, and it can also filter out unwanted traffic while logging activities. These logs may contain information about a break-in. The local area network may have a file server or network administration machine that controls and logs user access. There are also specific types of systems that may contain logs on the web server, mail server, FTP server and proxy servers. Each of these systems could potentially be a witness depending on the type of computer crime.

(5) A Computer Provides Digital Evidence

Digital evidence is data that indicates a crime has occurred. It is contained on digital devices previously mentioned. Investigators, cyber security personnel, witnesses, system managers or victims of a crime access or collect digital evidence and use it to prove a crime has been committed.

Digital Forensics

One of the key tools available to investigators and analysts to uncover all types of illegal activity is forensics. Forensics is the use of science and technology to investigate and establish facts in criminal or civil courts of law. "Computer forensics" is using scientific methodology to investigate and obtain facts in a criminal or civil case on computers, computer media, or computer hardware. Most law enforcement organizations are moving toward a more inclusive term, "<u>digital forensics</u>," to cover other digital media as mentioned before and to include Global Positioning System (GPS) devices, network devices, etc. Digital forensics entails extracting the information from the digital device by using standardized processes that eliminate or reduce the chance of altering the evidence. Many in the law enforcement community have studied the problems of digital forensics and have adopted community standards to process digital evidence. As with any forensic process, this will be a work in progress as new technology is developed and new programs and procedures are discovered.

The forensic laboratory brings standardization to the world of forensics. The accreditation authority for approximately 85% of all the crime labs in the US is the American Society of Crime Laboratory Directors (ASCLD). Its mission is to develop standardized procedures for many forensic disciplines to include fingerprint analysis, ballistics, DNA analysis, toxicology analysis, etc. There are many factors involved in accrediting a standardized process when it comes to forensics. In forensic disciplines, the tools must first be standardized and tested to ensure they function properly and as expected. An example would be a blood machine which must meet certain technical specifications in order to be able to conduct a DNA analysis. Also, many years of researching DNA were required to be able to categorize and draw conclusions about the DNA sample. Then a process had to be written without altering the sample such that it would skew the results.

In the year 2000, ASCLD began to develop standards for digital forensics as well. Digital forensics is in the embryonic stages of becoming a forensic discipline. Some laboratories will not incorporate it as a forensic discipline until specific processes are in place. For example, the forensic tools for digital forensics consist of several items: hardware platforms to conduct the analysis; a variety of different software programs that do a variety of tasks to complete the analysis; peripheral devices that assist with the analysis, e.g. adapters, cables, keyboards, printers, scanners, etc.; and protocols that address different configurations such as hardware platforms, operating systems, applications, networks, and so on. With technology moving forward at the speed of light and the next generation of computers only six months away, it is a formidable task to nail down hardware/software requirements, processes, and types of analysis steps for every possible scenario. This is especially the case since no two computers are configured exactly alike.

Making Digital Forensics a Discipline
The first step toward making digital forensics a real forensic discipline

is testing the tools and the platforms to ensure that no data is missed. There is a project at the National Institute of Standards and Technology (NIST) in the United States called the Computer Forensic Tool Testing (CFTT) Project. The US Department of Justice's National Institute of Justice (NIJ); federal, state, and local law enforcement; and NIST support the CFTT project. CFTT is designed to provide a measure of assurance in the results of investigations based on automated tools used in computer forensic examinations.

A second step toward enhancing digital forensics is another NIST project called the National Software Reference Library (NSRL). The NSRL is designed to collect software from various sources and incorporate file profiles computed from this software into a Reference Data Set (RDS) of information. This enables law enforcement, government, and industry to review files on a computer and attempt to match them with those in the RDS. The idea is to eliminate many superfluous files if they match the profile of a commercial software product. This will help investigators to quickly sift through the enormous number of files that computers contain and focus only on those files that have the potential for containing informational or evidentiary data.

A third step in making digital forensics an accepted forensic discipline is adopting community standards in the examination of digital media. In the United States, there are many scientific working groups that develop, promulgate, and research new technologies in many forensic disciplines. These scientific working groups are sponsored by government at the local, state, and federal levels, and they consist of experts from government, academia, and law enforcement. They publish their recommendations to the community for comment and acceptance. The Scientific Working Group for Digital Evidence (SWGDE) is responsible for the development, promulgation, and publishing of digital evidence standards. As with any discipline, a common terminology must be adopted. SWGDE has drafted and submitted to the International Organization on Computer Evidence (IOCE) the following definitions:[542]

- **Digital Evidence** – Information of probative value stored or transmitted in digital form.
- **Data Objects** – Objects or information of potential probative value that are associated with physical items. Data objects may occur in different formats without altering the original information.
- **Physical Items** – Items on which data objects or information may be stored and/or through which data objects are transferred.
- **Original Digital Evidence** – Physical items and data objects

---

[542] Definitions derived from conferences attended by Ms. Matthews in 1998-1999. They are available at fbi.gov/hq/lab/fsc/backissu/april2000/swdge.htm.

associated with such items at the time of acquisition or seizure.

- **Duplicate Digital Evidence** – An accurate digital reproduction of all data objects contained on an original physical item.
- **Acquisition of Digital Evidence** – A process that begins when information and/or physical items are collected or stored for examination purposes. The term "evidence" implies that the courts recognize the collector of evidence. The process of collecting is also assumed to be a legal process and appropriate for rules of evidence in that locality. A data object or physical item only becomes evidence when so deemed by a law enforcement official or designee.
- **Copy** – An accurate reproduction of information contained on an original physical item, independent of the original physical item.

Collecting and Exchanging Digital Evidence

Due to the very nature of the global economy and the accessibility of governmental, industrial, academic, and other information to hundreds of millions of people across the globe, it is necessary for law enforcement to collect and exchange digital evidence across jurisdictional and national boundaries. The US and international organizations seeking to assist the law enforcement effort provide the following resources.

National (US)

1. **National Infrastructure Protection Center (NIPC)** – The center is a joint government and private sector partnership whose mission is to prevent and respond to cyber attacks against US critical infrastructure systems. NIPC has become the US cybercrime point of contact for international inquiries into cyber intrusion issues. http://www.nipc.gov/

2. **US Department of Justice (USDOJ) Computer Crime and Intellectual Property Section (CCIPS)** – This is a section of the Criminal Division of the US Department of Justice. It drafts and recommends US laws for cybercrime issues; develops guidelines for US Attorneys and law enforcement in the handling of digital evidence and presentation of cases involving cybercrime in federal courts of law; assists local and state governments in the formulation of local and state laws involving cybercrime and digital evidence issues; represents the US on international organizations working on international cybercrime issues; and participates in a myriad of other tasks that promote legal issues addressing cybercrime and intellectual property. The Computer Crime and Intellectual Property Section (CCIPS) of the US Department of Justice

(USDOJ) published a guideline entitled "Searching and Seizing Computers and Obtaining Electronic Evidence in Criminal Investigations." This document gives examples of when it is best to seize a computer or search it at the site. These are guidelines and not policies since final decisions must be based on the facts surrounding   the   case. http://www.usdoj.gov/criminal/cybercrime/index.html

3. **Scientific Working Group on Digital Evidence (SWGDE)** – This organization of US law enforcement and forensic organizations establishes and promulgates forensic guidelines and definitions for the handling and analysis of digital evidence. http://www.for-swg.org/swgdehm.htm

4. **Federal Bureau of Investigation (FBI) Computer Analysis Response Team (CART)** The CART provides assistance to FBI field offices in the search and seizure of computer evidence as well as forensic examinations and technical support for FBI investigations involving computer systems, media, or data. http://www.fbi.gov/hq/lab/org/cart.htm

State/Local

1. **Regional Computer Forensic Laboratories (RCFL)** – These local, state, and federal law enforcement labs cooperate in the conduct of forensic analysis of digital evidence.

2. **FBI Field Offices** – Local FBI offices offer computer investigative support for state/local law enforcement for intrusion and/or computer forensic support. The FBI also conducts intrusion investigative training for state/local law enforcement.

International

1. **Council of Europe** – This intergovernmental organization of European nations addresses issues of human rights, the development of European culture, consolidation of European democracy, and it seeks solutions to problems facing European society to include issues needing legal cooperation. The Council of Europe established a cybercrime convention to address international cooperation of cross-boundary issues. http://www.coe.int/

2. **European Union** – This is an organization of European nations that seeks to establish European citizenship; ensure freedom,

security and justice; promote economic and social progress; and assert Europe's role in the world. This organization developed an international treaty for signatory countries to develop and promulgate cybercrime laws and to aid in the cooperation of investigations by other countries.
http://www.europa.eu.int/

3. **Interpol** – This is a law enforcement organization consisting of 168 countries. It is an organization that supports all law enforcement organizations. Specifically related to cybercrime, Interpol assists member law enforcement agencies with investigations into cyber issues and assists in obtaining digital evidence for member countries.
http://www.interpol.int/

4. **International Organization on Computer Evidence (IOCE)** – This is an international body of forensic and law enforcement organizations developing standards for acquiring, transferring, and analyzing digital evidence.
http://www.ioce.org/

The Need for Law Enforcement

During the 1980s and the 1990s law enforcement embarked on a new challenge. That challenge was investigating and solving the increased number of computer media criminal cases. At first the law enforcement challenge focused on stand-alone computer systems requiring computer forensic analysis. Expertise in this area was hard to find, especially in the law enforcement community. Also, in that era, bulletin board systems (BBS) became popular. If a computer owner was rich enough, he or she could buy a modem, which allowed a user to dial into these BBSs. Hacking the BBS became the first form of computer intrusion. Later as Internet access increased and businesses, the government, and universities installed local area networks connected to the Internet, cybercrime went global. Law enforcement now needed to handle network crimes as well as stand alone computer systems.

Fighting Computer Crime with a Computer

Two paths of investigation were necessary to solve such crimes. The first was the investigation into network-like crimes. This required knowledge of networks, methods that could lead to the identity of the subject, and knowledge about the evidence on those systems to prove the subject committed the crime.

The second investigation path was the analysis of computer media. Conducting computer forensics on computer evidence required tools and processes not utilized in standard investigations. Analysis required a computer that could process the data and specialized tools and processes. Necessity, being the mother of invention, resulted in some software tools being developed by law enforcement personnel in the early computer forensic days. Now, commercial, governmental research institutes, academia and even business are involved in developing forensic software and hardware tools.

The Internet is "governed" to some extent by the assignment of Internet Protocol addresses. Much like obtaining your phone number from the local phone company, one obtains an Internet phone number or Internet Protocol (IP) address from an Internet Service Provider (ISP) before connecting to the Internet. These Internet addresses are obtained and registered to a governing body, the Internic registry. The Internic registry maintains a registry database of all IP addresses. An investigator can start looking for the owner of an IP address using this tool. There are actually many databases based on geographical location. You can start at the main database, whois.arin.net. It will tell you what geographical database contains the pertinent IP address, e.g. whois.arin.net may point you to whois.apnic.net, which is the Asian Pacific regional registry database, which may point you to whois.twnic.net.tw, the registry database for Taiwan. Once a local ISP is located, the ISP may have logs that reveal which of their accounts were utilizing the IP address in question. Law enforcement can use the public database but to get further data from the ISP entails some legal complications such as jurisdictional boundary issues and obtaining legal authority documents.

Other information for law enforcement officials comes from company websites, department of motor vehicles (DMV) records, courthouse records (to some extent), search engines and other online services. Traditional crime investigations as well as cybercrime investigations can be enhanced by the information available on the Internet. In this manner, the Internet eventually became an important law enforcement tool.

Not long ago, in a well-publicized case, a 14-year old girl disappeared from her home in Salt Lake City, Utah. One of the investigative activities performed by the police was to seize (by consent) and search all of the family's computers. As the detective explained to the press, it is just a normal investigative step. A few years ago, that "normal" investigative step would have been rare. In the Salt Lake City case, there were no leads, and the hope was that digital evidence might point to online acquaintances. The point is, however, that digital evidence has become a mainstream method for law enforcement as another avenue for potential leads or evidence in almost any criminal act.

Investigative Electronic Tools and Techniques
Types of Tools and Techniques

Most law enforcement computer investigations can be categorized in terms of (1) extracting or retrieving stored data from digital processing systems such as data from the hard drive of a computer, (2) "capturing" data as it is transmitted across a digital or analog communications path, and (3) postprocessing analysis of either of the above or both combined with link analysis.

1. **Digital Forensic Analysis** – The goal of conducting digital forensic analysis is to retrieve evidence in a manner that does not alter the original media or change evidence and does not document the steps taken to extract data.

2. **Network Monitoring** – The goal of network monitoring is to capture digital data in transit to retrieve evidence or information about a crime from network traffic.

3. **Link Analysis** – The goal of link analysis is to fit the pieces of the puzzle together by identifying relationships between people or IP addresses, thereby building a comprehensive picture of all the digital data retrieved on a specific crime.

1. Digital Forensic Analysis

The basic premise of a forensic analysis is to avoid changing the media. Work should be done from a bit-for-bit copy if at all possible. "Document, document, document" is the rule to follow. With all the available technologies, hardware, software and configurations, it is impossible to know everything. The best practice is to consult with a subject matter expert and add that knowledge to yours for the future. Investigators, patrol officers, computer support personnel, and forensic laboratory examiners analyze digital evidence. The digital forensic community is a combination of experts and various forms of information technology support that assist law enforcement. This wide gamut of potential examiners of digital data is a necessity for many reasons.

First, investigations or first responders must ascertain immediately if a criminal event occurred which may require a system administrator to review logs and look for potential compromises. Second, investigators may need to view a file server on-site because the business will not let them seize their only system. Those investigators may rely on specialists since not all law enforcement officials or on-site system administrators are trained to examine digital data. Third, computer security personnel investigate per company policy,

314

and only if data suggests a crime, are law enforcement officials called. All of these are realistic scenarios. Trained forensic examiners may acquire the data at some point, or investigators may obtain enough evidence so that a forensic examiner is never requested. The potential problem is that a standard technique or tool is not utilized from this multitude of possibilities. One premise repeated in professional books on computer forensics is to know your limitations and call for help when your knowledge on a particular subject is exceeded. It is not OK to assume or continue an examination if you do not know what you are doing. Why a plethora of individuals to deal with digital information? The most important reason is time. How long will that evidence be there? Will seizing that computer by turning it off lose the critical data that the investigator needs?

Some data will be in memory and will be lost if the system is shut down or shut off for a bit-for-bit copy. This is called "volatile data." This information should be evaluated based on the case type, the computer or network server to be analyzed, and the likelihood that volatile data exists. If so, there are protocols developed to save this data. These protocols allow a copy of the process table to be copied out to a file. The process should be followed, and all steps, actions, and reasons for actions should be documented. Processes for retrieving static data follow the law enforcement agency's guidance or the national standard for preserving static data.

While the proliferation of digital forensic practices and training in the commercial as well as the law enforcement community is a fact, there is a down side. The methods, techniques, and tools can become common knowledge. When this happens, smart criminals create countermeasures to those methods. For example, not many people initially realized that erasing a file on a computer did not completely eliminate the data. Many criminals did not realize this either much to their chagrin. Today many people know that deleting a file does not fully remove it from the media. Tools have been developed that completely remove a file. A product called "Evidence Eliminator" professes to rid a Windows system of all traces of evidence.

Of the forensic processes used by law enforcement personnel, it is important to note the following as the main processes of digital forensics.

Identifying the Data Properly
The agency investigating the incident will have strict procedures and forms for this process. It is the typical police "bag and tag." Taking digital media into evidence is no different from any other type of evidence. It must be brought into a "chain of custody." When volatile information is captured and

transferred to a physical medium such as a diskette, it is the diskette that is "bagged" with a proper description of what it contains and how it was captured.

Preparing Hardware/Software Tools for Conducting Digital Analysis
The law enforcement officer or the lab examiner that conducts the forensic analysis should be working from a sanitized analysis work station— meaning that the system should be free of defects, viruses, and other case work. The computer forensic examiner should conduct an integrity check of the analysis workstation as well. Wiping the drive and reloading the software after each case is feasible with the current tools.

Obtaining Hardware or Processor Information from Suspect Computing Devices
Besides the data from the suspect's hard drive or floppy diskettes, there is other information necessary and important to the case. One is the date and time that is held in a firmware chip, called the basic input output system (BIOS). This type of investigative step, known as extracting data from the physical characteristics of the suspect computer, can be extremely important when trying to place a file of evidentiary value to a computer at a specific time.

Media Protection
Of course, a forensic examination starts with the protection of the original evidence from any tampering. There are two main methods of "write protection." A physical write protection method is any means to set a jumper, or disconnect the data cable, or alter the write function of the hard drive controller to keep ANYTHING from being written to the hard drive. The second means of write protection is a program that intercepts a write request and doesn't allow it to reach the hard drive. This allows processes such as creating an image of the hard drive to continue without fear of changing any data.

Processing the Data
A most important issue when processing the digital data is whether the procedure being performed is being done at the physical level of the medium or at the logical level. The following categories subdivide procedures into either physical or logical level analysis.

Physical Level Analysis
The physical aspects of a hard drive are those that are not operating system dependent. A hard drive is divided up into units called sectors. A sector is 512 bytes of data. These sectors of data are tracked, and metadata is created by the operating system. Data no longer tracked by the operating system may still be on the physical level of a disk.

Physical level analysis of a computer hard disk or other media is conducted regardless of whether the disk is formatted for Windows, Macintosh, or Unix. Such analysis and processes look directly at the physical disk at the sector level. No interpretation of the file system takes place. An operating system and specifically that operating system's file manager program arranges and tracks these sectors into a file system. Usually this file system keeps metadata about the data stored on the hard drive to find it easily. This metadata is a mixture of directory information, location information, and file attribute data.

Physical level analysis includes the following:

- **Bit-for-Bit Copy** – This creates an exact duplicate of the computer media. This method copies the media at the physical level from the starting sector of the computer media (such as a hard disk) to the ending sector of the disk (regardless of whether the sector is in use by a file or not).
- **File Header Searches** – This search uses a program that starts at physical sector 0 and looks for key strings that are known file headers (GIF87, JFIF - for some graphic file types).
- **String Searches** – Examiners search at the physical level or within the file system for a listing of keywords to the investigation. Encase and DiskSearch Pro are examples of programs that do this. The string search starts at sector 0 and looks for particular strings (for example, the words cocaine, coke, hash, etc.).
- **Regular Expression Searches** – This type of search utility helps an examiner find data that has some type of expression that is consistent but may not be a consistent string of characters. An example would be an email address. The consistent part of an email address is the "@" followed by a string of characters followed by a period followed by the rest of the domain name.
- **Maintenance Tracks or Other Areas of the Physical Disk Not Addressed by the File System** – A maintenance track is placed on the disk by the hardware manufacturer. It contains specific data about a disk when the hard disk is made. Special software tools are needed to read or write information to these tracks, and law enforcement must have access to such tools.
- **Recovering Sectors Marked as Bad** – When a hard disk is formatted, the formatting routine conducts a read/write test on each sector to ensure that it can be utilized by the file system. If this test fails, the routine can mark the sector as bad and tell the file system to skip this sector. There are also other utilities that can mark

sectors as bad. A person wanting to hide data could potentially write data to a sector, mark it as bad, and that data would not be found using standard file viewing programs. Therefore, as part of a forensic process of recovering data, utilities to seek out bad sectors and review the contents of those sectors are essential.

Logical Level Analysis

Logical level analysis of computer media requires interpretation of the file system structure that is on the disk. For instance, for a disk in which Windows 2000 was installed, the logical level analysis would have to interpret the NT File System (NTFS) utilized by Windows 2000. These processes include finding data within the file space addressed by that file system utilizing tools that interpret that type of file system. The object of the analysis may be to obtain the directory structure, the metadata about the data or file, and the file attributes.

Logical level analysis includes the following:

- **Directory Listings** – The directory lists directories of subfolders that contain files tracked by the file system. The utility in creating this listing is the chance to poll the file system for this data, thus it must understand the file system.
- **Authentication Algorithms** – Message Digest 5 (MD5) programs that calculate the contents of a file result in a unique number. If the file is changed in any way and another MD5 calculation run, the result will not yield the same number.
- **File Listings** – This is a complete listing of system files, archive files, regular files, hidden files, and, if possible, a listing of deleted files plus the directory path or directory structure of where these files are stored.
- **File Viewing** (such as graphics, text, and audio) – These programs will allow the examiner to open and view a variety of file formats for graphics files and text-based files. Also included are programs that will play a variety of audio formats.
- **Erased File Recovery** – This uses a logical file system to determine where erased data may reside and then goes to those physical parts of the disk pointed out by the file system that once had files but are now no longer being tracked by the logical file system.
- **Slack Extraction** –This uses a logical file system to determine the actual length of a file and the size of the allocation unit designated for the file. The remainder of the space from the file in the allocation unit is then recovered using the physical addresses.

- **File Comparison Utilities** – This utility compares a file to another file to see if it has been changed. A file might have been altered or had its evidentiary value changed. These utilities assist in discovering this.
- **Recovering Erased Files** – An operating system will have a method to delete or erase a file from the file system. It would be analogous to removing a directory card from the old card catalog index file. There would no longer be a "pointer" to where the book resides on the library shelves, but the actual book would still be there. The same holds true for a lot of operating systems in that the file remains even when the pointer is erased. The degree of data that you lose is dependent on the operating system. In a forensic analysis of a computer, recovering this data can provide a wealth of information and evidence.
- **Extracting Slack** – Slack is the space from the actual end of a file to the logical end of file space. For instance, you may create a word document that is only 50K but the operating system creates a logical block or "clusters" that may be 32K in length. In this example, this file would take two clusters. Cluster One allocated to this file would be filled. Cluster Two, however, would have only 18K of data from the document. The extra space, in this case, which would be 14K, would be considered slack space. What happens to the remaining space? The operating system may use this space to dump excess data from the memory. Or it could contain data from a previous file that has been deleted. Slack can give an investigator clues, but it is hard to put into context because it may only be partial fragments of a file.
- **Recovering and Interpreting Swap Files** – Some operating systems create a portion of the disk to use as a paging storage area or a temporary area to store information from the processor. This "swap space" can have some valuable information. There are some new tools on the market to help investigators recover and interpret this data.
- **Recovering or By-Passing Passwords** – Many programs such as word processing or spreadsheet programs allow a user to "password" protect their files. This is not encrypting the file but rather requiring a key (the password) to open the file. When these files are encountered during forensic processing, the forensic examiner must be able to crack the password or somehow by-pass that password to obtain the data. There are many methods to do this, such as using available programs or obtaining the passwords through interviewing the suspect.

- **Compressing/Decompressing Files** – Compression utilities such as WinZip are used quite frequently. These utilities use different algorithms to compress the size of a file. The files created, if not decompressed by forensic examiners, can be problematic. For instance, if the forensic examiner is doing a word search for a subject's name on a compressed file, the word search may fail because compression may not allow that string to be seen even though in the decompressed version it can be seen. Therefore, forensic examination entails detecting and decompressing compressed files either manually or by using automated search utilities that can perform this function.
- **Encrypting/Decrypting Utilities** – Because encryption is now prolific, the ability to detect encrypted files and decrypt them is imperative in a forensic examination. Products such as "Pretty Good Privacy" (PGP) have brought strong encryption to everyone. This process is problematic for law enforcement. There are some lesser encryption methods that law enforcement can deal with, but this area will always be a concern. As new and better encryption becomes available, new methods for law enforcement must be found to expose the encryption.
- **Detecting Steganography Utilities** – Steganography is hiding a file within a file. For example, one takes a word document and hides it within a graphic file. If those utilities are known to be used by the suspect or if steganography tools are found on the computer being examined, it is prudent for the forensic examiner to try to uncover the steganography program. This is a new problem area for law enforcement.

Imitating the Suspect's Operating Environment

A final static data process is to create a common operating environment. This process involves establishing a similar operating environment as the one on the suspect's computer in order to run his programs (from an image, not from the evidence disk), to check programs, to view files in a manner like the suspect, and to view the directory structure. This gives investigators an idea of how the evidence could have been obtained, processed, or viewed by the subject. It also will allow a visual inspection of the suspect's configuration setting for network connections, computer settings, and user and group settings.

One other type of analysis that should be conducted during a forensic examination is a *chronological or timeline analysis*. When a traditional crime takes place, three things come together at a certain time—the victim, the suspect, and the location. A timeline of the sequence of events and activities of each element is a standard way of fleshing out the activities and, perhaps, even the intent of the crime. In cyberspace, this is a little bit more difficult because a suspect can be miles away from the scene. Still a useful tool for a forensic examination of a computer system is a timeline analysis. A timeline analysis includes important files or data obtained from the physical and logical level analyses, users and dates, and times of computer usage, file creation, file deletion, or file changes that might pertain to the case. It is imperative to know who created or downloaded a file of information with value to the computer being analyzed, how it got there, and when it got there. Many case types benefit from this type of analysis, such as intrusion cases, fraud cases, and plagiarism cases.

Login logs, audit logs, system logs, and dial-up logs may provide additional information for this type of analysis. Intrusion cases are especially dependent on the sequence and timeline analysis of events. System logs include Intrusion Detection System (IDS) logs, web application logs, firewall logs, router logs, operating system logs and other application logs. The file attributes that an operating system's file system stores about a file can include such important timeline items as file creation date (when a file was created), file modified date (the last time it was changed), last file access date (last time that file was opened or viewed), and last archived date (last time the file was backed up or archived). An example would be a co-conspirator of a hacker who broke into a computer card site. A timeline analysis could show when the subject acquired the information as, for example, an attachment to an email from the original hacker. This type of information may help make the case to prove that the subject was part of the crime and decided what to do with the information. Perhaps the file was attached to another email and sent out to another co-conspirator as proof of his hacker buddy's "work well done."

2. Technology Used in Network Forensics or Investigations

Today many crimes have associated network data that can be used as evidentiary information. If a crime is committed at work, the Local Area Network (LAN) can offer additional information. An example of this is an individual who uses a workplace computer to download or upload pornography from the Internet, communicates with others about uploading and downloading pornography, or uses the Internet chat rooms to converse about illicit sexual conduct. The network file server could contain some of the images if the worker used his network home directory or perhaps the public areas of the file server's disk to place some of the evidence. The network server probably has logs regarding when the worker's account was logged in, and it may also contain the download records of what account downloaded what file and from where. This type of evidence would be obtained from the servers on the network and not the worker's computer. Other areas on the network that may contain evidence are mail servers, which could contain not only email but also attachments to the email, and the email logs. The site may keep web server logs that would show which websites a user may have visited. The network or domain servers may show login data, file download data, application usage, privilege levels, directory permissions, and a multitude of other data that may be useful in an investigation. Security testing records may show the configuration of a user's workstation that may be helpful in certain types of investigations.

Besides the computers on the network, other network devices may contain useful information. These devices include firewalls which may have some useful data in the firewall logs, border or intranet segregating routers which may have data in router logs, intrusion detection systems, web servers, DNS servers, and so on. Any of these devices, logs, or information may help in an investigation to determine what happened, when it happened, how it happened, and to or by whom. Network forensics is time consuming and usually requires the assistance of the network administrator or expert help. Since, in most cases, a court is not going to give law enforcement permission to seize a whole network, it usually requires that a search be completed on-site. This increases the possibility of missing valuable information. Usually the search has to be completed within a time limit, and that means that law enforcement has little time to respond to a configuration or system that is not familiar to them. Much preparation is required to conduct a network search. Law enforcement officials can help themselves by gathering data that helps determine configurations such as operating system types, hardware issues, storage issues, application issues, and so on. If an investigator knows he is going to have to search a local area network with one file server running an NT server with ten workstations running Windows 98 and that the application most likely to have the data they are seeking is Microsoft Access, then he should prepare for this eventuality. He must insure he has the capability on hand to search the network.

There are many methods to uncover data from a remote access, or to change or acquire data. The system logs may be the best starting place. If data were changed, older versions of the file should then be compared. Some files are stored temporarily, and these may also be a source for comparison. If this system were part of a network, file servers may store backups of these files. Again, a file comparison can be used. All network access devices have the capability to store audit or login logs, and these may be very useful in determining the source of a remote entry into a system.

Network Monitoring
Some data as we have mentioned before is volatile. Some data such as the commands a hacker might issue from a remote location will be lost if the investigator does not capture the activity in progress. The stored digital data may show the result, but what transpired and how it was done may best be answered using a network monitoring program. There are many types of network monitoring programs such as commercial, shareware, and freeware for different types of operating systems. There are even post processing programs that interpret the captured data back into a playback session which can show what the hacker typed, how fast he typed it, and even his spelling mistakes. The network monitoring program used by the FBI is Carnivore or FBI DCS 1000—an intercept program that captures network traffic and has post processors that tie the packets back into network sessions, such as Simple Mail Transfer Protocols (SMTP, sometimes called port 25 traffic) back to an email session.

3. Link Analysis
With so many kinds of data to analyze in a networking case, it may be useful to use some tools to view and grasp the whole picture of what transpired on a network and the locations that data has traversed. These tools assist in that type of analysis:

1. **Starlight**—a form of link analysis using Extensible Markup Language (XML) tags so that different types of records can be compared to one another, such as the comparison of phone records to computer logs.
2. **Spire**—a visual analysis program that searches text-based files for correlation of data. This includes log files, email, and IRC logs.
3. **Intrusion Detection Systems (IDS)**—located on networks that have been attacked. Data from the IDS can include transaction logs of the attacker's activity that may include the source of the attack. It may contain content data that will help investigators determine the type of attack.

There are many difficulties in investigating a cybercrime whether it be digital forensics or network forensics. The examples above demonstrate a few that law enforcement officials face. Because of these difficulties, other traditional law enforcement methods may need to be employed. These include nontechnical means, such as physical surveillance, online sources, sting operations, and criminal intelligence.

Receiving a Complaint about a Cybercrime
How does a cybercrime come to the attention of law enforcement officials? Sometimes it is because law enforcement officials take the initiative and educate corporations on cybercrime prevention. In the United States, the

FBI created a partnership program with industry called Infraguard. Its purpose is to provide legal and preventative information to corporations to enhance the corporation's ability to first prevent a cybercrime and then to respond effectively when a cybercrime occurs.

An initial complaint can be received by law enforcement in a variety of ways. The most common is through reports from the victims themselves—either a person or a company. The company may have an information technology shop and/or network security personnel. They may be the ones to detect an incident, investigate and gather facts, and then decide on the course of action. That course of action may be to notify or turn the incident over to law enforcement. As regards corporate security, the corporations may complete incident investigations on their own. The company may deem these cases as having little effect on business and may not wish to report them to law enforcement. There are several reasons for this, but mainly this is because of time, money, and resources. If the case involves an e-commerce site, for example, the decision may be to do anything to maintain or restore operations rather than investigate.

The next common method of receiving complaints is from other victims. Especially in intrusion cases, law enforcement may be notified by Internet Service Providers of attacks through their systems to downstream clients. This often happens with prolific hackers who have many victims. In investigating one victim, law enforcement may find evidence of multiple victims previously unknown to them. In addition, underground sources or agents of law enforcement may report illegal activity to law enforcement. They may assist law enforcement in determining the illegal activities or the identity of the perpetrators.

An example of a complaint would be a report of illegal remote access to obtain/change data in a system. The initial investigative steps would revolve around who conducts the investigation and what to look for. A system administrator or perhaps a user may notice an anomaly or an event that transpired at an odd hour from an Intrusion Detection System or from reviewing access logs. From the initial notice, a multitude of things will seemingly take place in parallel. They include informing management and gathering more security log data from network level devices such as firewall logs, intrusion detection logs, router logs, host-based intrusion detection logs, system logs, and, perhaps, application logs. If a company is experienced, it may have adopted good incident response procedures that would include gathering this data as law enforcement would—in a documented and forensic-like analysis process. Notifications to system managers and upstream Internet Service Provider may also happen. Usually in a corporate setting with critical servers, immediate disaster recovery steps are taken to get the system back online. This may or may not affect the subsequent investigation into what happened, who did it, and why. If the decision is made by management to bring in law enforcement, it will be necessary to present the data collected so far and to conduct interviews of all involved. Another parallel process should involve an ongoing damage assessment to include what it will cost the company to repair the damage and to support the investigation. Law enforcement officials will take similar steps. They will gather data via a forensic process to protect data of informational or evidentiary value and document the steps.

Legal Processes in a Cybercrime Investigation

Cybercrime investigations involve several legal steps and processes that must be accomplished in order to expand the search. Some of the elements that assist law enforcement authorities are explained below:

- **Consensual Searches** – The first questions to answer are who conducts the search and what is to be looked at. Initial investigative steps for an intrusion are to collect data about who, what, when, where, why, and how an intrusion occurred. The data collection begins when a complaint is received. Immediate attention must be given to data that is volatile and can readily be deleted or changed. In most instances, the company with a complaint may have already backed up the data and taken action to return the system to operational status. Law enforcement realizes that a company cannot usually afford to have a system tied up as evidence for long periods of time. Getting all the pertinent information about the system, the network, the access controls, the hardware and software configuration of the affected system, the protection measures of the network, and information from any other system that could potentially hold data of value is extremely important to the investigation. A parallel track for law enforcement is to preserve the account transaction records that the network provider or the ISP may have.

- **Use of Banners** – Banners at the entry or initial connection to a computer are much like the sign at the gate of a military installation. Those signs basically say that if you enter, you are giving consent to search. These banners have been reviewed by many legal experts and can give a company much leeway in what they decide to monitor regarding the usage of the company's network or computers.

- **Subpoenas** – These must be obtained by law enforcement personnel. An Internet Service Provider can give law enforcement access to subscriber-type information such as who owns the account and the billing information, name, address, etc. This type of legal authority does not extend to transactional data or content-monitoring data.

- **2703d Court Orders** – This order is usually given to Internet Service Providers that are electronic communications providers. With a letter of notification to the ISP stating the intent of the law enforcement organization to obtain a 2703d order, the actual data can be preserved immediately. The transaction logs will give data about accounts, much like the data that is on your phone bill. Whatever is asked for in the 2703d order up to, but not including the content of the transactions, will be provided, such as the time and date the account was activated, the log in logs, the connection logs, and so on.

- **Search Warrants** – A search warrant will give law enforcement the ability to seize and analyze whatever is listed. Thus, if you are investigating an intrusion and you have probable cause, you can search and seize the objects listed in the items to be searched or seized.

- **Trap and Trace Orders** – If a suspect is using a phone line, part of an investigation may be to find the number that the subject is using to access the Internet. A trap and trace order can be obtained to serve to the phone companies.

- **Title III Wiretap Authorities** – If complete content monitoring is warranted from an ongoing investigation, a Title III wiretap authority may be needed. The Title III process is cumbersome. It is the last resort in an investigative process.

- **Evidence Recovery Procedures** – There are two types of data that can be of use in a remote access or intrusion incident. The first, of course, is evidence. The second is data that has informational value which means it demonstrates the commission of the crime or evidence of the crime.

Limits to Control Measures under National Legislation

What are the limits to such investigative measures under national legislation? Naturally, this depends on several factors, not the least of which are the computer attacker's identity, law enforcement's ability to characterize intent, and the laws of the country concerned. In the US, for example, there are specific laws that govern what a government agency can and cannot do when attacked. That law grows fuzzier when the military is involved since the latter's activities are guided by the 1878 Posse Comitatus Act that prohibits the military from taking on a law enforcement function or from executing civil laws.

John Brinkerhoff, an expert on the Posse Comitatus Act, noted that the real intent of Posse Comitatus was "that it restored to the president the sole authority for authorizing the use of armed force to enforce the laws of the US."[543] This apparently means that the president could authorize the armed forces to protect ITSELF from information attacks and to actively seek and destroy the perpetrators. More important for the Information Age, Brinkerhoff added that a new law is required, one that sets the conditions for the use of the armed forces in the homeland security and modern (Information Age) context. The National Guard, which has state troops under the control of a state governor, does not fall under the act.

A US Department of Justice site (http://www.usdof.gov/criminal/cybercrime) lists US federal computer intrusion laws. Recent legislation includes two actions: the USA Patriot Act of 2001 and field guidance on new authorities relating to computer crime and electronic evidence enacted in the USA Patriot Act. The Patriot Act is designed to unite and strengthen the US by providing the appropriate tools required to intercept and obstruct terrorism. It establishes a counterterrorism fund in the Treasury, amends federal criminal code to authorize enhanced surveillance procedures (to include computer fraud and abuse), provides guidelines for investigating money laundering concerns, removes obstacles to investigating terrorism (granting the FBI authority to investigate fraud and computer related activity for specific cases), and strengthens criminal laws against terrorism, among other issues.[544]

The second new authority, Field Guidance on New Authorities that Relate to Computer Crime and Electronic Evidence Enacted in the USA Patriot Act of 2001, provides authority to do several things. This includes intercepting voice communications in computer hacking investigations, allowing law enforcement to trace communications on the Internet and other computer networks within the pen register and trap and trace statute ("pen/trap" statue), intercepting communications of computer trespassers, writing nationwide

---

[543] John Brinkerhoff, "Inside IT," Homeland and Security and Information Technology insert to <u>Defense News</u>, p. 18.

[544] See http://thomas.loc.gov/cgi-bin/bdquery/z?d107:HR03162:@@@L&summ2=m&.

search warrants for email, and deterring and preventing cyberterrorism. The latter provision raises the maximum penalty for hackers that damage protected computers (and eliminates minimums); states that hackers need only show intent to cause damage, not a particular consequence or degree of damage; provides for the aggregation of damage caused by a hacker's entire course of conduct; creates a new offense for damaging computers used for national security and criminal justice; expands the definition of "protected computer" to include computers in foreign countries; counts prior state convictions of computer crime as "prior offenses"; and defines computer "loss." In addition, the guidance develops and supports cybersecurity forensic capabilities.[545]

US federal criminal code related to computer crime includes the following:

- 18 USC. 1029, Fraud and Related Activity in Connection with Access Devices
- 18 USC. 1030, Fraud and Related Activity in Connection with Computers
- 18 USC. 1362, Communicationlines, Stations, or Systems
- 18 USC. 2511, Interception and Disclosure of Wire, Oral, or Electronic Communications Prohibited
- 18 USC. 2701, Unlawful Access to Stored Communications
- 18 USC. 2702, Disclosure of Contents
- 18 USC. 2703, Requirements for Governmental Access.

In peacetime, not only nation-states but the United Nations may have some power in the computer area. For example, the UN Security Council (UNSC) may have limited power to authorize computer actions by countries electronically attacked by other nations. Chapter VII provides the UNSC with the power to authorize the "use of coercive measures, including military force, to maintain or restore international peace and security, where it determines a threat to the peace exists, or a breach of the peace, or act of aggression has occurred."[546] A computer network attack (CNA) causing widespread damage, economic disruption, and loss of life might precipitate such a response from the UNSC. The intent of the offender and the consequences of the offending action would be examined. The UN Charter's Article 51 also includes the doctrines of anticipatory self-defense and self-defense in neutral territory as reasons for

---

[545] See http://www.cybercrime.gov/PatriotAct.htm.
[546] LTC Jordan, "Information Operations," Handout from the International and Operational Law Department of the Judge Advocate General's School, Charlottesville, Virginia, p. 46.

attack.[547] Such action is justified since Article 2 (4) states that "unarmed, non-military physical force may produce the effects of an armed attack prompting the right of self-defense laid down in Article 51."[548] Any computer countermeasures must be guided by the principles of necessity and proportionality.

It is believed that international law places restrictions on a state's activities in cyberspace. This especially applies to destructive attacks on another state's critical infrastructure.[549] Here the consequences and results of the attack are as or more important than the means used.[550] Further

- Any state activity in cyberspace that intentionally causes any destructive effect within the sovereign territory of another state is an unlawful use of force.
- Any computer network attack that intentionally causes any destructive effect within the sovereign territory of another state is an unlawful use of force within the meaning of Article 2 (4) that may produce the effects of an armed attack prompting the right of self-defense.[551]

In short, CNA's can result in victim nations responding either with another CNA or by conventional military means for self-defense.

Active defense against a computer attack can be used when there are constant unauthorized intrusions indicating a danger or when a single attack causes significant damage. The latter can also minimize issues of proportionality.[552] Again, this will also depend to a great degree on the ability of the victim to ascertain the identity and location of the intruder or if his intent is unclear. Responses against state-sponsored attacks are generally considered to fall in line with the concept of self-defense, whereas other attacks generally do not. The general procedure under international law is that a nation whose interests are damaged by the conduct of an individual acting within the territory of another state will notify the government of that nation and request its cooperation.[553] This procedure takes time, and the victim nation may lose its patience during the process. In order to investigate a computer attack

---

[547] Ibid.
[548] Ibid., p. 48.
[549] Ibid., p. 50.
[550] Ibid.
[551] Ibid., p. 51.
[552] Ibid., pp. 52-53.
[553] Ibid., p. 55.

originating from country X, law enforcement agencies in the US must first write a note to the US State Department that in turn must deliver the request to the embassy of the country concerned in order to receive permission to conduct the investigation beyond US borders. Perhaps the creation of an international cyber circuit court could shorten the process, but the eventually of this development ever occurring is remote. On the other hand, if the requested nation is unable or unwilling to prevent another attack, then the doctrine of self-defense permits the injured nation to act in self-defense inside the territory of another nation. However, the immediate danger presented to a nation, and to what degree the sanctuary government is likely to object, and how the world community is likely to respond, may play decisive roles in the action taken by the government.[554] While it may be possible for a government or key civilian infrastructure system to specify itself as vital to national security, attacks are also greatly influenced by the fact that this type of activity using public communications networks as an attack means is not a violation of a nation's sovereignty.[555]

What this means is that if nations decide not to negotiate a treaty that addresses computer attacks, then international law will develop through a trial and error routine based on the actions nations take as events unfold. There are great implications for both national and international security systems under such conditions.

Legal Challenges Presented by Information Operations
Clearly the characteristics of a computer attack complicate the application of traditional national and international law. Laws were originally developed in response to more traditional crimes and uses of force, such as those conducted by criminals or terrorists in peacetime, or by troops, aircraft, and kinetic weapons in wartime.[556] Computer attacks make it very difficult to ascertain combatants from noncombatants, especially since most criminal or terrorist activity occurs during peacetime. In time of war, civilians making direct contributions to the war effort may be attacked, along with objects whose damage or destruction would produce a significant military advantage based on location and purpose.[557] In peacetime, criminals and terrorists may still be attacked under certain circumstances and according to the following logic. An information weapon is an indiscriminate weapon since its consequences are unknown. International law bans the use of indiscriminate weapons, but this law, written before the advent of the computer, focused on bacteriological

---

[554] Ibid., p. 56.
[555] Ibid.
[556] Ibid., p. 36.
[557] Ibid., p. 37.

weapons and poison gas. Nations can site the use of an information weapon to suspend, modify, or terminate certain treaties related to indiscriminate weapons, since "a fundamental change of circumstances may justify a party to regard its treaty obligations as suspended or terminated."[558]

Possible Future Law Enforcement Techniques

There are several techniques that law enforcement agencies can use to intervene in the contents of international networks, but each must be coordinated with the appropriate authorities of the network and country concerned. The urgency of protecting critical infrastructure may in fact push the development of a properly designed active defense concept that is "precleared" by the courts for action.[559]

Computer systems may be developed that prevent the sabotage or destruction of friendly systems. As computers are unbounded systems, "no one has complete and precise knowledge of the topology or state of the system. Central control is nonexistent or ineffective."[560] Programming pioneer David Fischer developed just such a system, known as Easel, to work around unbounded systems such as the power grid. Easel can perform abstract reasoning easier than older programming methods. This allows Easel to predict how a new cyberpathogen or software bug might cripple a system. Law enforcement agencies would benefit from his expertise.

Closer cooperation between the National Institute for Standards and Testing's Information Technology Laboratory (ITL, mentioned earlier) with law enforcement agencies is another way to increase law enforcement techniques. There has been past cooperation. For example, the ITL's National Software Reference Library compares the files' electronic "fingerprints" to those in its database, allowing investigators to focus on suspicious or unknown files identified during a sweep. This automatically eliminates 40-95% of the files, and saves hundreds of man-hours. ITL also is working to protect the Internet Infrastructure from cyber terrorism, and it just helped develop the Advanced Encryption Standard for protecting sensitive, nonclassified information. The computer security division recently put out guidelines for federal agencies on risk management and contingency planning. Finally, work is being done to strengthen the security of the domain name system since the

---

[558] Ibid., p. 39.
[559] Ibid., p. 54.
[560] W. Wayt Gibbs, "Survival in an Insecure World," Scientific American, May 2002, p. 39.

system is globally distributed and provides a means of two-way mapping between names and Internet addresses. The latter is of utmost importance.[561]

Conclusion

Just as the capabilities of computers and their associated devices and functions have expanded exponentially, the capacity for criminal use expands with it. Law enforcement is creating cross-disciplinary guidelines and standards to deal with this new type of crime. There have been great strides made in gathering and collecting evidence both in the laboratory setting and in the field. The intent of the user may show persistence and sophistication of methods; however, law enforcement is ready to tackle head on the challenges offered by these cybercriminals. A variety of methods are available to thwart them.

---

[561] Regina Galvin, "IT Lab Brings Spy Novel Research to Life," Homeland Security and Information Technology insert, Defense News, p. 3.

Bibliography for Appendix 3

Casey, Eoghan. <u>Digital Evidence and Computer Crime</u>. San Diego, California: Academic Press, 2000.

Casey, Eoghan, editor. <u>Handbook of Computer Crime Investigation, Forensic Tools, and Technology</u>. San Diego, California: Academic Press, 2002.

Clark, Franklin and Ken Dilierto. <u>Investigating Computer Crime</u>. Boca Raton, Florida: CRC Press, Inc., 1996.

Department of Justice, Computer Crime and Intellectual Property Section (CCIPS), Searching and Seizing Computer and Obtaining Electronic Evidence in Criminal Investigations, Department of Justice, 2001.

Icove, David, Karl Seger, and William Von Storch. <u>Computer Crime: A Crimefighter's Handbook</u>. Sebastopol, California: O'Reilly and Associates, 1995.

Middleton, Bruce. <u>Cybercrime Investigator's Field Guide</u>. Boca Raton, Florida: Auerbach Publications, a CRC Press Company, 2002.

Northcutt, Stephen, Mark Cooper, Mat Fearnow and Karen Frederick. <u>Intrusion Signatures and Analysis</u>. Indianapolis, Indiana: New Riders, 2001.

About the author:

Timothy L. Thomas is a retired US Army Lieutenant Colonel. He received a Bachelor of Science degree from West Point and a Master of Arts degree from the University of Southern California. He was a US Army Foreign Area Officer who specialized in Soviet/Russian studies. His military assignments included serving as the Director of Soviet Studies at the United States Army Russian Institute (USARI) in Garmisch, Germany; as an inspector of Soviet tactical operations; and as a Brigade S-2 and company commander in the 82nd Airborne Division. Mr. Thomas has done extensive research and publishing in the areas of peacekeeping, information war, psychological operations, low intensity conflict, and political-military affairs. He is an adjunct professor at the US Army's Eurasian Institute; an adjunct lecturer at the USAF Special Operations School; and a member of three Russian organizations, the Academy of International Information, the Academy of Natural Sciences, and the Academy on Problems of Security, Defense, and Law Enforcement.